Flood Estimation Handbook

Volume 5

Flood Estimation Handbook

Volume 5
Catchment descriptors

Adrian Bayliss

Institute of Hydrology

© NERC (CEH) 2008

ISBN for complete set of 5 volumes: 978-1-906698-00-3
ISBN for this volume: 978-1-906698-05-8

Originally published by the Institute of Hydrology 1999

Centre for Ecology & Hydrology

Maclean Building, Benson Lane, Crowmarsh Gifford

Wallingford, Oxfordshire OX10 8BB

UK

General and business enquiries: 01491 692562
E-mail: enquiries@ceh.ac.uk
Website: www.ceh.ac.uk

Cover photo: © Fotolia. All rights reserved.

Cross-referencing

Cross-references to other parts of the Handbook are usually abbreviated. They are indicated by the relevant volume number preceding the chapter, section or sub-section number, with the volume number in bold (e.g. **4** 2.2 refers to Section 2.2 of Volume 4). Cross-references conventionally prefixed by Chapter, Section or § are to the current volume.

The Flood Estimation Handbook should be cited as:
Institute of Hydrology (1999) Flood Estimation Handbook (five volumes).
Centre for Ecology & Hydrology.

This volume should be cited as:
Bayliss, A. C. (1999) Catchment descriptors. Volume 5 of the Flood Estimation Handbook.
Centre for Ecology & Hydrology.

Contents

Preface

The research for the Flood Estimation Handbook was undertaken at the Institute of Hydrology, Wallingford, Oxfordshire. The Institute is an integral part of the Centre for Ecology and Hydrology, and a component institute of the Natural Environment Research Council. The research programme ran from 1994 to 1999.

Contributors

The core research team comprised Duncan Reed (team leader), Adrian Bayliss, Duncan Faulkner, Helen Houghton-Carr, Dörte Jakob, David Marshall, Alice Robson and Lisa Stewart. David Jones acted as an internal consultant, advising on all aspects of the research. The WINFAP-FEH software package was principally developed by Lawrence Beran, and the FEH CD-ROM was designed and developed by Kevin Black. The Handbook is dedicated in memory of Tanya Jones, a team member whose contribution to hydrological research was tragically cut short by cancer.

Major contributions were also made by David Morris, Susan Morris, Christel Prudhomme and Robert Scarrott, with additional contributions by Val Bronsdon, Victoria Edmunds, Beate Gannon, Stephanie Hills and Nick Reynard.

The team was supported by 1-year Sandwich Course Students from Luton and Sheffield Hallam Universities, including: Mark Bennett, Robert Brookes, Russell Brown, Louisa Coles, Nick Davie, Philip Davies, David Hewertson, Catriona Kelly, Marina Syed Mansor and Paul Nihell.

Sponsors

The research programme was funded by the Ministry of Agriculture Fisheries and Food (MAFF), the Environment Agency, the Department of Agriculture Northern Ireland, and a consortium led by the Scottish Office. The budget for the programme totalled about £1.7m. Indirect support was provided by the Centre for Ecology and Hydrology, the Meteorological Office and river gauging authorities. Costs of final editing and publication of the Handbook, and development of the WINFAP-FEH software, were met by the Institute of Hydrology.

Advisers

The research was reviewed by the Flood Estimation Handbook Advisory Group, comprising:

David Richardson, MAFF Flood and Coastal Defence *(Chair)*
Linda Aucott, Environment Agency
Alan Burdekin, Scottish Office
John Clarke, Department of Agriculture, Northern Ireland
Christopher Collier, University of Salford
Conleth Cunnane, University College Galway, Ireland
John Goudie, MAFF Flood and Coastal Defence *(Technical Secretary)*
Richard Harpin, Sir William Halcrow and Partners
David MacDonald, Binnie Black and Veatch
Andrew Pepper, Consultant to the Environment Agency *(Observer)*
Duncan Reed, Institute of Hydrology
Richard Tabony, Meteorological Office
Howard Wheater, Imperial College

Testers

The main participants in the user test programme were:

David Archer, Consultant to Jeremy Benn Associates
Alan Barr and Grace Glasgow, Kirk McClure and Morton
Don Burn, University of Waterloo, Canada
Jonathan Cooper, Owen Bramwell and Brian Darling, WS Atkins North West
Con Cunnane and Savithri Senaratne, University College Galway
Steve Dunthorne, Sir Alexander Gibb and Partners
Jim Findlay, Murray Dale, Stuart King and Birol Sokmenor, Babtie Group
Mark Futter, Montgomery Watson
Malcolm MacConnachie, Scottish Environment Protection Agency
David MacDonald, Binnie, Black and Veatch
Ian Rose, Emma Blunden and Rob Scarrott, Halcrow
Peter Spencer and David Rylands, Environment Agency
Peter Walsh, Bullen Consultants Ltd
Paul Webster and Anna Lisa Vetere Arellano, University of Birmingham
Howard Wheater and Christian Onof, Imperial College

Acknowledgements

The Flood Estimation Handbook is a product of strategic research funding at the Institute of Hydrology in the 1990s. It would not have happened without the lead shown by MAFF, in particular by Reg Purnell and David Richardson. The dedication of Advisory Group members and the testers is gratefully acknowledged. Alan Gustard (IH) is thanked for managerial assistance in a research programme that did not fit a standard mould.

General thanks go to all those who exchanged ideas with members of the team during the research programme. Those having greatest impact on the course of the research were Don Burn and Jon Hosking. A more general acknowledgement is to all earlier researchers in UK rainfall and flood frequency estimation. It would be invidious to list some and not others.

Coastlines, rivers and lake shorelines shown in the Handbook are based on material licensed from Ordnance Survey and are included with the permission of the controller of Her Majesty's Stationery Office © Crown copyright. Place names are from a gazetteer licensed from AA Developments Ltd.

More specific acknowledgements to individuals and organisations co-operating in the research are made in the relevant volume.

Volumes

1 Overview
2 Rainfall frequency estimation
3 Statistical procedures for flood frequency estimation
4 Restatement and application of the *Flood Studies Report* rainfall-runoff method
5 Catchment descriptors

Notation

The following are the main symbols and abbreviations used throughout this volume
of the Flood Estimation Handbook. Other symbols have just a local meaning and
are defined where they occur. All the units are metric unless otherwise stated

AREA	Catchment drainage area (km^2)
ALTBAR	Mean catchment altitude (m above sea level)
ASPBAR	Index representing the dominant aspect of catchment slopes
ASPVAR	Index describing the invariability in aspect of catchment slopes
BFI	Baseflow index
BFIHOST	Base flow index derived using the HOST classification
CORINE	Co-ordination of information on the environment
DANI	Department of Agriculture Northern Ireland
DPLBAR	Index describing catchment size and drainage path configuration (km)
DPSBAR	Index of catchment steepness (m/km)
DTM	Digital terrain model
FARL	Index of flood attenuation due to reservoirs and lakes
FEH	Flood Estimation Handbook
FEH CD-ROM	A software package of particular relevance to the use of Volumes 2 and 5
FSR	Flood Studies Report
HOST	Hydrology of soil types classification
IH	Institute of Hydrology
IHDTM	Institute of Hydrology digital terrain model
ITE	Institute of Terrestrial Ecology
LAKE	FSR index of flood attenuation
LCMGB	ITE land cover map of Great Britain
LDP	Longest drainage path (km)
MORECS	Met. Office rainfall and evaporation calculation system
MSL	FSR catchment characteristic describing main stream length
NERC	Natural Environment Research Council
NGR	National grid reference
OS	Ordnance Survey
OSNI	Ordnance Survey Northern Ireland
POT	Peaks-over-threshold
PROPWET	Index of proportion of time that soils are wet
RITE	ITE land cover data that has been refined at IH
RMED	Median annual maximum rainfall (mm)
RMED-1D	Median annual maximum 1-day rainfall (mm)
RMED-2D	Median annual maximum 2-day rainfall (mm)
RMED-1H	Median annual maximum 1-hour rainfall (mm)
SAAR	1961-90 standard-period average annual rainfall (mm)
SAAR$_{4170}$	1941-70 standard-period average annual rainfall (mm)
SEPA	Scottish Environment Protection Agency
SMD	Soil moisture deficit defined by MORECS
SMDBAR	Mean SMD for 1961-90 (mm)
SOIL	Index of winter rainfall acceptance potential
SPR	Standard percentage runoff (%)

Catchment descriptors

SPRHOST	SPR derived using the HOST classification
$URBAN_{FSR}$	FSR index of fractional urban extent
URBCONC	Index of concentration of urban and suburban land cover
URBEXT	FEH index of fractional urban extent
$URBEXT_{1990}$	FEH index of fractional urban extent for 1990
URBLOC	Index of location of urban and suburban land cover
WINFAP-FEH	A frequency analysis package for use with Volume 3

Chapter 1 Introduction

1.1 The need for catchment descriptors

Flood peak data are available at a large number of gauging stations throughout the UK, but for many of the sites where flood estimation is required there are no such data. It is useful to quantify the physical and climatological properties of a catchment so that flood peak data may be transferred and applied to hydrologically similar catchments and so that ungauged sites can be allocated to an appropriate pooling-group. Most importantly, relationships between key variables (such as the median annual flood *QMED*) and catchment descriptors provide a technique for deriving a flood estimate at an ungauged site. Estimates produced in this way are (in nearly all cases) far less reliable than those obtained by using flood peak data, but they can nevertheless be considered for use in minor flood design schemes, and they are useful in providing a provisional assessment when more major works are being proposed.

1.2 Catchment characteristics from maps

The estimation of flood variables from catchment characteristics is discussed in Volume 1 (Chapter 4) of the *Flood Studies Report* (FSR) (NERC, 1975). Here a boxed set of thematic maps (such as Standard Period Average Annual Rainfall 1941-70) allowed the user to calculate catchment values by overlaying a catchment boundary onto the required map. Details on how to derive morphometric variables (for example, mainstream length) from Ordnance Survey (OS) maps were also given. Before this derivation of catchment average values could take place, a boundary was drawn on an OS topographic map, by interpreting the contour and stream network information, and then transferred to a translucent medium such as tracing paper. This manual procedure was time-consuming and required skill to define the watershed accurately and compute the required characteristic. In addition, since this was a manual computation, and there was an element of subjectivity in some of the procedures, the values calculated by users were often inconsistent.

1.3 Catchment descriptors from digital spatial data

A number of organisations now have access to digital terrain models, where elevations are held digitally over a regular grid. The Institute of Hydrology Digital Terrain Model (IHDTM), described by Morris and Flavin (1990), uses digitised river information taken from 1:50000 OS maps to position river valleys correctly. This means that the IHDTM is more suited to hydrological applications than other digital terrain models. Based on the steepest route to neighbouring grid nodes, the IHDTM includes a 50 m × 50 m grid of drainage path directions, from which a catchment boundary can be derived automatically (Morris and Heerdegen, 1988). This boundary can, with the appropriate software, be applied to any gridded dataset to generate catchment values, and offers the user speed, accuracy and consistency.

The move away from deriving catchment descriptors from maps offers far more than the advantages provided by automation. Descriptors calculated from maps need to be computationally straightforward, since the operation is performed manually. Freed from this restriction, the use of digital datasets allows catchments to be described with greater subtlety. For example, the indexing of catchment urbanisation can now take account of the delineation of suburban areas within settlements, and the *location* of built-up areas within the catchment relative to the gauging station or site of interest. Similarly, it was impractical for the FSR to recommend the use of mean land slope as an index, because this would have been difficult and time-consuming to calculate. This is no longer a problem now that the IHDTM is available.

1.3.1 Selection of catchment descriptors

Since the choice of catchment descriptors is no longer limited by the need to be able to compute descriptor values manually and the availability of appropriate maps, the number of descriptors that could be derived from digital data is potentially large. Although in practical terms the choice is still limited to available datasets, the use of automated derivation techniques means that the selection of descriptors is not restricted to those that are computationally straightforward. A list of approximately 50 descriptors was drawn up for consideration.

Newson (1975; 1978) describes the process of selecting catchment characteristics for use in the FSR. The choice of an initial set of characteristics was largely governed there by judgement of what was likely to be successful: partly by intuition and partly by inspection of results from other studies. The selection of catchment descriptors for use in the Handbook followed similar lines and was, of course, influenced by what had been successful in the FSR. From an initial list of 50 possible descriptors, software was developed for 30 of the descriptors that were thought to be most useful and practical to compute.

Details of nine of the catchment descriptors required by the flood estimation procedures defined in the Handbook are described in Chapters 3, 4, 5 and 6. A further eleven descriptors, thought to provide useful additional information about the catchment, are also described. Those descriptions are not repeated here, but some discussion is warranted regarding the important differences between the map-based characteristics presented in the FSR and the Handbook's digitally-based descriptors.

Drainage networks

Catchment drainage density is represented in the FSR by a count of the number of stream junctions per unit area (STMFRQ) taken from the OS 1:25000 map series. Mainstream length (MSL), in part a measure of catchment size, and mainstream slope (S1085), are also reliant on this 'blue line' information in their derivation. Rivers and streams, taken from OS 1:50000 maps, have been digitised by IH, and are vital to the production of a hydrological DTM, but the prohibitive cost of digitising the stream networks present on OS 1:25000 maps has meant that this information is not yet held digitally. Descriptors based directly on blue line information could not be used, because digitised stream networks were not available to the Handbook at an appropriate scale.

The IHDTM provides drainage directions connecting each node to a neighbour. Stream networks, depicted at any scale, can be simulated for *individual* catchments by applying a suitable threshold of catchment area to the IHDTM drainage path network. Then, from a point along each drainage path where the area draining to that point exceeds the threshold, the drainage path is treated as a blue line. Applying a threshold to a number of catchments in a consistent way presents more difficulties. The blue line information found on maps reflects other factors, such as wetness and local soil types. Using the same threshold across catchments of differing soils and climate regime would produce, for some of the catchments, simulated stream networks that are inconsistent with conventional mapping. Stream networks based on a catchment descriptor model for the index flood (see Chapter 3 of Volume 3) is a possibility for future research. Descriptors developed for the Handbook are therefore not based on mapped stream networks, but use the IHDTM drainage path network, which connects to (and is representative of) the *whole* catchment.

Flood attenuation

Flood attenuation attributable to reservoirs and lakes is represented by the FARL index (Chapter 4). The descriptor takes into account *all* on-line water bodies within the catchment, which the FSR characteristic LAKE was unable to do. There, the need to keep the manual derivation simple meant that only the *first* upstream lake or reservoir on each tributary that satisfied the necessary criteria was included.

The FSR recognised the desirability of an index representing channel or flood plain storage, but was unable to define a procedure that could derive such an index from maps for any site in the UK. The availability of a DTM brings the realisation of such an index nearer, but the development of a flood plain storage descriptor for the Handbook was not possible within the time constraints of the study.

Soils

An important development in the FSR was the production of the Winter Rain Acceptance Potential (WRAP) map to describe the role of soils in flood generation. This five-class map has now been superseded by the 29-class Hydrology Of Soil Types (HOST) classification, which is seen as a step forward towards more accurate estimation. Standard Percentage Runoff (SPR) and Base Flow Index (BFI) values are estimated using catchment HOST soil values (Chapter 5).

Urban land cover

FSR procedures recommend that fractions of urban land cover are derived manually by evaluating the extent of flesh-coloured areas shown on OS 1:50000 maps. To aid map clarity, the symbolisation of built-up areas on these maps tends to exaggerate the true extent of the impervious area. In addition, small non-urban areas within settlements are often not represented. A major improvement to the indexing of urbanisation is the use of gridded 50 m land cover data (Chapter 6), which reflect more accurately the true extent of built-up areas, define 'green areas' within the conurbation and delineate between urban and suburban land cover, allowing a more subtle descriptor to be derived using an automated technique.

1.4 Provision of catchment descriptors

1.4.1 Descriptors for gauged catchments

Catchment descriptors are listed in the Appendix, and are also provided on a CD-ROM (enclosed with Volume 3), for 943 of the 1000 gauged sites for which flood peak data are held at IH. Section 2.2.1 describes how 57 catchments were rejected because of problems defining the boundary using the IHDTM. Descriptor values are not given for these sites.

In addition, uncertainty about the quality of flood peak data for a small number of catchments meant that not all of the descriptor values given for the 943 sites were used in the statistical analyses (Volume 3), nor in revision of the rainfall-runoff method (Volume 4). However, these descriptors have still been listed, because even though problems relating to the flood peak data have led to their exclusion from some parts of the analyses, the DTM has defined their catchment boundaries adequately and the descriptors do represent the catchments concerned.

1.4.2 Descriptors for ungauged catchments

Use of digital data, and an automated procedure for generating catchment descriptors, provide benefits in timesaving and consistency to those wishing to derive the variables needed for flood estimation at an ungauged site. Replacing the manual procedure, which involved catchment boundary overlays and maps, is the provision of catchment descriptor values on CD-ROM. Values are provided for catchments of 0.5 km² or more, on a 50 m grid, for the descriptors used in the generalised flood estimation procedures, as well as some other variables, which were chosen to give additional information about the catchment. Chapter 7 introduces the FEH CD-ROM and its use.

Chapter 2 Catchment boundaries from the IHDTM

2.1 Selecting the correct grid node

Use of the IHDTM allows a catchment boundary to be generated from any point on the 50 m grid. However, the appropriate grid node must be selected if the derived boundary is to be the correct one for the site of interest. For individual catchments this can be checked visually by plotting the boundary at a suitable scale.

Figure 2.1 illustrates how one of the five IHDTM grids gives information regarding the number of other grid nodes draining to that point (effectively a 50 m grid of drainage areas). For clarification, drainage direction has been added to this example grid. In addition to these DTM-derived drainage areas, catchment areas are usually calculated for gauged sites, by the measuring organisation. A comparison of DTM-derived areas, and those supplied by the gauging authority, is used as a guide to selecting the correct grid-node and, later, as a validation tool. Since visually inspecting the location of the boundary is too onerous where a large number of catchments is involved, this procedure has been automated with software, which endeavours to select the best match between these two areas within a defined search area, to ensure that the correct grid node is chosen.

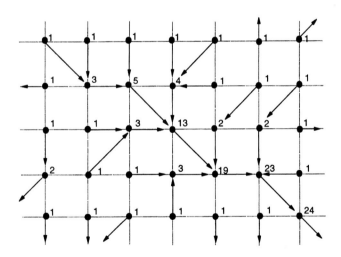

Figure 2.1 Cumulative catchment area grid and drainage direction

2.2 Validation of 1000 catchment boundaries

Catchment boundaries were derived, using the IHDTM, to all 1000 gauging stations for which flood peak data are held at IH, along with their respective drainage areas. Drainage area is an important variable in its own right, but its computation also enabled the accuracy of the DTM-derived boundary to be assessed. Each DTM-derived drainage area was compared with the catchment area, obtained manually from maps supplied to the National River Flow Archive by the gauging authority. Figure 2.2 shows that the IHDTM-derived catchment area is within 2%

of the manually-derived area for more than 70% of catchments, while 87% of catchments are less than 5% different. It is also evident that the IHDTM does not consistently produce either smaller or larger values. This comparison of areas shows that the IHDTM can be used to produce catchment boundaries quickly and accurately for the majority of catchments.

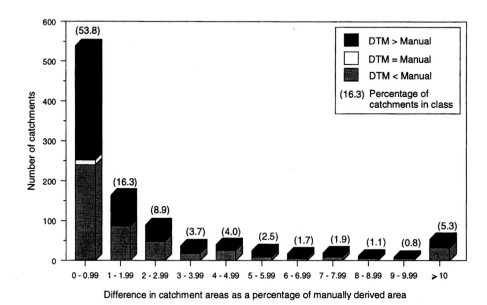

Figure 2.2 *Comparison of catchment areas produced from manually-drawn and IHDTM-derived boundaries*

2.2.1 Problem catchments

A few catchments (5%) differ in area by 10% or more. Where the ratio of larger to smaller area exceeded 1.1, the descriptors defined by these boundaries were deemed to be unreliable and were not used in the analyses. Some of these catchments have boundaries which, through drainage diversion, do not always follow the topography, which of course a DTM-derived watershed, defined using elevation information, must always do. In other cases, the generation of IHDTM-drainage paths has been flawed, in some small areas, by difficulties encountered when using digitised rivers to fix the location of valleys. Problems may arise when rivers appear (from the supplied river and contour information) to flow uphill; or where two digitised rivers are located within 50 m of each other, the 'capture' of one river by the other can occur. Planned improvements to the IHDTM are likely to resolve many of these difficulties, but the automated production of effective descriptors will probably remain problematic for catchments where drainage works or groundwater effects override the topography.

A pragmatic approach to adjusting catchment descriptor values where the DTM-derived boundary is considered inappropriate is described in Section 7.2.

Chapter 3 Land form descriptors

3.1 Introduction

The Institute of Hydrology Digital Terrain Model comprises five square grids of data: surface type, ground elevation, outflow direction, inflow pattern and cumulative catchment area. Drainage direction allows the automatic computation of catchment boundaries, which underpins the derivation of catchment values from thematic data sets. However, the IHDTM grids themselves offer the potential to describe the physical or morphometric attributes of a catchment in ways too onerous to contemplate when using maps. From an extensive list of possible descriptors, those thought to be most useful and practical to compute were developed further.

3.2 Size and configuration

In addition to the catchment drainage area, defined by the DTM-derived boundary, two further indices have been produced, which principally describe catchment size, but also give information regarding drainage path configuration.

3.2.1 Longest drainage path (LDP)

The IHDTM defines a drainage direction for each 50 m grid node based on the steepest route to one of its eight neighbours (Morris and Heerdegen, 1988). From each source node, therefore, a drainage path can be traced and measured down to the catchment outlet. The maximum distance from source to outlet (LDP) can thus be defined (Figure 3.1). LDP is similar to the mainstream length (MSL) used in the Flood Studies Report — they are both measures of catchment size — but some brief discussion of their differences is worthwhile.

MSL is derived from the 'blue line' depiction of river networks found on Ordnance Survey 1:25000 topographical maps. These networks expand and contract seasonally, but the fixed representation found on maps still reflects the soil and wetness conditions found in the area. For instance, the network is likely to be more extensive on impermeable clays in the north and west than on the chalk of southern England. MSL therefore represents catchment wetness and soils in addition to catchment size. This is not true of LDP, since it is derived from the DTM, where all parts of the catchment are connected by drainage paths. LDP does not reflect catchment soils and wetness, but does give information about catchment size and (in association with AREA) shape.

Values of LDP have been computed for 943 catchments in the UK. Figure 3.2 shows that the majority of catchments have index values in the range 10-40 km, that small catchments are reasonably well represented in the dataset (index values less than 10 km), and that there is a small number of large catchments, where LDP is greater than 200 km. Although the distribution of values is skewed, all but one class is represented by one or more catchments.

Figure 3.3 shows the spatial distribution of LDP by means of circles, located at the catchment outlet, of size proportional to the index value. The larger catchments can clearly be seen on the lower Thames, Severn and Wye, while a range of index values is evident in most parts of the country.

Values of LDP are also influenced by drainage path configuration. Two adjoining catchments — the Severn at Bewdley (54001) and the Trent at Shardlow

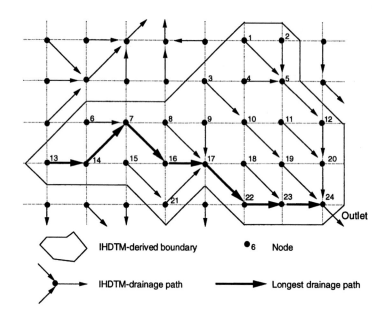

Distance to outlet (m)

1	241.4	7	291.4	13	412.1	19	70.7	**LDP = 412.1 m**
2	220.7	8	241.4	14	362.1	20	50.0	
3	212.1	9	220.7	15	312.1	21	241.4	**DPLBAR = 193.0 m**
4	220.7	10	141.4	16	220.7	22	100.0	
5	170.7	11	120.7	17	170.7	23	50.0	
6	341.4	12	100.0	18	120.7	24	0.0	

Figure 3.1 Derivation of LDP and DPLBAR

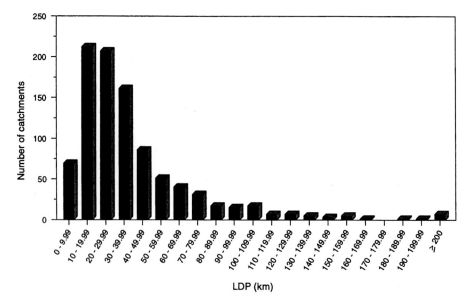

Figure 3.2 Numerical distribution of LDP values

(28007) — are almost exactly the same size (4330 km² and 4414 km² respectively), but their LDP values are quite different. The more sinuous catchment of the Severn has an LDP value of 216.8 km, whereas in contrast, the longest drainage path computed for the more fan-shaped configuration of the Trent catchment is 131.5 km (Figure 3.4).

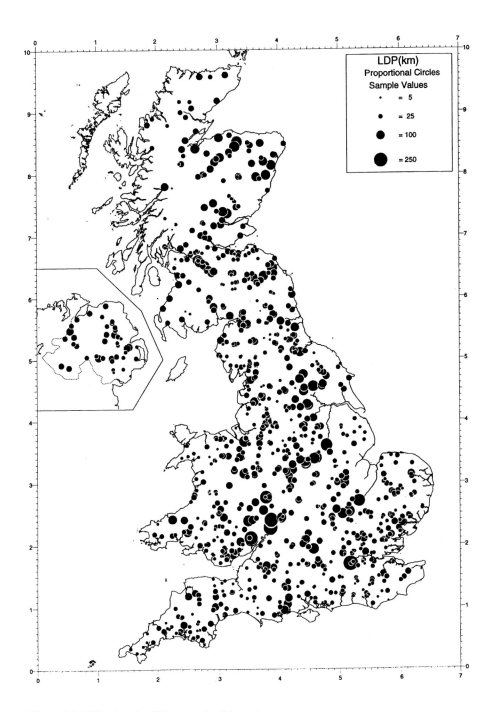

Figure 3.3 *LDP values for 943 gauged catchments*

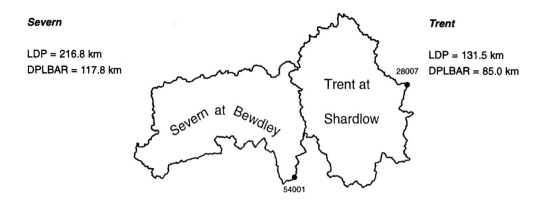

Severn

LDP = 216.8 km
DPLBAR = 117.8 km

Trent

LDP = 131.5 km
DPLBAR = 85.0 km

Figure 3.4 *Contrastingly-configured catchments*

3.2.2 Mean drainage path length (DPLBAR)

Using the IHDTM drainage paths, the distance between each node and the catchment outlet is calculated (Figure 3.1). The mean of these distances is used to standardise the distance along the drainage paths of urban and suburban development, from the catchment outlet, in the computation of the urban location index (URBLOC) described in Section 6.6. This mean distance (DPLBAR) is listed here as an alternative measure of catchment size.

The distribution of DPLBAR values for the 943 catchments (Figure 3.5) has a similar appearance to that shown by LDP (Figure 3.2), in that the data are skewed and there is a large range of values. Values for the contrasting catchments shown in Figure 3.4 are 117.8 km for the Severn and 85.0 km for the Trent, indicating that DPLBAR also reflects the drainage path configuration. Figure 3.6 shows the spatial distribution of DPLBAR values.

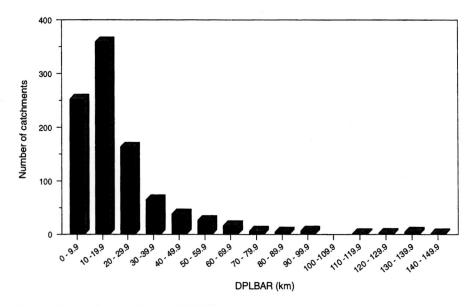

Figure 3.5 *Numerical distribution of DPLBAR values*

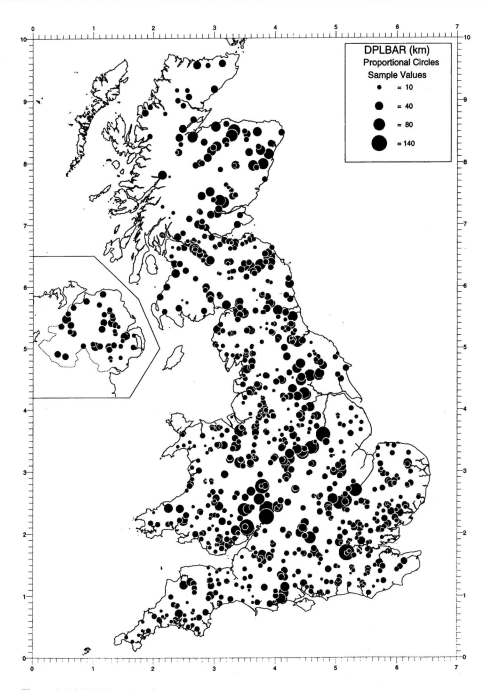

Figure 3.6 *DPLBAR values for 943 gauged catchments*

3.3 Altitude

3.3.1 Mean altitude (ALTBAR)

One of the IHDTM's five square grids is the altitude above mean sea level. At each 50 m grid node, the altitude of that point, interpolated from Ordnance Survey contours by a procedure described by Morris and Flavin (1990), is held to a vertical resolution of 0.1 m. Figure 3.7 shows how all altitude values defined as being within the catchment are used to calculate the mean altitude (ALTBAR).

The skewed nature of the data represented in Figure 3.8 reflects both the terrain of the UK and the preponderance of gauges in lowland areas (generally upstream of major confluences), sited there for water resource assessment. However, the sites analysed here do depict catchment type for a large range of altitude, from the low-lying fens of East Anglia to the Cairngorms in Scotland (Figure 3.9).

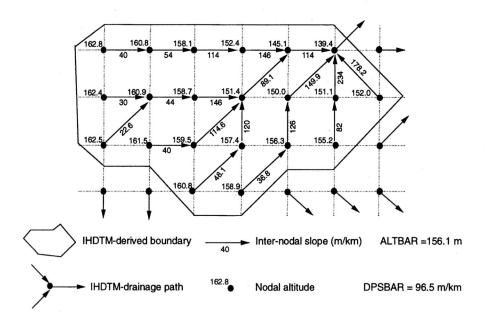

Figure 3.7 Derivation of ALTBAR and DPSBAR

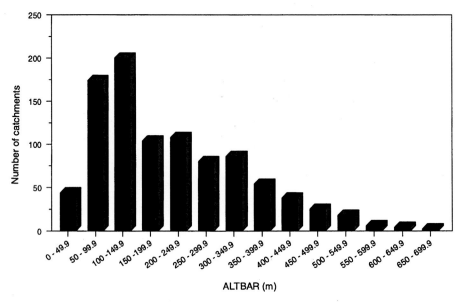

Figure 3.8 Numerical distribution of ALTBAR values

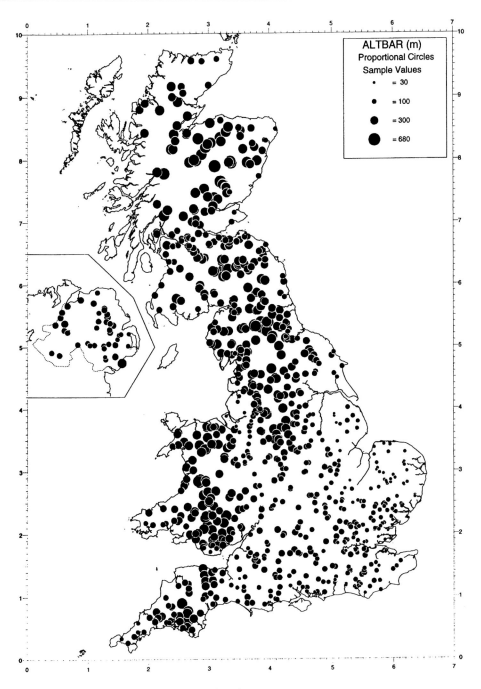

Figure 3.9 *ALTBAR values for 943 gauged catchments*

3.4 Slope

3.4.1 Mean drainage path slope (DPSBAR)

At each grid node the IHDTM defines an outflow direction (based on the steepest route) to one of its eight neighbouring nodes. Using the difference in altitude, and the distance between the two nodes, the internode slope is calculated. The

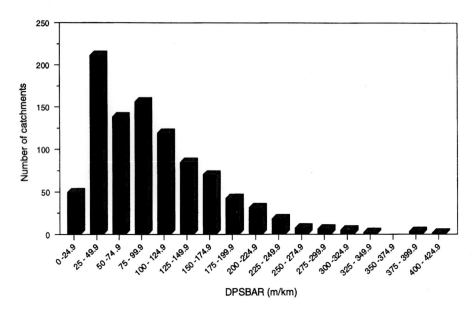

Figure 3.10 *Numerical distribution of DPSBAR values*

procedure is adopted for all nodal pairs within the catchment (Figure 3.7) to give the mean drainage path slope (DPSBAR).

The numerical distribution of DPSBAR values (Figure 3.10) again reflects the terrain of the UK and the concentration of river flow gauges in lowland areas, and correspondingly the dominance of catchments with moderate slopes. However, sites representing a wide range of values are present in the dataset, including a small number of very steep catchments in the Scottish Highlands (Figure 3.11).

3.5 Aspect

3.5.1 Mean aspect (ASPBAR)

The direction of each nodal outflow is recorded as a bearing, which increases clockwise between zero and 360°, starting from the north. Figure 3.12 shows how the mean direction is calculated using the procedure defined by Fisher (1993). This represents all the directions (θ) as a weight of unit mass on the circumference of a circle and then finds the centroid of these weights to give the mean direction ($\bar{\theta}$), referred to here as ASPBAR. Since the outflow direction follows the steepest slope, ASPBAR is indicative of the dominant aspect of catchment slopes.

Figure 3.13 shows the distribution of ASPBAR values (e.g. 50 catchments have slopes with a mean aspect of between 75° and 85°). The figure indicates that a large proportion (nearly 40%) of the 943 catchments analysed are dominated by catchment slopes with a mean aspect between 75° and 155° (approximately east to south-south-east).

The spatial distribution of ASPBAR values is given in Figure 3.14, where the arrowhead marks the catchment outlet and the direction of the arrow the mean aspect of catchment slopes. Although the picture is confused in areas where a lot of gauges are close to each other, the dominance of easterly- and south-easterly-facing catchments supports the impression given by Figure 3.13.

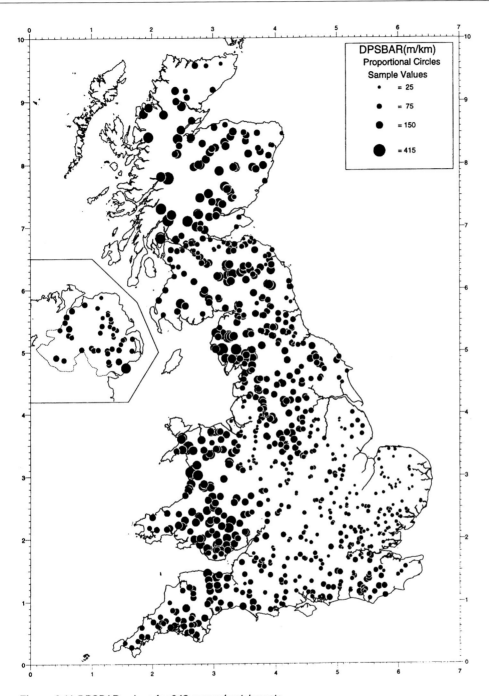

Figure 3.11 *DPSBAR values for 943 gauged catchments*

It is apparent from these two figures that the vast majority of rivers in Great Britain flow in an easterly or southerly direction, and the number flowing in a westerly direction is relatively small. In Northern Ireland, catchment values of ASPBAR are more varied, since the convergent stream network centred on Lough Neagh dominates much of the drainage in the Province.

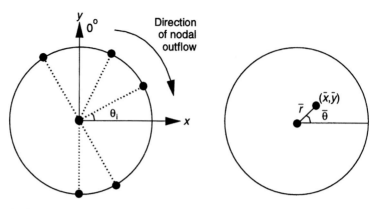

Figure 3.12 *Calculating the mean aspect (ASPBAR) and invariability of slope directions (ASPVAR)*

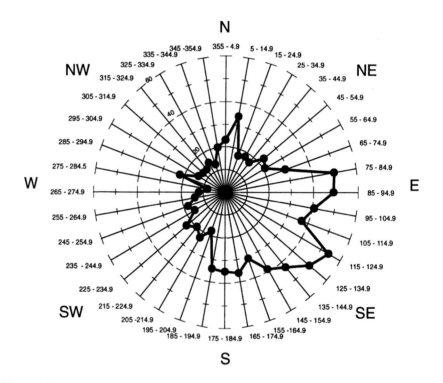

Figure 3.13 *Numerical distribution of ASPBAR values*

3.5.2 Invariability in aspect (ASPVAR)

In addition to calculating the mean direction, Figure 3.12 shows how circular statistics have been used to compute the 'mean resultant', which gives some indication of the spread in the direction data, where a value close to one indicates that the data are strongly directional. This would mean that catchment slopes tended to face in one particular direction. Conversely, where the mean resultant (referred to here as ASPVAR) is close to zero, then there is considerable variability in the data, the catchment slopes do not favour any one direction and the value of ASPBAR is less meaningful.

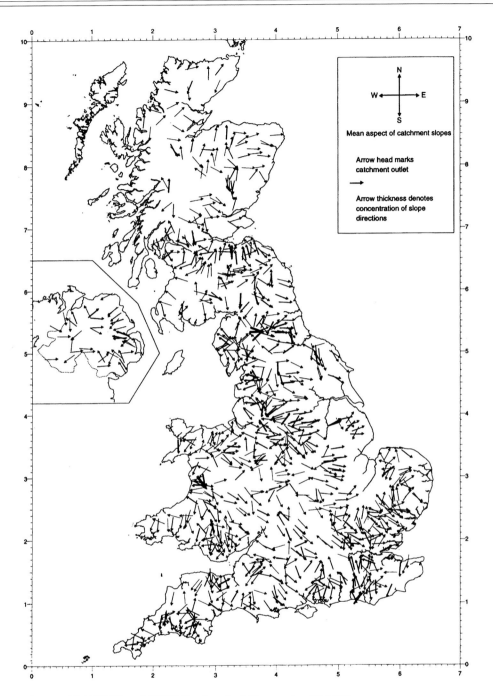

Figure 3.14 ASPBAR and ASPVAR values for 943 gauged catchments

The numerical distribution of ASPVAR values is given in Figure 3.15 and shows that for the majority of catchments there is considerable variability in slope directions.

Figure 3.16 suggests that variability increases with catchment size. Intuitively this would seem correct: with fewer slope directions present for a smaller catchment,

Catchment descriptors

there would be a greater likelihood of one direction dominating (i.e. a value of ASPVAR close to one). Conversely for large catchments, with a great number of slope directions, it is likely that there would be more variability in the data.

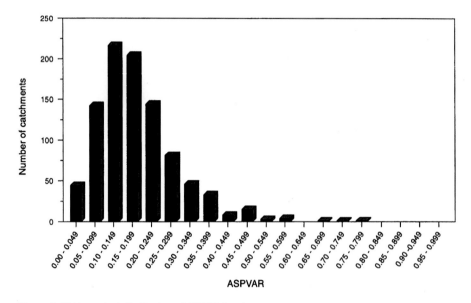

Figure 3.15 *Numerical distribution of ASPVAR values*

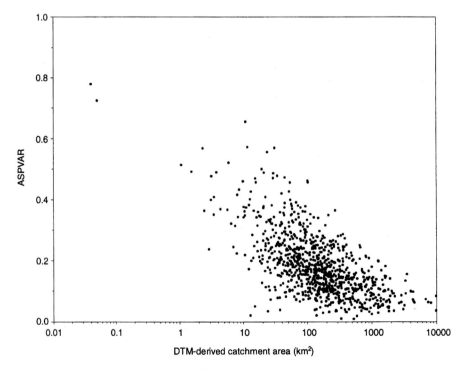

Figure 3.16 *Relationship between ASPVAR and catchment area*

Chapter 4 Indexing the attenuation effect attributable to reservoirs and lakes

4.1 The effect of lakes and reservoirs on flood regime

The storage of flood flows, in lakes and reservoirs, often results in attenuation of the flood hydrograph. Lakes that have a small surface area and a correspondingly small storage capability are likely to have little impact on the flood regime. Similarly, if the area draining to the lake is minor, in relation to the overall catchment, the attenuation effect is also likely to be small. Larger lakes however, have more storage potential, and are therefore likely to modify the catchment flood response to a greater extent.

A full reservoir will behave in a similar way to a lake of equal size. However, if the level is drawn down, potential storage is increased, and the impact on the flood regime is greater. Quantifying the effect of reservoirs within a generalised method is difficult, since the impact of the reservoir depends on the operating policy in force at each site. Where reservoirs are found to be within the catchment, it is recommended that details be sought from the operator.

4.2 Development of a new index

The FSR catchment characteristic *LAKE* was based on the first upstream lake or reservoir on each tributary whose surface area covered more than one per cent of its own subcatchment area. This meant that water bodies of considerable size, and with a potentially large impact on flood flows, would be ignored if they were upstream of a lake or reservoir which had satisfied the necessary criteria. In addition, apart from deciding whether the water body exceeded the 1% threshold, surface area was not taken into account in evaluating the index, so that a small lake (which just exceeded the threshold) would be treated in the same way as a large one. Index values were defined as the fraction of the catchment that drained through significant lakes and reservoirs, and the degree of flood attenuation was expected to increase as values of *LAKE* increased. The index had to be relatively simple to calculate, because the necessary data had to be extracted manually from Ordnance Survey maps.

Reservoir and lake shoreline vector data, generally taken from the 1:50 000 Landranger and Discoverer map series, were supplied by the OS and OS Northern Ireland respectively. Typically these data relate to the 1980s, and reservoirs built later will not be present in the dataset. Freed from the requirement to derive the descriptor from maps, the digital data associated with the IHDTM allow fresh ideas to be explored in defining a new index. The objectives behind the derivation of a new index are:

- To assess the effect of *all* lakes and reservoirs;
- To allow for the location of lakes and reservoirs within a catchment;
- To include the effect of nested lakes and reservoirs;
- To produce a smooth index, rather than the stepped 1% threshold technique used in the FSR;
- To improve the speed, accuracy and consistency of calculating the index.

4.3 Flood Attenuation by Reservoirs and Lakes (FARL) index

4.3.1 Defining on- and off-line reservoirs and lakes

Any reservoirs or lakes within a catchment will tend to have some affect on flood response, but it is those directly linked to the stream network that are most likely to produce a flood attenuation effect. However, it must be remembered that where storage is available in isolated reservoirs and lakes, there will still be some effect, since precipitation falling directly on the reservoir or lake surface will be lost from the flood generation process. Nevertheless, in general, an isolated lake with no stream inflows or outflows has less effect than a similar lake that is part of the stream network. The location of water bodies in relation to the local stream network is termed 'on-line' where there is a direct link and 'off-line' where the reservoirs and lakes are isolated from the network. Pictorial representations of the definitions of on- and off-line lakes and reservoirs as used here are presented in Figures 4.1, 4.2 and 4.3. For the purpose of this definition the rivers used are taken from a gridded digital version of the 'blue line' information on OS 1:50000 maps.

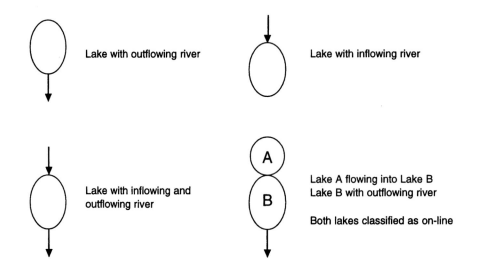

Figure 4.1 Reservoirs and lakes treated as on-line

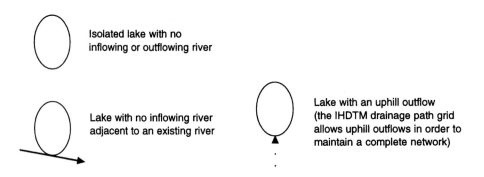

Figure 4.2 Reservoirs and lakes treated as off-line

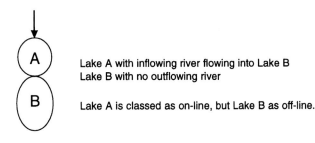

Figure 4.3 *Reservoirs and lakes treated as special cases*

4.3.2 Indexing the effects of individual reservoirs and lakes

It was decided that only on-line water bodies would be used in index evaluation, to reflect the likelihood that they have a more important role in flood attenuation. This effect for individual reservoirs and lakes is indexed by:

$$\alpha = \left(1 - \sqrt{r}\right)^{w} \tag{4.1}$$

where r is the relative size of the reservoir or lake to its subcatchment, i.e.

$$r = \frac{surface\,area}{subcatchment\,area} \tag{4.2}$$

and w is a weight which reflects the importance of the reservoir or lake in terms of the flood behaviour at the catchment scale, defined by:

$$w = \frac{subcatchment\,area}{catchment\,area} \tag{4.3}$$

A reservoir or lake immediately upstream of the catchment outlet will have a w value of one. Figure 4.4 gives illustrated examples of how the local index value α is evaluated.

In reality, the attenuation effect depends on both the storage characteristics of the reservoir or lake (typically well represented by the surface area) and the discharge characteristics of the outlet. The outlet characteristics cannot be represented without design or survey information of the reservoir or lake respectively. However, the most influential factor is likely to be the length of the outlet weir (in the case of a reservoir) or the width of the channel (for a natural lake).

The choice of the square root transformation in Equation 4.1 was motivated by a simple geometric representation. If one considers two subcatchments, one twice the size of the other, containing lakes of surface area in the same ratio, then one would expect the attenuation effect in each case to be the same. The flood attenuation effect is largely influenced by the width of the outlet control to the lake. In geometric terms, the channel width at the outlet will have increased only by a factor of $\sqrt{2}$, because the width is of dimension L, whereas the catchment and lake areas are of dimension L². In order for the attenuation effect to be the same in both cases, the square root of the relative significance value r must be taken: this is shown in Figure 4.5.

Catchment descriptors

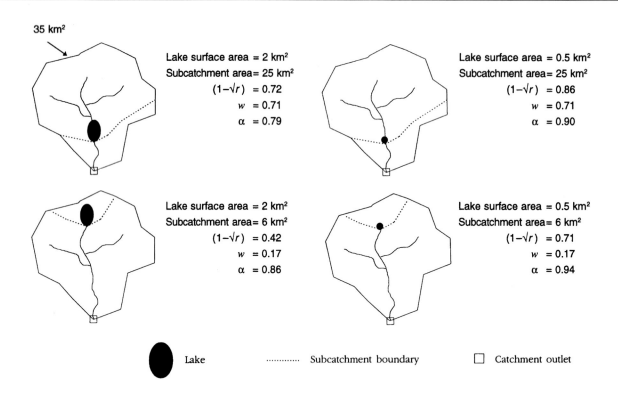

Figure 4.4 *Example evaluations of the local α index*

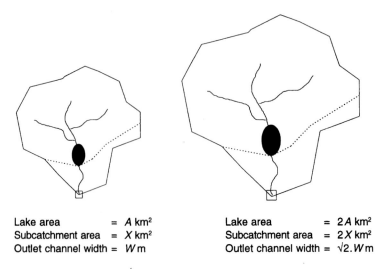

Figure 4.5 *Rationale behind the √r transformation*

4.3.3 Evaluating a composite attenuation factor – the *FARL* index

The catchment descriptor *FARL* is the product of the individual local index values where:

$$FARL = \prod_{i \in reservoirs\ and\ lakes} \alpha_i \qquad (4.4)$$

The *FARL* index value is close to one when there is little flood attenuation due to reservoirs and lakes. As attenuation effects become more important, the value of the index decreases. In contrast to the *LAKE* variable in the FSR, the *FARL* index is a 'smooth' function, and free from any threshold effect. As the number of lakes and reservoirs increases, *FARL* decreases proportionately. An example of how the index behaves in response to increasing numbers of lakes and reservoirs with the same α_i value can be can be seen in Figure 4.6. The index value decreases proportionately as the number of lakes and reservoirs increases.

Since the catchment index assesses the flood attenuation potential of all the on-line lakes and reservoirs, the effect of those nested within the subcatchment of another are included. As Figure 4.7 shows, nested and non-nested reservoirs and lakes are represented as having the same effect.

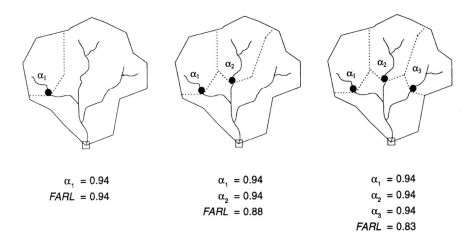

α_1 = 0.94
FARL = 0.94

α_1 = 0.94
α_2 = 0.94
FARL = 0.88

α_1 = 0.94
α_2 = 0.94
α_3 = 0.94
FARL = 0.83

Figure 4.6 *Index behaviour in response to the number of reservoirs and lakes*

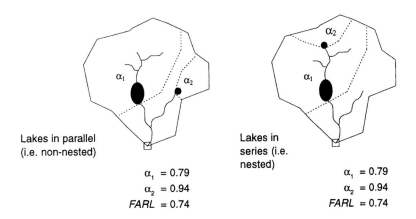

Lakes in parallel (i.e. non-nested)

α_1 = 0.79
α_2 = 0.94
FARL = 0.74

Lakes in series (i.e. nested)

α_1 = 0.79
α_2 = 0.94
FARL = 0.74

Figure 4.7 *Examples of nested and non-nested reservoirs and lakes*

4.4 Distinguishing between lakes and reservoirs

In developing the *FARL* index, additional software was written to distinguish reservoirs from lakes, using IHDTM elevation data. Reservoirs are generally artificial impoundments, with dams to retain the water. The steeper slope found at a reservoir outlet, generally reflected in the elevation data, was used to differentiate between a reservoir and a lake. If the gradient exceeded 10% at any point up to 150 m downstream from the outlet, the water body was assumed to be a reservoir. If this threshold was not exceeded it was recorded as a lake. The success of the reservoir identification procedure was assessed visually using OS maps and by reference to the Building Research Establishment register of British dams (Tedd *et al.*, 1992). It appeared that the criteria we had applied were too simplistic: although identifying reservoirs in this way was successful in a large number of cases, it could not be relied upon.

4.5 FARL values for 943 gauged catchments

Figure 4.8 illustrates that index values are in the range 0.557 to 1.0 with 151 catchments (16%) not influenced by lake or reservoir attenuation (i.e. *FARL* = 1.0). There are 71 catchments (7.5%) with *FARL* values below 0.9, indicating that significant attenuation is likely at these sites. The lowest index value (0.557) for a small catchment in north-west Scotland indicates that the presence of Fionn Loch will markedly attenuate flood flows measured on the Little Gruinard (95801), some 8 km downstream.

Figure 4.9 depicts the spatial distribution of *FARL* index values: the larger circles denote greater attenuation effects. Those catchments with the largest *FARL* values are found mainly in north Wales, Cumbria, Northumberland, Scotland and Northern Ireland, reflecting the large number of water supply reservoirs, natural lakes and lochs in upland areas.

Attenuation from reservoirs is also a feature of some lowland catchments. For example, Figure 4.9 shows a large circle in Lincolnshire, corresponding to the

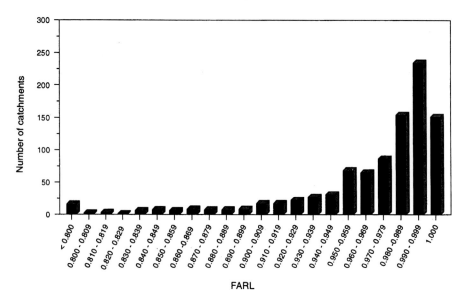

Figure 4.8 Numerical distribution of FARL values

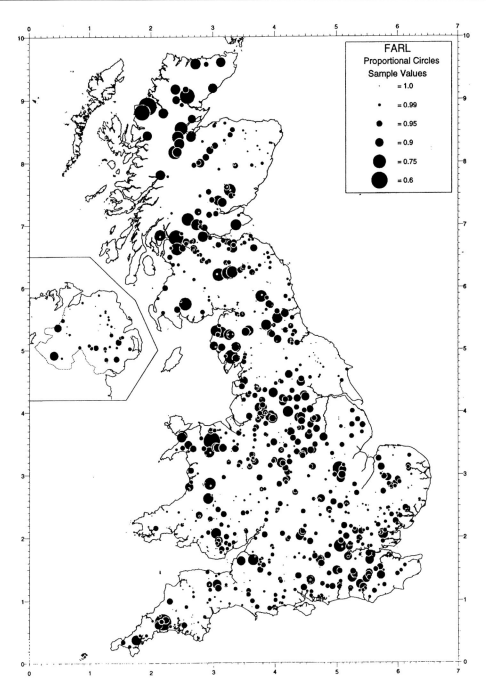

Figure 4.9 *FARL values for 943 catchments*

Gwash at Belmesthorpe (31006), where the gauging station is 13 km downstream of Rutland Water (Figure 4.10). The reservoir dominates the catchment, and this is borne out by the low *FARL* value of 0.758.

A major advantage of the *FARL* index over the FSR *LAKE* index is that it takes account of all on-line reservoirs and lakes in the catchment. The Derwent at Camerton (75002) in north-west England has a number of large on-line reservoirs which are 'nested' in the subcatchment of those further downstream (Figure 4.11). The *LAKE* index would only be evaluated on those farthest downstream, whereas the *FARL* index also embraces the likely flood attenuation effects from the nested reservoirs and lakes.

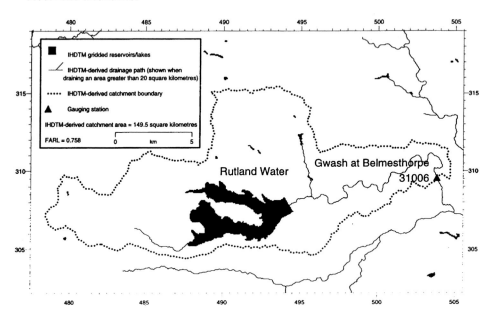

Figure 4.10 *The Gwash at Belmesthorpe: a lowland catchment dominated by a reservoir*

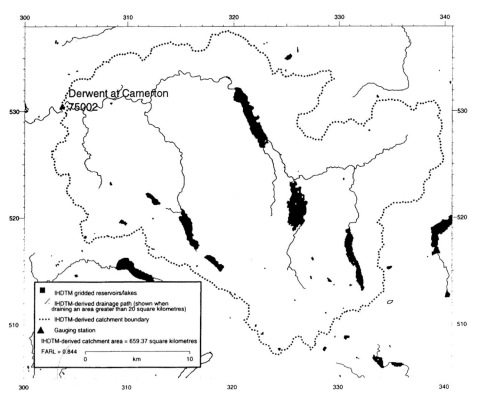

Figure 4.11 *The Derwent at Camerton: nested reservoirs and lakes*

Chapter 5   Climate and soils

5.1 Introduction

Catchment boundaries derived automatically using the IHDTM have the advantage that they can be applied, quickly and accurately, to any gridded thematic dataset to produce catchment average values. Several such datasets, relating to climate and soils, are described here; catchment average values, derived from these datasets, are listed for 943 gauged sites in the Appendix.

5.2 Standard-period Average Annual Rainfall (SAAR)

Average annual rainfall for the standard period 1961-90 in Great Britain and Northern Ireland (SAAR) is provided by The Met. Office on a 1 km grid, with average rainfall held to a resolution of 1 mm.

In Figure 5.1, catchment values based on data for the 1961-90 standard period are compared with those calculated using a 1 km grid generated from a digitised version of the SAAR 1941-70 map provided with the FSR. For the 943 catchments shown, $SAAR_{4170}$ values are 24.3 mm higher on average.

Catchment values of average annual rainfall for the standard period 1961-90 are listed in Table A.1 of the Appendix, whilst 1941-70 values are provided, for information only, in Table A.2.

5.3 Median annual maximum rainfall (RMED)

Median annual maximum rainfall, for a number of different durations, have been produced as 1 km grids. The interpolation of RMED between gauges uses sophisticated variables which have been developed to take account of the influence of topography on extreme rainfall, notably in relation to the prevailing direction of rain-bearing winds. Volume 2 gives a full account of the interpolation process in Chapter 7.

A grid was produced for each of the following durations: 1-hour (RMED-1H), 1-day (RMED-1D) and 2-day (RMED-2D).

5.4 Standard Percentage Runoff from the Hydrology Of Soil Types classification (SPRHOST)

UK soils have been delineated according to their hydrological properties to produce the 29-class Hydrology Of Soil Types (HOST) classification. The HOST dataset is available as a 1 km grid which records, for each grid square, the percentage of the 1 km × 1 km area given to each HOST class present (Boorman *et al.*, 1995). Figure 5.2 shows the dominant HOST class for each 1 km square in the UK. The area of lake or reservoir in each grid square is also held. The application of DTM-derived boundaries to these data enabled the computation for each site of the percentage of the catchment attributed to each HOST class, and the lake or reservoir surface area.

Boorman *et al.* (1995) give Standard Percentage Runoff (SPR) and Base Flow Index (BFI) values for each HOST class (reproduced below as Table 5.1) and conclude that estimating SPR from HOST classes – rather than using the five-class SOIL classification presented in the FSR – is a step towards more accurate estimation.

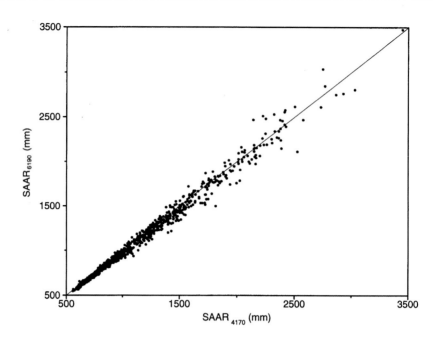

Figure 5.1 *Comparison of SAAR$_{4170}$ and SAAR$_{6190}$ values for 943 catchments*

Table 5.1 *SPR and BFI values for HOST classes*

HOST class	SPR (%)	BFI	HOST class	SPR (%)	BFI
1	2.0	1.000	16	29.2	0.778
2	2.0	1.000	17	29.2	0.609
3	14.5	0.900	18	47.2	0.518
4	2.0	0.791	19	60.0	0.469
5	14.5	0.900	20	60.0	0.524
6	33.8	0.645	21	47.2	0.340
7	44.3	0.792	22	60.0	0.315
8	44.3	0.560	23	60.0	0.218
9	25.3	0.734	24	39.7	0.312
10	25.3	0.520	25	49.6	0.170
11	2.0	0.927	26	58.7	0.244
12	60.0	0.170	27	60.0	0.259
13	2.0	1.000	28	60.0	0.581
14	25.3	0.380	29	60.0	0.226
15	48.4	0.380			

Therefore SPR was estimated for each of the 943 catchments, using the HOST classification and an area-weighting method. Since areas of lake or reservoir had not been assigned to a HOST class, an adjustment to catchment HOST values had to be made in catchments containing lakes or reservoirs in order that the weighting was not biased. The area of lake or reservoir in the catchment was deducted from the total catchment area and the HOST class percentages were recalculated using the reduced area (representing HOST classified areas only). The calculation of SPR for the Roden at Rodington (54016) illustrates this adjustment (Table 5.2).

Figure 5.2 Dominant HOST class for each 1 km grid square

Table 5.2 HOST classes for the Roden at Rodington (54016) and the calculation of SPR

HOST class	Area (km²)	Fraction	Adjusted fraction	SPR for class	SPR × adjusted fraction
3	16.44	.0628	.0629	14.5	0.912
4	5.33	.0204	.0204	2.0	0.041
5	70.92	.2708	.2711	14.5	3.931
7	3.57	.0136	.0136	44.3	0.602
8	0.19	.0007	.0007	44.3	0.031
9	6.67	.0255	.0255	25.3	0.645
10	12.81	.0489	.0490	25.3	1.240
11	19.83	.0757	.0758	2.0	0.152
13	0.53	.0020	.0020	2.0	0.004
18	27.05	.1033	.1034	47.2	4.881
19	0.25	.0010	.0010	60.0	0.060
21	2.90	.0111	.0111	47.2	0.524
24	95.09	.3631	.3635	39.7	14.431
Lake/resr.	0.32	.0012			
	$\Sigma = 261.90$				$\Sigma = 27.454$

The total surface area of lakes and reservoirs in this catchment is small (0.32 km²), and consequently only a minor adjustment is necessary in computing the SPR value of 27.5. However, where a significant area of surface water exists, this adjustment becomes important to avoid underestimating the value of SPR.

The production of a 1:250 000 soil map for Northern Ireland and subsequent provision of a HOST classification on a 1 km grid were not completed until 1996. References by Boorman *et al.* (1995) to the HOST classification in Northern Ireland relate to a provisional dataset only. The work undertaken by the Agriculture and Environmental Science Division of the Department of Agriculture for Northern Ireland to produce a HOST dataset consistent with that produced for Great Britain is described by Higgins (1997). Descriptors derived using the HOST classification in Northern Ireland are based on this new dataset.

For some small catchments, the use of SPRHOST values based on a summary of the HOST classes present in each 1 km grid square may be inappropriate. In these cases, a value may be derived manually, based on more detailed soil information, using the methodology described in Volume 4, Appendix C (§ C.3.2). Soil maps at '1 inch', 1:50 000 and 1:25 000 scale are available for some areas. The Macaulay Land Use Research Institute (MLURI) can provide details of the availability of mapping in Scotland; information on soil maps for England & Wales may be obtained from the Soil Survey and Land Research Centre (SSLRC), and soil maps for Northern Ireland are available from the Ordnance Survey of Northern Ireland (OSNI).

5.5 Base Flow Index from the Hydrology Of Soil Types classification (BFIHOST)

In addition to Standard Percentage Runoff, Boorman *et al.* (1995) also give Base Flow Index (BFI) values for each HOST class. BFIHOST values are calculated automatically by the same methodology used to evaluate catchment values of

SPRHOST. Similarly, detailed soil mapping may be used to derive BFIHOST values manually, where appropriate.

5.6 Indexing soil wetness

Dry soils tend to inhibit flood formation, in contrast to the saturated soil conditions that precede many large flood events. Generalised soil moisture deficit data may well be useful in describing antecedent soil wetness.

5.6.1 Soil moisture deficit data

Generalised soil moisture deficit (SMD) data are produced by the Meteorological Office Rainfall and Evaporation Calculation System (MORECS) for the UK. For Great Britain, the data described here are those produced by the MORECS model detailed by Thompson *et al.* (1981), since MORECS Version 2.0 data were not available at that time. In Northern Ireland, MORECS data were not provided by the Met. Office until the Version 2.0 model was run for the Province in 1998, and consequently data from the more recent model were used.

Month-end values are derived from meteorological variables (rainfall, sunshine, temperature, wind speed and vapour pressure) measured at over 120 synoptic sites around the country. After standardisation procedures, the daily average values are interpolated to obtain values for 40 × 40 km squares. Soil moisture deficits derived from daily rainfall, less actual evaporation, are added to the previous day's soil moisture deficit to produce a month-end value for that square. The *month-end* SMD dataset gives the required geographical coverage at reasonable cost. For Great Britain the data used here were calculated for grassland with soil of medium water availability. The model allows SMD values to vary between zero (field capacity) up to a maximum deficit of 125 mm. Version 2.0 data do not have a maximum deficit that applies to all MORECS squares, since available water capacity is calculated for each individual square based on the soils present. There is no provision in either model to take into account the length of time for which the SMD is at the extreme limits.

Thompson *et al.* (1981) report close agreement between neutron probe SMD values and those derived by the MORECS system at the ten test sites. However, given the assumptions of the model, the relatively sparse meteorological station network and the large size of the grid squares, the SMD value can only be considered a generalised indication of average soil moisture conditions.

In Great Britain MORECS 40 × 40 km grid squares are numbered 1 to 190, starting in the north-west of Scotland and moving east and south. In Northern Ireland, squares are numbered from 191 to 201 in the same way. Some coastal areas of mainland Britain lie outside the 40 × 40 km grid, so to produce complete coverage, adjacent grid squares have been extended to incorporate all of mainland Britain (Figure 5.3). Where possible, an adjacent grid square with the most similar properties (i.e. proportion of coast and orientation) has been extended. For example, SMD data have not been calculated by the Met. Office for Square 82 (St. Bees Head, Cumbria) so, for completeness, the values from Square 76 immediately to the north of it have been used. Square 89 covers only open sea and consequently has no SMD data.

Similarly, in Northern Ireland some coastal and border areas lie outside the Met. Office's defined 40 × 40 km grid. For example, SMD data are not provided for the southernmost areas, and in this instance squares 198 to 201 have effectively been extended southwards.

31

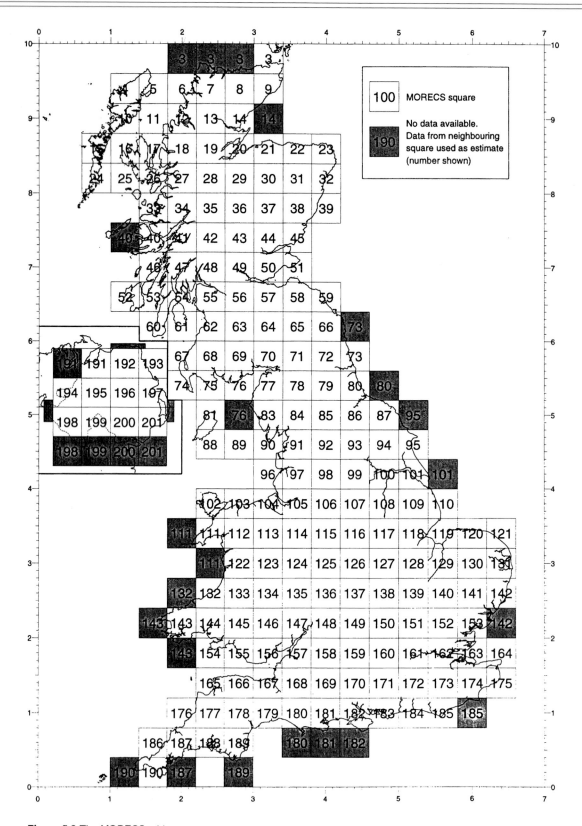

Figure 5.3 *The MORECS grid*

5.6.2 Derivation of catchment values of daily SMD

The fraction of the catchment that relates to each MORECS grid square was calculated and used as a weight to derive catchment SMD values. Figure 5.4 and Table 5.3 show an example of a catchment, the Teme at Tenbury, occupying parts of four MORECS squares.

Month-end SMD values were calculated for each of the 943 catchments for the period 1961-1990 using the catchment weights. These were then converted to daily values by linear interpolation between month-end values. The first 30 days of January 1961 were set to 'missing', since no data were available for the preceding month-end from which to interpolate. The maximum number of daily values is consequently reduced to 10957.

5.6.3 Definition of a wet catchment

A catchment is most likely to produce a flood response to rainfall when the soils are at field capacity (i.e. SMD = 0). However, such a narrow definition of field

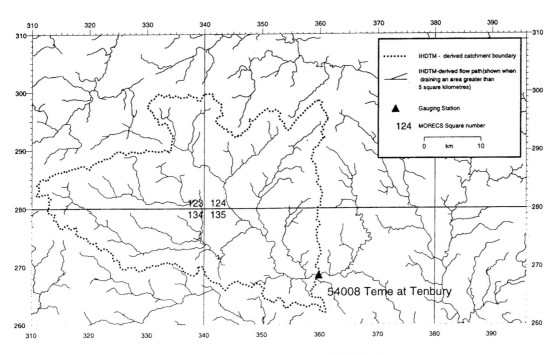

Figure 5.4 *The Teme at Tenbury (54008), covering parts of four MORECS grid squares*

Table 5.3 *Calculation of catchment weights for the Teme at Tenbury (54008)*

MORECS square	Area km²	Fraction of catchment
123	310.03	0.276
124	313.40	0.279
134	212.30	0.189
135	287.56	0.256
Total	1123.29	1.0

Catchment descriptors

capacity would be misleading in this case. The SMD values are theoretical and are allocated to a large and often heterogeneous area, as discussed previously. For this reason it was decided to define a wet catchment as one that was at or near to field capacity. Rather than picking an arbitrary threshold, peaks-over-threshold (POT) flood peak data were used to try to identify the soil moisture conditions when floods are most prevalent. The POT data used are all defined to a standardised threshold (Bayliss, 1994) to ensure greater consistency.

The daily SMD data can be divided into those days when a POT flood was recorded and those when no flood occurred. If these are plotted as percentages of each subset, it is apparent that at an SMD of 5.7 mm the lines cross (Figure 5.5). At this intersection, the antecedent conditions (represented by SMD) can be considered typically neutral to flood formation. When SMD values are less than 5.7 mm the probability of a flood occurring increases. Conversely, with SMD values greater than 5.7 mm the soil moisture conditions are more likely to inhibit flood formation. This intersection, rounded to 6 mm, is taken as the threshold above which the catchment is defined as dry.

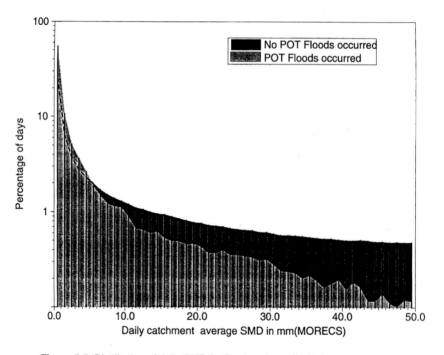

Figure 5.5 *Distribution of daily SMD for flood and non-flood days*

5.6.4 Derivation of wet and dry spells

Each day of the daily record was defined as either wet or dry, according to the 6 mm threshold. A series of n consecutive days with SMD greater than 6 mm is defined as a dry spell of n days duration. Conversely a series of consecutive days with SMD less than, or equal to, 6 mm is defined as a wet spell.

The number of consecutive days above or below the 6 mm threshold was calculated for 943 gauged catchments over the 30 year period 1961-90. The spell at the start of the data (beginning on 31 January 1961) was discarded, as was the final spell (terminating on 31 December 1990), because they are limited by the availability of data. Consequently, the total number of days in the analysis varies between catchments, depending on the length of the two spells discarded. These tend to be wet spells, since the data start and end in the winter months, and hence the majority of spells start with an SMD value exceeding 6.0 mm.

5.7 The catchment wetness indices

5.7.1 Mean daily Soil Moisture Deficit (SMDBAR)

Mean daily SMD (SMDBAR) values are calculated on the catchment daily SMD series generated using the area-weighting method described in Section 5.6.2. The bimodal distribution in Figure 5.6 represents SMDBAR values for the period 1961-90, computed for 943 catchments. Figure 5.7 shows that values range from less than 10 mm in northern Scotland to more than 50 mm in eastern England. Generally SMDBAR values increase as you move southwards and eastwards.

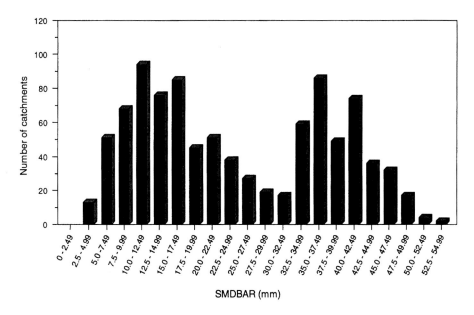

Figure 5.6 *Numerical distribution of SMDBAR values*

5.7.2 Proportion of time catchment soils are wet (PROPWET)

The proportion of the time that catchment soils are defined as wet (PROPWET) was calculated for 943 gauged catchments, using the catchment daily 'wet or dry' data described in Section 5.6.4. The numerical distribution of PROPWET values is presented in Figure 5.8. The highest PROPWET values are found in northern Scotland: e.g. the Cassley at Duchally (3801) has a PROPWET value of 0.84 (i.e. the SMD threshold was exceeded for 84% of the time during the period 1961-90).

The 'barcode' plots (Figure 5.9) enable catchment soil wetness to be compared visually, where the black bands depict dry spells and the white bands wet spells (relative to the 6 mm threshold). The width of the bands (x-axis) denotes

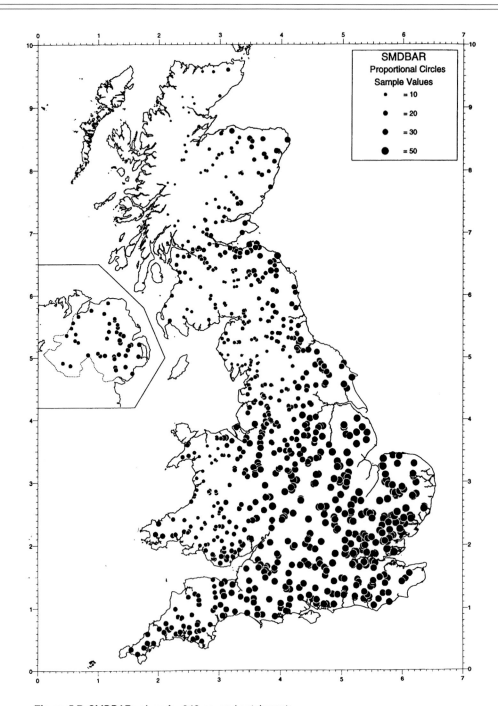

Figure 5.7 *SMDBAR values for 943 gauged catchments*

the duration of the wet or dry spell. The Glen at Kates Bridge (31002) has a PROPWET value of 0.22, which is typical of the drier parts of eastern England: wet spells are infrequent and of relatively short duration, while the proportion of time the catchment is dry (78%) means that a prevailing soil moisture deficit inhibits flood generation for much of the time. The other examples, from Yorkshire

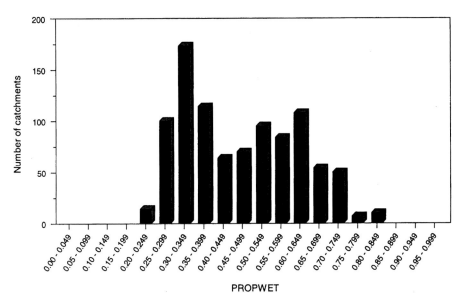

Figure 5.8 *Numerical distribution of PROPWET values*

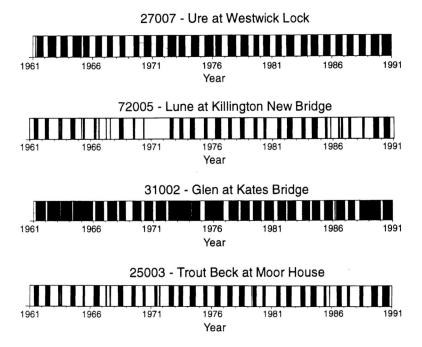

Figure 5.9 *Barcode plots for contrasting catchments*

(Ure at Westwick Lock), Cumbria (Lune at Killington New Bridge) and Northumbria (Trout Beck at Moor House), illustrate that catchment soils are typically wetter for a greater proportion of the time in the north and north-west, reflecting the increase in reliable frontal rainfall and lower evapotranspiration rates. This is borne out by the spatial distribution of PROPWET values shown in Figure 5.10.

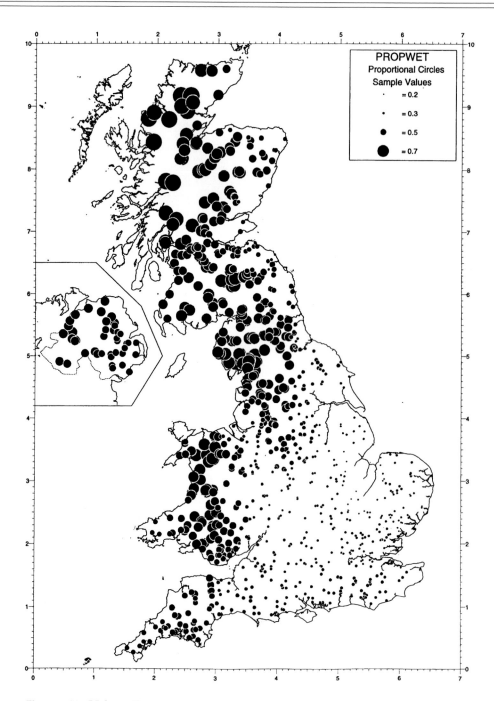

Figure 5.10 *PROPWET values for 943 gauged catchments*

Chapter 6 Urban and suburban land cover

6.1 Introduction

Urbanisation exerts considerable influence on the flood generation process, and often results in a more immediate and intense response to rainfall. Urban land use features strongly in flood estimation procedures and its importance has been emphasised in work on improving the estimation of small catchment response times (Marshall and Bayliss, 1994) and in Volumes 3 and 4 of the FEH. It is important, therefore, that indices describing catchment urbanisation be derived from an accurate source. In addition, the advantages of calculating catchment descriptors automatically using boundaries computed from the IHDTM, dictate that the source of urban land cover is in spatial digital form.

An early assessment of potential sources of urban land cover data suggested that a Land Cover Map of Great Britain, produced by the Institute of Terrestrial Ecology (ITE), could meet these requirements if the problem of overestimating urban land cover in rural areas could be overcome. In Northern Ireland, the European Commission programme "Coordination of Information on the Environment" (CORINE), provided combined land cover and land use mapping.

6.2 A land cover map for Great Britain

A land cover map, showing 25 cover types, was produced from a semi-automated classification of 30 m pixels recorded by the Landsat Thematic Mapper and is held at ITE on a 25 m grid. Key landscape features, where the spectral signature is strong, show patterns down to a minimum mappable unit of 0.00125 km² (0.125 ha). The use of a combination of seasonal images helped distinguish arable fields, bare in winter and vegetated in summer, and permanently bare surfaces, such as urban (Fuller *et al.*, 1994a). The target date for imagery was 1990, plus or minus two years, but with particularly good weather between 1988 and 1990, the majority of the coverage used came from this period. Cloud-speckle, and occasionally lying snow, often meant that the target summer and winter seasons had to be extended, sometimes by up to six weeks, and even with this compromise 11% of the coverage used remained single season (Fuller *et al.*, 1994b).

6.2.1 Urban and suburban

The discrimination of built-up areas into two land cover classes, urban and suburban, attempts to differentiate the density of development. The urban class comprises all developments which fill individual pixels and tends to include large areas of concrete and tarmac that can be found in cities and major industrial and commercial sites. The suburban class includes pixels where a mixture of built-up land and permanent vegetation has been recorded. This cover type is typical of housing developments found in city suburbs, small towns and villages. These two classes, urban and suburban, were supplied to the Institute of Hydrology, after generalisation, as a 50 m grid, to be consistent with the IHDTM.

6.2.2 Use of additional wavebands

Despite the use of summer and winter images to assist in discriminating between bare earth and built-up areas, there appears to be frequent misclassification of tilled land, and other areas, as urban or suburban. At the request of IH, a short study was undertaken by ITE, with the objective of evaluating the use of four

 A.C. Bayliss & R.M.J. Scarrott **39**

Thematic Mapper (TM) wavebands not previously used in the classification, in the hope that this would result in a more accurate definition of urban and suburban. A review of TM scenes held at ITE revealed that very few summer images were available with the additional bands sought (Groom and Fuller, 1995). However, the use of winter TM data alone offered greater possibilities for widespread improvement since many more scenes with the required data were available. Nevertheless much of Great Britain would remain outside the scope of existing data holdings. In the two pilot areas chosen for re-evaluation using the additional data, the results were mixed, with improvement in some areas but only limited success in others.

Since an improved ITE Land Cover Map of Great Britain, based on satellite imagery alone, was unlikely to be available before the FEH programme of research was complete, the decision was made to assess, using map information, the validity of each 50 m grid square classified by ITE as urban and suburban.

6.2.3 Validation using Ordnance Survey Strategi settlement data

Digital data from the Ordnance Survey (OS) 1:250000 Travelmaster Series are available under the product name Strategi. Although the digital representation of urban areas is available at more detailed scales (e.g. 1:10 000), the use of Strategi settlement data was seen as an accurate way of defining built-up areas in Great Britain at a reasonable cost. Settlement data are provided in vector format and define not only the outer limits of built-up areas but also non-urban areas, such as parks, within settlement polygons.

Since the OS Travelmaster Series is essentially a route-planning aid, accuracy is sometimes compromised for the sake of lucidity, in order that its primary function is fulfilled. As a consequence of scale, the settlement polygons are often generalised, and sometimes slightly displaced to improve clarity. In an attempt to overcome any effect that these spatial inaccuracies may have on the validation procedure, all polygons were extended with a 250 m buffer.

6.2.4 The validation process

The settlement polygons, with buffers, were used as an urban mask to test each individual 50 m square (throughout Great Britain), classified by ITE as urban or suburban. If the grid square fell within the polygon or buffer it was accepted, but if it lay outside the mask it was rejected. Figure 6.1 illustrates the validation process for an 8 km × 11 km area in Oxfordshire. The four shades of orange and pink represent ITE urban and suburban areas which have been accepted, since they fall within an OS settlement polygon (dark grey areas) or the 250 m buffer (light grey areas). ITE urban and suburban areas which did not fall within the polygons or associated buffers, have been rejected (dark and light green areas).

6.2.5 Evaluating the procedure's success

To determine the success of using a buffer of 250 m, and the validation procedure in general, plots covering approximately 24% of Great Britain in total (34 areas, each 40 km × 40 km) were examined and compared with the equivalent OS 1:50 000 Landranger sheets. This check confirmed that a buffer was necessary to prevent authentic ITE urban and suburban areas being rejected as a result of slight spatial inaccuracies in the OS settlement polygons. For a small number of 1:250000 settlement polygons the 250 m buffer appeared to be too large, with the result that apparently spurious ITE data just outside the polygons were being accepted, and in a few instances the buffer appeared to be too small, resulting in authentic data being rejected. However, for the majority of polygons a buffer size of 250 m was found to be a satisfactory compromise. In addition, since the ITE Land Cover Map is more contemporary than the OS settlement polygons, the use of a buffer often includes development on the outskirts of towns, which are not incorporated into the polygons, but have been identified on the TM images.

Figure 6.1 demonstrates the purpose of extending the settlement polygons with a buffer. For example, a significant proportion of ITE urban and suburban (dark and light orange areas) falls within the buffer (light grey areas) surrounding the polygon representing the town of Witney. Overlaying the plot on the relevant map from the OS 1:50 000 Landranger Series confirms that the polygon is slightly inaccurate and the presence of the buffer has meant that ITE urban and suburban has not been mistakenly rejected.

6.2.6 Manual additions to settlement polygons

The comparison of 34 validation plots with OS 1:50 000 maps indicated that overall the use of Strategi settlement polygons to correct ITE mapping of urban and suburban land cover classes resulted in a significant advancement of the dataset. However, further improvements were achieved by expanding the number of settlement polygons to include authentic urban and suburban areas identified by ITE, but which were not shown as built-up in the Strategi dataset. These areas include some airports, industrial estates, works and depots. In addition, although the majority of settlements are on the OS Travelmaster maps, a few villages have been omitted where they appear to be locally unimportant in the context of route planning. An assessment based on the number of falsely rejected areas, identified in the aforementioned plots, indicated that the manual digitising of polygons around these areas, for the whole of Great Britain, would be a manageable task, if a minimum threshold size of 0.25 km^2 was used. This work resulted in a further refinement of the dataset.

6.2.7 Summary of refinement procedure

The use of OS Strategi settlement polygons in validating urban and suburban areas, depicted by the ITE Land Cover Map of Great Britain, has seen a significant advancement in the accuracy of this digital dataset. Although some rejected built-up areas will be authentic, and a small number of spurious areas are likely to have been accepted, in general the classification is vastly improved. Manual additions to the OS set of polygons have provided further enhancement. The resultant validated dataset offers considerable advantages over using the OS data alone, since not only are built-up areas discriminated into two classes, but there are the additional benefits of a high definition grid (50 m) and the delineation of open spaces within settlements.

6.3 A land cover map for Northern Ireland

In 1985 the European Community (EC) set up a programme for the Coordination of Information on the Environment (CORINE) for member states. A major initiative within this framework is to establish a digital inventory of land cover within the EC, and in particular produce maps at a scale of 1:100 000, depicting 44 land cover and land use classes, with a minimum mappable unit of 0.25 km^2 (25 ha). The methodology comprises a semi-automated interpretation of satellite images with additional inputs from aerial photography and topographic mapping.

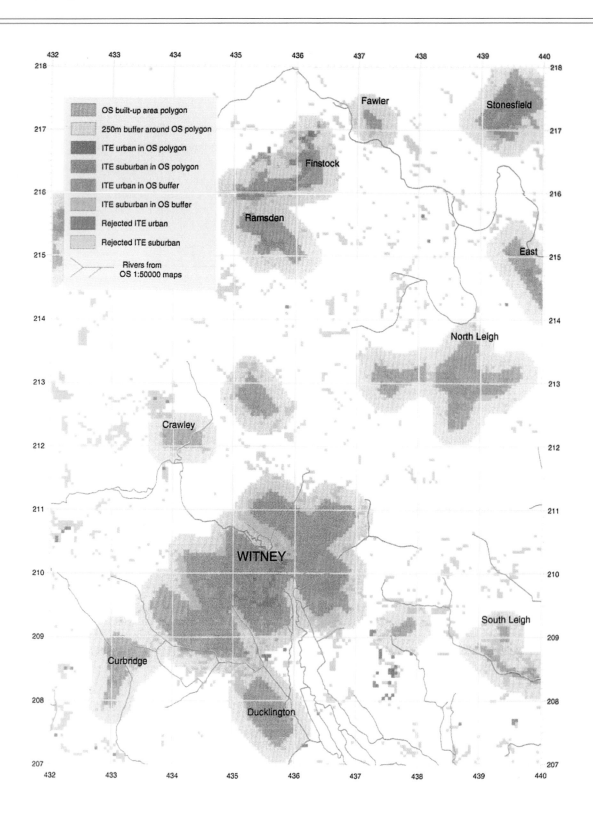

CORINE-standard mapping has been produced for Ireland (Brand and Mitchell, 1993) and as a result, data are available for all catchments within, or draining into, Northern Ireland. The CORINE nomenclature embraces land cover classes defined at three levels. The Level 1 group defined as 'artificial surfaces' (Table 6.1), includes a number of sub-classes which appear synonymous with the ITE Land Cover Map of Great Britain (LCMGB) classes urban and suburban. Vector data were obtained for all eleven Level 3 classes in the artificial surfaces group from the Ordnance Survey of Northern Ireland (OSNI).

Table 6.1 *The CORINE nomenclature for the Level 1 class 'artificial surfaces'*

Level 1	Level 2	Level 3
1. Artificial surfaces	1.1 Urban fabric	**1.1.1 Continuous urban fabric**
		1.1.2 Discontinuous urban fabric
	1.2 Industrial, commercial and transport units	**1.2.1 Industrial or commercial units**
		1.2.2 Road and rail networks and associated land
		1.2.3 Port areas
		1.2.4 Airports
	1.3 Mines, dumps and construction sites	1.3.1 Mineral extraction sites
		1.3.2 Dump sites
		1.3.3 Construction sites
	1.4 Artificial non-agricultural vegetated areas	1.4.1 Green urban areas
		1.4.2 Sport and leisure facilities

Emboldened font denotes those Level 3 classes judged equivalent to LCMGB urban and suburban classes

Polygons for these classes were plotted at 1:50000, to enable comparison with OSNI topographic maps at the same scale. CORINE data are based on satellite imagery taken between 1989 and 1990, and since the majority of maps relate to a similar period, their use in a validation procedure was feasible. With assistance from Rivers Agency staff at DANI, a number of misclassified areas were corrected and several new polygons added which were above the minimum mappable unit present in the CORINE dataset. The corrected vector data were regenerated as a regular 50 m grid using ARC/Info, to be consistent with the IHDTM and LCMGB data already held.

6.3.1 Equivalent urban and suburban classes

To ensure that the use of land cover data in Great Britain and Northern Ireland was carried out as consistently as possible, it was important to select equivalent classes in the two datasets. For Great Britain the ITE land cover types urban and suburban have been chosen as the most appropriate to represent urbanisation. Equivalent classes needed to be found from the artificial surfaces group in the CORINE mapping of Northern Ireland.

Comparable classes are suggested by Fuller and Brown (1996), in their description of the production of a CORINE equivalent map for a pilot area of Great Britain. CORINE cover type 1.1.1 (continuous urban fabric) is identified as being comparable to urban and 1.1.2 (discontinuous urban fabric) shown as equivalent to suburban. Five other CORINE classes, namely cover types (1.2.1, 1.2.2, 1.2.3, 1.2.4 and 1.4.2) are identified as being partly made up of both urban and suburban areas.

A comparison of the CORINE polygons with contemporary OSNI maps showed that the extent of urban and suburban land cover in two of these five mixed-cover classes was minimal. In the context of Northern Ireland, including CORINE classes 1.2.3 (port areas) and 1.4.2 (sport and leisure facilities) would unduly exaggerate the extent of urbanisation, and these classes were therefore rejected from the definition of equivalent urban and suburban areas. CORINE class 1.2.2 (road and rail networks and associated land) was also rejected, since in Great Britain, roads and railways were not included as urban or suburban land cover in the refined ITE data, except when running through built-up areas. The use of the Strategi polygons to reject spurious data (§6.2.3) meant that roads and railways in rural areas, even where large enough to be identified in the satellite data, were not included in the validated dataset.

In relation to Northern Ireland, CORINE land cover type 1.1.1 (continuous urban fabric) and 1.2.1 (industrial or commercial units) were judged to be equivalent to the refined ITE class urban. As regards equivalent suburban classes in the CORINE dataset, cover types 1.1.2 (discontinuous urban fabric), and 1.2.4 (airports), appeared to be comparable since they represented a mixture of built-up land and permanent vegetation. Table 6.1 shows these selected urban and suburban equivalent CORINE classes in bold type.

Although equivalent land cover classes were chosen to represent urban and suburban areas in Great Britain and Northern Ireland, it is evident that the level of detail shown by the CORINE classes (minimum mappable unit 0.25 km²) is far below that depicted by the LCMGB (minimum mappable unit of 0.00125 km²). The four CORINE classes described above, represent built-up areas in Northern Ireland reasonably well, but the resolution of the data means that at the scale required here, the delineation of urban and suburban areas is not sufficiently accurate.

6.4 Indexing catchment urbanisation

The indexing of catchment urbanisation has for many years involved the manual extraction of information from maps. However, the availability of gridded urban and suburban land cover data, and the capability to produce catchment boundaries from the IHDTM, offered the chance to automate the procedure and to consider spatial aspects of urbanisation too onerous to contemplate using manual techniques.

IHDTM-derived catchment boundaries can be produced both quickly and accurately for the majority of catchments and can be applied automatically to any gridded dataset. The refinement of urban and suburban data taken from the ITE Land Cover Map of Great Britain, using a validation process based on OS polygons representing built-up areas (§6.2.4) and manually digitised polygons representing industrial estates, airports and other important omissions from the OS data, meant that the validated urban and suburban data could be used with confidence. In Northern Ireland, corrections to the CORINE dataset identified by Rivers Agency staff, and the selection of equivalent urban and suburban classes, meant that automated procedures could be extended there.

6.5 Extent of urban and suburban land cover

6.5.1 Introduction

The 1970s Flood Studies Team found in early regression trials that a measure describing the extent of built-up areas within a catchment was significant and asked the Department of Environment (DoE) to provide recent 1:625000 maps showing these areas. The urban fraction of each catchment was calculated by using catchment boundary overlays and these fractions are listed in Volume IV of the Flood Studies Report (NERC, 1975). It was realised that this was a crude estimate, given the scale of the maps being used, and subsequent advice was to estimate the built-up fraction of the catchment from the flesh-coloured areas on OS 1:50000 scale maps. However, even at this larger scale it is not easy to discriminate between different types of development and as a consequence the urban value calculated includes all categories of housing and industrial development.

6.5.2 Comparison of digital and map-based techniques

The Land Cover Map of Great Britain does discriminate between urban and suburban areas (Fuller *et al.*, 1994a). The urban class comprises all developments large enough to completely fill individual pixels (30 m square), typically cities and large town centres, major industrial and commercial sites. The suburban class describes pixels where a mixture of built-up land and permanent vegetation has been recorded, and is characteristic of lower-density housing and rural development. IHDTM-derived boundaries were used to compute urban and suburban fractions automatically from the refined gridded data.

Figure 6.2 compares urban values for 647 sites calculated manually from maps (principally those published in the FSR, with some subsequent corrections

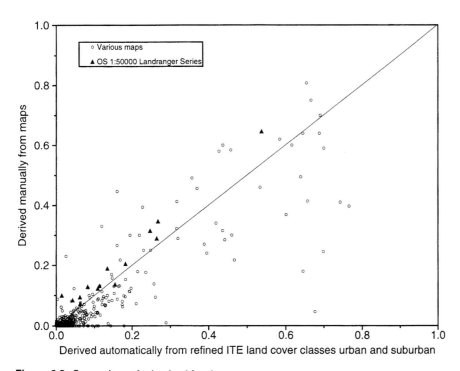

Figure 6.2 *Comparison of urbanised fractions*

and additions) and those derived from gridded data. The urban and suburban fractions taken from the refined ITE data have been added together so that they are consistent with the map-derived values in that they include all types of urban development.

Those map-derived values known to have been taken from the OS 1:50000 Landranger Series are shown as filled triangles: with the exception of one catchment, they are consistently higher than those calculated from the refined ITE data. This may seem surprising, given that the Landranger maps used are *circa* 1983 and the majority of the satellite imagery used to derive the ITE data were images taken between 1988 and 1990 (Fuller *et al.*, 1994b). The expectation is that urbanisation would increase not decrease. However, the symbolisation of built-up areas on OS 1:50000 maps tends to exaggerate the true extent of the buildings to aid map clarity and, in addition, the maps tend not to distinguish small non-urban areas within the urban polygon. In contrast, these small 'green areas' within built-up areas are evident in the refined ITE data held at IH as a 50 m grid. The time-consuming nature of manual extraction of urban information from maps also means that, where small non-urban areas within built-up areas are shown on the OS map, they may get overlooked. The automatic derivation of urban and suburban values from the gridded data always takes into account these green areas within towns and cities. The higher Landranger-based values, therefore, are likely to reflect differences in the nature of the two datasets, and the relative inaccuracy of the manual-derivation when compared with an automated technique, rather than any differences in catchment urbanisation between 1983 and 1990.

Figure 6.2 shows that, although values taken from the Landranger Series tend to be higher than those derived from the gridded data, there is considerable scatter when comparing the refined ITE data with the other map-derived urban fractions (open circles). The map-based values are principally those derived by the Flood Studies Team using the 1:625000 DOE built-up area maps, with some corrections and additions from OS 1:50000 First and Second Series maps. An examination of outliers seemed to show errors in the map-derived values, most likely as a result of misregistration of the catchment boundary overlay on the source map.

6.5.3 A composite index (URBEXT) for Great Britain

The urban and suburban fractions (URB_{EXT} and $SUBURB_{EXT}$), based on the refined ITE (RITE) data, were combined into a single index. However, rather than merging the two indices by simple addition, intuitively it would seem logical to give more weight to the urban fraction since it is known that the types of development included by ITE in this class (e.g. city centres, major industrial and commercial sites) have, because of the greater density of impermeable surfaces and the presence of storm-water sewerage, a greater influence on the flood generation process.

To determine an appropriate weighting for urban and suburban fractions, in the calculation of a composite index, urban values ($URBAN_{50K}$) were extracted from OS 1:50000 Landranger maps (using the FSR methodology), for 25 of the catchments used in the Volume 3 analyses. This gave $URBAN_{50K}$ values in the range 0.053 to 0.850. For the same 25 catchments, urban and suburban fractions were calculated from the RITE data. By regression the following relationship was established:

$$URBAN_{50K} = 2.05 \, (URBAN_{EXT} + 0.495 \, SUBURB_{EXT}) \qquad (6.1)$$

Box 6.1 Categories of catchment urbanisation

Six categories of catchment urbanisation are distinguished in the FEH, according to their URBEXT values.

Essentially rural	$0.000 \le URBEXT < 0.025$
Slightly urbanised	$0.025 \le URBEXT < 0.050$
Moderately urbanised	$0.050 \le URBEXT < 0.125$
Heavily urbanised	$0.125 \le URBEXT < 0.250$
Very heavily urbanised	$0.250 \le URBEXT < 0.500$
Extremely heavily urbanised	$0.500 \le URBEXT \le 1.000$

Thus, it can be seen that the urban index used in FSR, based on the manual extraction of information from maps will give, on average, a value approximately twice that derived automatically from the refined ITE data. It is also evident that an appropriate weighting for $SUBURB_{EXT}$ would seem to be about 0.5. This is supported by the fact that the suburban class consists of pixels where a mixture of built-up land and permanent vegetation have been recorded, so on average you might expect urban development to occupy one-half of each pixel in this land cover class. Thus, a composite index of urban extent is given by

$$URBEXT = URB_{EXT} + 0.5\ SUBURB_{EXT} \tag{6.2}$$

6.5.4 An urban index for Northern Ireland

In Northern Ireland, four CORINE classes, thought to be equivalent to the LCMGB urban and suburban classes, are taken to represent urban development (§6.3.1). A catchment value of urban extent (URB_{CORINE}) is defined by computing the sum of the fractions for these four classes, where

$$URB_{CORINE} = CORINE_{111} + CORINE_{112} + CORINE_{121} + CORINE_{124} \tag{6.3}$$

The composite index URBEXT, provided for use in Great Britain, incorporates an appropriate weighting of 0.5 for the suburban component (Equation 6.2). Differences between the LCMGB and the CORINE datasets mean that the application of the same weighting to equivalent suburban classes could not be justified. Indeed the low resolution of the data does not warrant using urban and suburban equivalent classes independently.

In addition, since the CORINE dataset has a minimum mappable unit of 0.25 km², many small rural settlements are not represented, and conurbations are depicted in a generalised way. Comparisons with OSNI maps reveal that the CORINE dataset tends to underestimate urban development in rural areas but often exaggerates the extent of major conurbations. It is therefore important that an adjustment procedure is applied to URB_{CORINE} values so that they are consistent with the $URBEXT$ values used in Great Britain (§6.5.6).

6.5.5 Relationship between URBAN$_{50K}$ and URBEXT

Section 6.5.3 describes the relationship between urban and suburban extent, derived automatically from refined ITE data, and urban fraction, taken from OS maps using the FSR methodology ($URBAN_{50K}$). Combining Equations 6.1 and 6.2 yields

$$URBAN_{50K} = 2.05\ URBEXT \qquad (6.4)$$

Thus, an $URBAN_{50K}$ index value is likely to be, on average, approximately twice that of an equivalent $URBEXT$ value. The symbolisation of built-up areas on OS 1:50000 maps tends to exaggerate and does not always distinguish small non-urban areas within the urban polygon. In contrast, the refined ITE (RITE) classes urban and suburban, used to define $URBEXT$ values, do not systematically overestimate and do generally preserve 'green areas' within towns and cities.

Equation 6.4 was established by regression using $URBAN_{50K}$ and $URBEXT$ values for 25 gauged catchments, where the maximum $URBEXT$ value is 0.423 (Figure 6.3). However, there are many small ungauged catchments where $URBEXT$ values approaching one are found. There was some concern that this relationship may not apply to extremely heavily urbanised catchments, so some additional $URBAN_{50K}$ and $URBEXT$ values were calculated (represented as triangles in Figure 6.3), and as expected these indicate a relationship closer to 1:1. For these sites, the composite index $URBEXT$ is able to reflect the difference between a very heavily urbanised catchment and an extremely heavily urbanised catchment, which OS urban mapping at 1:50000 scale is unable to do.

Clearly the relationship established between $URBAN_{50K}$ and $URBEXT$ (Equation 6.4) cannot apply to extremely heavily urbanised catchments since this would yield values of $URBAN_{50K}$ greater than one. Considerations such as those

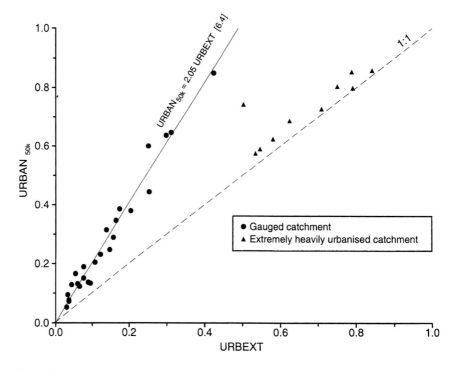

Figure 6.3 *Relationship between URBAN$_{50K}$ and URBEXT*

described above, led to the general recommendation that FEH flood frequency estimation procedures (both in Volume 3 and Volume 4) should not be routinely applied to extremely heavily urbanised catchments (i.e. where $URBEXT \geq 0.5$).

6.5.6 An adjustment procedure for Northern Ireland

The CORINE dataset tends to underestimate urban development in rural areas and often exaggerates the true extent of major settlements (§6.5.4). It is important that URB_{CORINE} values are adjusted so that they are consistent with the $URBEXT$ values produced for Great Britain. Comparison of LCMGB and CORINE data for the same area would enable a procedure to be derived whereby $URBEXT$ values could be estimated from URB_{CORINE} values. However, as the two datasets are not currently available for the same area, an indirect approach has been taken.

First, a relationship between automatically-derived URB_{CORINE} values and manually-derived $URBAN_{50K}$ values (using OSNI 1:50000 maps) is required. $URBAN_{50K}$ and URB_{CORINE} values were computed for 29 catchments in Northern Ireland (Figure 6.4). For essentially rural catchments, the CORINE mapping (with a minimum mappable unit of 0.25 km²) tends to underestimate urban and suburban extent so that URB_{CORINE} values need to be increased if they are to be equivalent to those taken from maps. Other, more urbanised catchments, tend to include towns and major conurbations which have been exaggerated by the CORINE mapping. These URB_{CORINE} values need to be reduced to be equivalent to $URBAN_{50K}$ values.

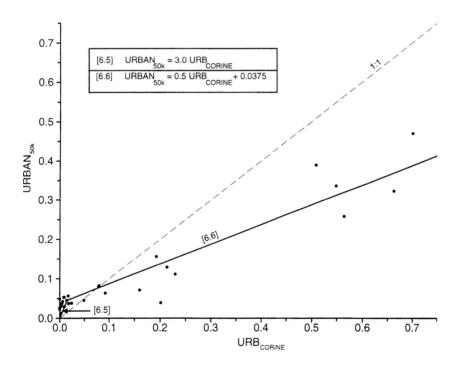

Figure 6.4 *Relationship between $URBAN_{50K}$ and URB_{CORINE}*

Fitting using a least-squares method produced unsatisfactory results, so a straight line relationship, with an appropriate break point, was fitted by eye (Figure 6.4). The respective equations are:

$$URBAN_{50K} = 3.0 \ URB_{CORINE} \qquad \text{when } URB_{CORINE} \leq 0.015 \qquad (6.5)$$

$$URBAN_{50K} = 0.5 \ URB_{CORINE} + 0.0375 \qquad \text{when } URB_{CORINE} > 0.015 \qquad (6.6)$$

Second, by reversing the relationship defined in the previous section (Equation 6.4), $URBEXT$ values can be estimated from values of $URBAN_{50K}$ using the equation below:

$$URBEXT = URBAN_{50K} \ / \ 2.05 \qquad (6.7)$$

This adjustment procedure provides a technique for automatically defining $URBEXT$ values in Northern Ireland. However, for some small catchments, the generalised nature of the CORINE mapping may be inappropriate for use in defining URB_{CORINE}, and subsequently an $URBEXT$ value. In this situation it is recommended that an $URBAN_{50K}$ value is derived by calculating the extent of flesh-coloured areas on OSNI 1:50000 maps. This manually derived $URBAN_{50K}$ value can then be used to estimate a value of $URBEXT$ using Equation 6.7.

6.5.7 URBEXT values for 943 gauged catchments

Values of $URBEXT$ have been calculated for 901 catchments in Great Britain, using refined LCMGB data and the methodology described in §6.5.3. In Northern Ireland $URBEXT$ values for 42 catchments have been based on CORINE data (§6.5.4), and adjusted to be approximately comparable with those derived in Great Britain (see §6.5.6).

Figure 6.5 shows that, although the majority of these catchments are essentially rural, a significant proportion (over 22%) have values greater than or equal to 0.025 and 13 percent have values greater than or equal to 0.05.

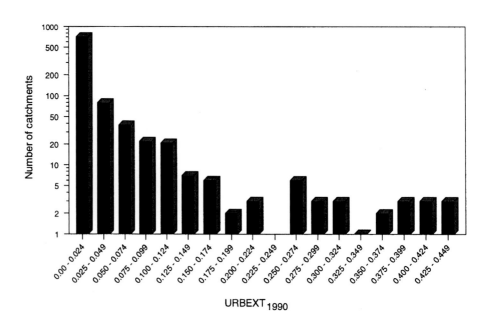

Figure 6.5 *Numerical distribution of URBEXT$_{1990}$ values*

Figure 6.6 shows the spatial distribution of *URBEXT* values with a circle, located at the catchment outlet, whose size is proportional to the index value.

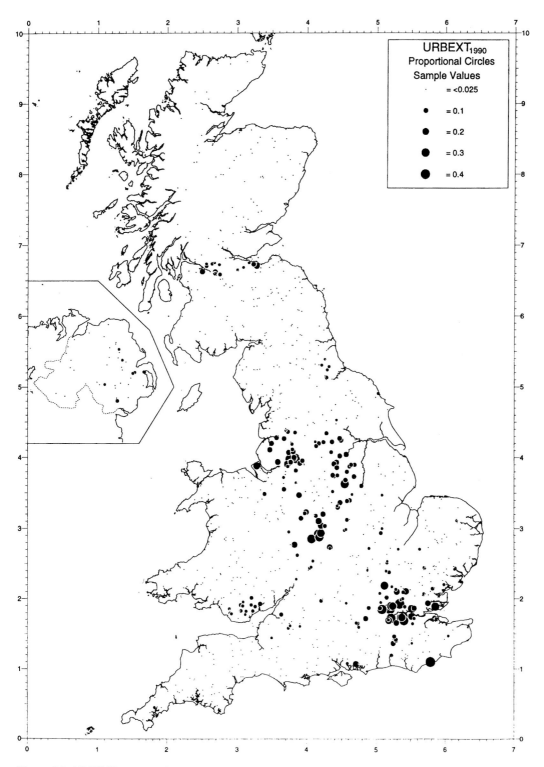

Figure 6.6 *URBEXT$_{1990}$ values for 943 gauged catchments*

Partly urbanised catchments are evident, notably in South Wales, Yorkshire, Nottinghamshire, Glasgow and Edinburgh, but the most heavily urbanised catchments are found mainly in London, Birmingham and Manchester. In Northern Ireland, most of the 42 catchments shown are essentially rural. Figure 6.7 shows a small catchment in South London (39058 – Pool at Winsford Road) which is dominated by urban and suburban land cover, and this is reflected in the high index value of 0.432.

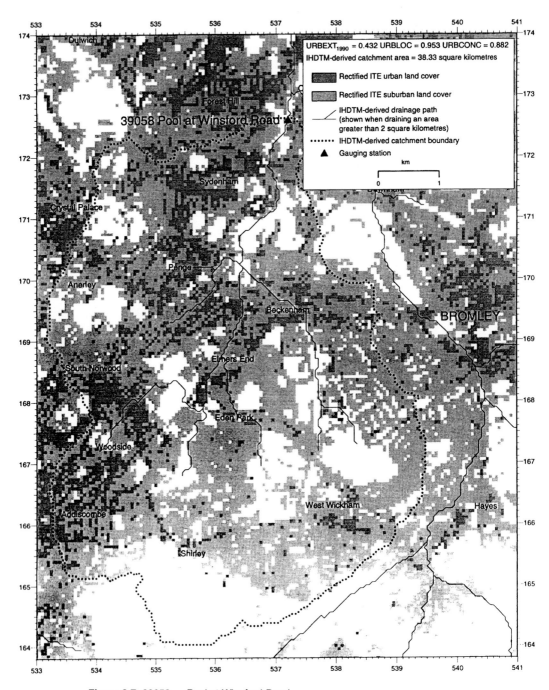

Figure 6.7 *39058 — Pool at Winsford Road*

6.5.8 Adjusting URBEXT to relate to the period of record in use

The Land Cover Map of Great Britain, produced by ITE, is based on satellite imagery whose target date was 1990 (§6.2). The CORINE land cover classification in Northern Ireland is also based on imagery taken from the same period. Since the extent of a land cover class such as suburban, generally changes with time, the *URBEXT* values derived from these two classifications relate to the situation in 1990. The data presented in Figures 6.5 and 6.6 for 943 gauged catchments therefore, describe urban and suburban development around 1990 (denoted by the use of the 1990 subscript).

Many of the flood records that are available for use in the UK are typically 'centred in time' earlier than 1990. If no adjustment is made to the $URBEXT_{1990}$ value then, in many cases, the level of urbanisation related to flood records would be too high. At these sites, any effect on the flood regime that is attributable to urban extent has been produced by less urban and suburban development than reflected in the $URBEXT_{1990}$ index. It is therefore desirable, to adjust the 1990 value to a level of urbanisation which more closely relates to the period of record being used.

'Urban area' values for English counties and regions, relating to 5-yearly 'snapshots' during the period 1945-1990, have been published by the Council for the Protection of Rural England (CPRE, 1993). These have been used here to compute the urban area in England, as a fraction of the 1990 value, for each of these 5-yearly points. The growth in land under urban development, shown in Figure 6.8, suggested a model based on an inverse tan function. The urban area is represented as a fraction of the 1990 value, termed the urban expansion factor (*UEF*). The model fitted to the data was:

$$UEF = 0.8165 + 0.2254 \tan^{-1}\left\{(Year - 1967.5)/21.25\right\} \qquad (6.8)$$

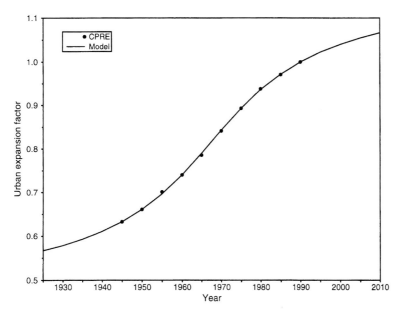

Figure 6.8 *Urban expansion based on data published by CPRE (1993)*

$URBEXT_{1990}$ values have been adjusted in this way for use in the modelling of $QMED$ in Volume 3 and $Tp(0)$ in Volume 4. The model is based on urban area figures for England, and the rate of increase in urbanisation between 1945-90 may well be different in Wales, Scotland and Northern Ireland. However, the adjustment procedure has been applied throughout the UK, since a broad approximation of urban area before 1990 in these regions is preferable to using an unadjusted $URBEXT$ value.

6.6 Location of urban and suburban land cover

6.6.1 Introduction

The location of urban and suburban land cover is likely to be influential in determining how and when a catchment responds to rainfall. Although the possible scenarios are manifold, and their likely effect depends on other factors (e.g. soil type), indexing the location of built-up areas (whether they be near to the catchment outlet or centred in the headwaters) should improve understanding of how spatial variations in urban and suburban land cover affect the flood hydrograph.

The IHDTM defines a drainage direction for each 50 m grid node based on the steepest route to one of its eight neighbours (Morris and Heerdegen, 1988), from which a complementary grid of inflow data has been generated. Rather than use the straight-line distance from the catchment outlet to each grid node in the derivation of a location index, it is more appropriate to use the distance along the IHDTM defined drainage paths. By using the inflow grid this distance can be calculated for any grid node in the catchment.

6.6.2 A composite index (*URBLOC*) for Great Britain

The urban and suburban location parameters (URB_{LOC} and $SUBURB_{LOC}$) are calculated by computing the mean drainage path distance to all RITE urban grid nodes and to all suburban nodes, respectively. Both are expressed as a fraction of the mean distance to all nodes that fall within the catchment, as given in the following equations:

$$URB_{LOC} = \frac{URBDIST_{MEAN}}{DIST_{MEAN}} \qquad SUBURB_{LOC} = \frac{SUBURBDIST_{MEAN}}{DIST_{MEAN}}$$

Figure 6.9 shows the derivation of these parameters for a small catchment with two suburban grid nodes. Firstly, the distances A to outlet and B to outlet, along their respective drainage paths, are calculated. Secondly, the mean of these two distances is expressed as a ratio of the mean distance of all grid nodes in the catchment, to give the suburban parameter ($SUBURB_{LOC}$). The urban parameter (URB_{LOC}) is undefined in this instance as no urban land cover is present.

In keeping with the indexing of the extent of urban and suburban land cover, a composite index, combining the urban and suburban parameters, has been calculated. The fraction of the catchment given to the respective land cover classes has been used to weight the addition of the urban and suburban location parameters.

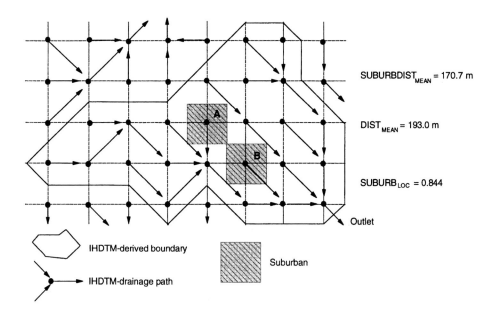

SUBURBDIST$_{\text{MEAN}}$ = 170.7 m

DIST$_{\text{MEAN}}$ = 193.0 m

SUBURB$_{\text{LOC}}$ = 0.844

Outlet

⬡ IHDTM-derived boundary

↙ IHDTM-drainage path

▨ Suburban

Figure 6.9 *IHDTM drainage paths are used to define the distance to the catchment outlet*

Thus

$$URBLOC = \frac{URB_{\text{EXT}} \; URB_{\text{LOC}} + \frac{1}{2} \, SUBURB_{\text{EXT}} \; SUBURB_{\text{LOC}}}{URB_{\text{EXT}} + \frac{1}{2} \, SUBURB_{\text{EXT}}}$$

The urban and suburban location parameters, and hence the composite index, are not defined when the catchment is completely rural and are poorly defined when it is nearly so. Therefore, when *URBEXT* is less than 0.005, the location parameters are not evaluated.

6.6.3 An URBLOC index for Northern Ireland

In Northern Ireland, the poor resolution of the data does not justify delineating between urban and suburban land cover in the computation of the urban location index (*URBLOC*). Here, the drainage path distance is calculated to all grid nodes which are designated as CORINE classes 1.1.1, 1.1.2, 1.2.1 and 1.2.4 (i.e. those that are judged to be equivalent to the RITE classes urban or suburban). The *URBLOC* index is then defined as the mean of these distances (*CORDIST*$_{\text{MEAN}}$), divided by the mean of distances between all nodes within the catchment and its outlet. Thus

$$URBLOC = CORDIST_{\text{MEAN}} \; / \; DIST_{\text{MEAN}} \tag{6.11}$$

6.6.4 *URBLOC* values for 516 catchments

URBLOC has been calculated for all 516 sites where *URBEXT* is greater than or equal to 0.005. Since the catchment mean distance is generally at a point half-way between its outlet and most distant watershed, a built-up area close to the gauged point gives *URBLOC* values close to zero, while development in the most remote parts of the catchment will produce values approaching two. Figure 6.10 shows that the location index takes on values between 0.1 and 1.6. The distribution shows that development is less prevalent in the catchment headwaters than in the area around the catchment outlet, where the land is generally flatter.

Figure 6.11 illustrates the spatial distribution of *URBLOC* values in the UK, where the larger circles represent catchments which have urban and suburban development further from the catchment outlet than those depicted by a small circle. No strong spatial pattern is evident. Figure 6.12 shows the location of urban and suburban land cover for the Roding catchment to Redbridge (37001). Much of the development in the catchment is sited near the river gauging station, which is reflected in a low index value of 0.427.

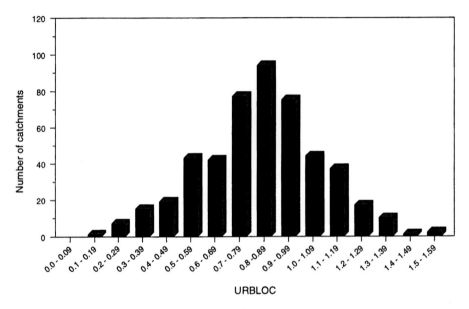

Figure 6.10 *Numerical distribution of URBLOC values*

6.7 Concentration of urban and suburban land cover

6.7.1 Introduction

In addition to the *extent* and *location* of urban and suburban land cover, the degree to which built-up areas are *concentrated* within a catchment is likely to have some effect on the flood regime. If catchment development comprises a large number of small settlements, then a significant proportion of storm-water following a rainfall event is likely to enter soakaways, with the soil usually acting as a buffer to catchment response, dependent on the prevailing wetness conditions. Conversely, if that same amount of development was concentrated into a single conurbation then it is likely that storm-water sewerage would be present and catchment response accelerated.

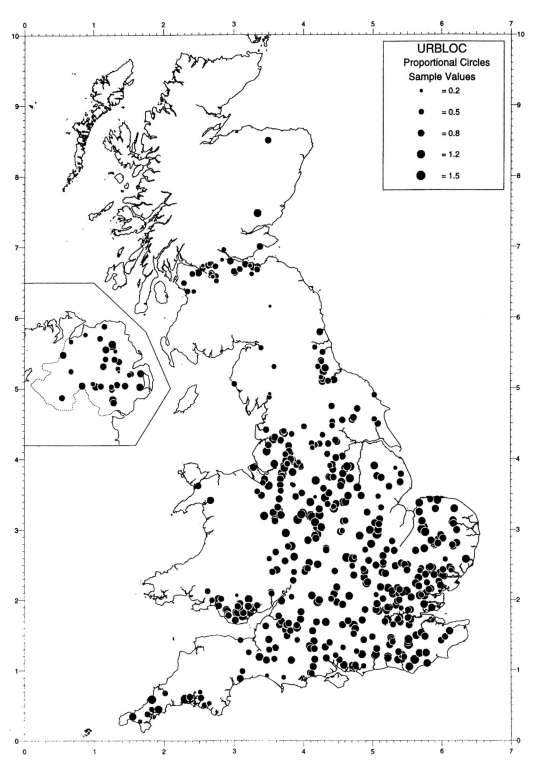

Figure 6.11 *URBLOC values for 516 gauged catchments*

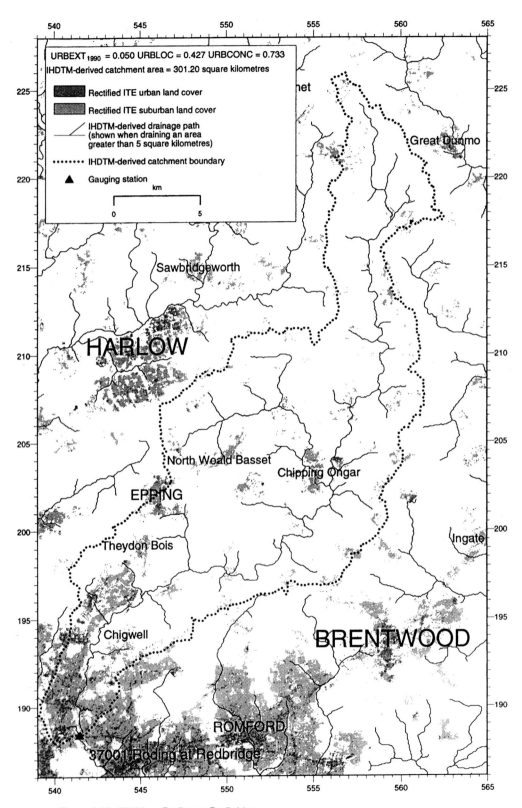

URBEXT$_{1990}$ = 0.050 URBLOC = 0.427 URBCONC = 0.733
IHDTM-derived catchment area = 301.20 square kilometres

Rectified ITE urban land cover

Rectified ITE suburban land cover

IHDTM-derived drainage path
(shown when draining an area
greater than 5 square kilometres)

IHDTM-derived catchment boundary

▲ Gauging station

km

0   5

Figure 6.12 37001 — Roding at Redbridge

6.7.2 A concentration index (URBCONC)

The first step in the indexing procedure dictates that, for each urban and suburban grid node within the catchment, the number of adjacent nodes flowing to the point under examination, along IHDTM-derived drainage paths, is computed ($INFLOW_{TOTAL}$). Those grid nodes with no other points flowing to it are ignored. When this count is made the number of inflowing nodes which are urban or suburban is also noted ($INFLOW_{URB/SUBURB}$). Urban and suburban nodes are not differentiated and the procedure adopted for both land cover types is the same (Figure 6.13).

The concentration index describes the 'connectivity' of urban and suburban nodes, and it is inappropriate to differentiate urban and suburban elements. Thus the concentration index is derived by finding the catchment total number of inflows to urban or suburban nodes, which are themselves urban or suburban, and expressing this total as a fraction of the catchment total number of inflows to urban or suburban nodes, and is given by

$$URBCONC \ = \ \frac{\sum_{1}^{n}INFLOW_{URB/SUBURB}}{\sum_{1}^{n}INFLOW_{TOTAL}}$$

In Northern Ireland, the coarse resolution of the CORINE land cover data means that urban and suburban areas generally *appear* to be more concentrated than they are in Great Britain. This is the result of differences in the resolution of the data rather than real differences in settlement patterns. Consequently, as they are likely to be misleading, *URBCONC* values have not been computed for Northern Ireland.

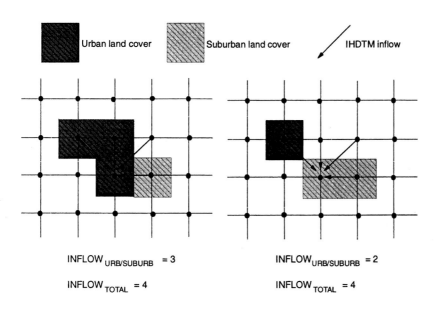

Figure 6.13   *Computing the number of inflowing grid nodes and the number that are urban or suburban*

6.7.3 *URBCONC* values for 484 gauged catchments

The concentration index is defined for 484 catchments in Great Britain where *URBEXT* is greater than, or equal to, 0.005, and the distribution of these values is shown in Figure 6.14. The modal value is between 0.6 and 0.65 which indicates that, for these catchments, typically, nearly two thirds of neighbouring nodes which flow to urban or suburban nodes, are themselves urban or suburban.

Figure 6.15 indicates that no strong spatial patterns are evident but high *URBCONC* values are more commonly found in, or close to, the major conurbations. The Trent catchment to Drakelow Park (28019) includes much of the city of Birmingham in its headwaters (Figure 6.16) and this is reflected in a high concentration index value of 0.821 and a high location index value of 1.199.

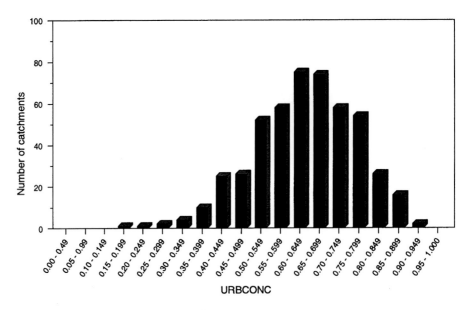

Figure 6.14 *Numerical distribution of URBCONC values*

6.8 Summary

IHDTM-derived catchment boundaries have been applied automatically to the refined ITE urban and suburban land cover data in Great Britain, and equivalent classes taken from CORINE data for Northern Ireland, to produce an index describing the extent of catchment urbanisation for 943 catchments with flood peak data. For catchments which have an URBEXT value greater than or equal to 0.005, indices relating to the location and concentration of built-up areas have been defined for 516 catchments in respect of the former, and 484 catchments in respect of the latter.

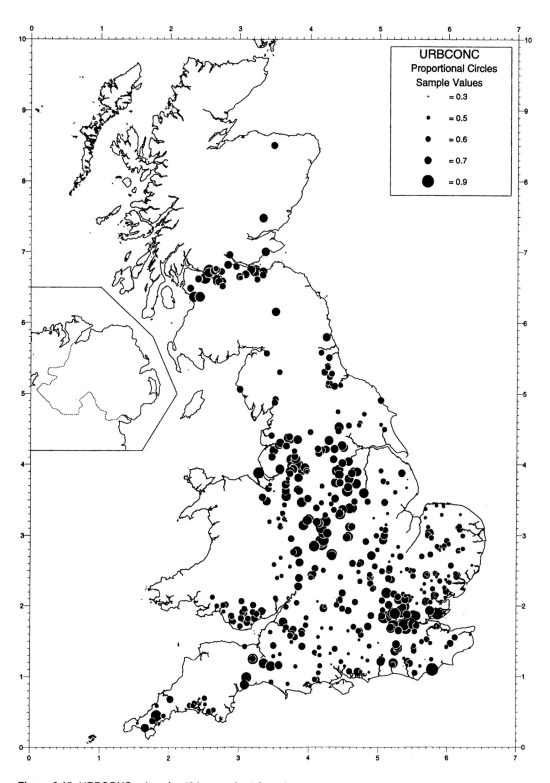

Figure 6.15 *URBCONC values for 484 gauged catchments*

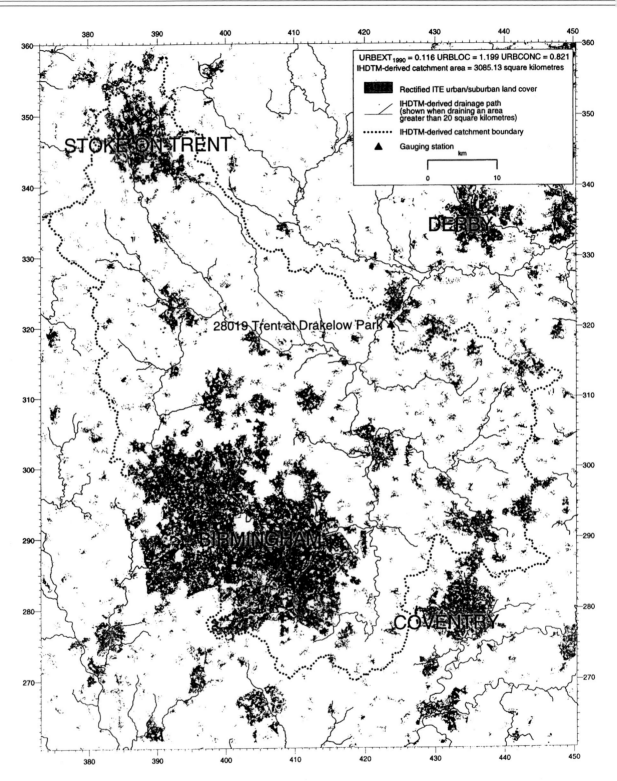

Figure 6.16 *28019 — Trent at Drakelow Park*

The relationships between the three indices are presented for these catchments, on a logarithmic scale, in Figure 6.17. Index values of location against extent (Diagram A) show the scatter of points around a dashed line denoting an URBLOC value of 1.0 (the mean distance to the outlet from all nodes within the catchment). The greater number of points below the line indicates that urban and suburban development is more prevalent on the generally flatter land of the lower catchment, than the often steeper slopes of the catchment headwaters. Diagram B supports the conclusion that catchments which have high index values of concentration are found in the most heavily urbanised areas, while Diagram C indicates there is considerable scatter when comparing the location and concentration index values for the 484 catchments.

The computation of an index describing the extent to which the catchment is urbanised, using automated procedures and based on recent satellite imagery, is seen to have advantages of accuracy, reproducibility and currency, over the manual map-based techniques used in the past. The availability of urban and suburban data in a gridded form has also allowed the derivation of two new indices describing spatial aspects of urbanisation not previously considered.

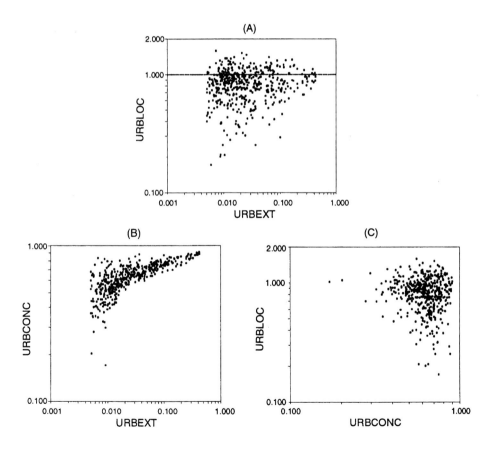

Figure 6.17 *Relationship between the extent, location and concentration index for 484 gauged catchments*

Chapter 7 Catchment descriptor values for an ungauged site

7.1 FEH CD-ROM

Catchment descriptors for ungauged sites are supplied on the FEH CD-ROM, which is available from the Institute of Hydrology. They are provided at all locations on drainage paths with a catchment area of at least 0.5 km², for mainland Britain, Northern Ireland, the Isle of Wight and Anglesey. In addition to the descriptors, catchment average values of the six parameters of the rainfall depth-duration-frequency model (Volume 2) are also provided at these locations.

When retrieving data from the CD-ROM, it is important to select the appropriate point on the drainage path: 'browser' software is provided to assist in this. Initially, a map of the UK is displayed to help locate the area that contains the subject site, which is achieved using the mouse and the zoom facility. Alternatively the grid reference can be typed in if known, or a place name can be selected from the gazeteer. For the chosen area, the browser displays the catchment boundary, together with drainage paths, urban areas, place names, gauging stations, lakes, reservoirs and coastline, if applicable (Figure 7.1). By moving the mouse pointer across the map around the site, the software illustrates the catchment that drains to each selected location. This enables the appropriate location to be chosen, based on the catchments displayed. The user must have a preconceived idea of what the catchment should be before using the browser. This may be based on published material defining the catchment or derived from an inspection of OS maps.

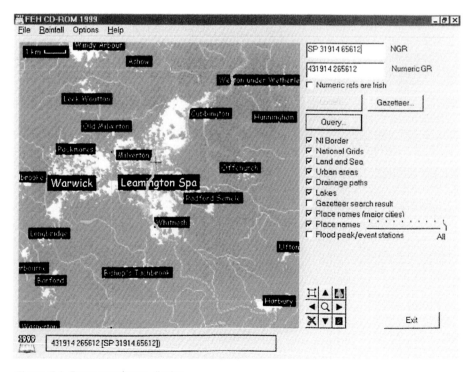

Figure 7.1 Browser software display

When the required catchment has been found, the user can abstract the catchment descriptors from the database. The values are reported on the screen and can be saved as a file or exported into the WINFAP-FEH software package.

7.2 Manual adjustment of descriptor values

Visualisation of the chosen catchment using the FEH CD-ROM browser is provided, to allow users to ensure that the boundary derived by the IHDTM is accurate. Before dismissing the DTM-derived boundary as incorrect, it is worth rechecking any pre-existing view of what the catchment should be. A number of catchment areas that have been in use for decades have been found to be incorrect, as a result of comparison with DTM-defined areas.

7.2.1 Component drainage areas

In cases where the DTM-derived boundary of the site is found to be incorrect, the catchment descriptor values that relate to this site, provided on the CD-ROM, will in most cases be inappropriate. Through the browser software (Section 7.1) it is possible to identify whether the correct estimate of the catchment boundary is made up of one or more component DTM-defined catchments. Once this has been done, an adjustment procedure allows descriptor values for the component parts to be used to estimate descriptors for the desired catchment.

The catchment draining to Olton Reservoir, in Birmingham, serves to demonstrate this procedure (Figure 7.2). The user-defined boundary to the reservoir outlet (dashed line) gives a catchment that is seen to be larger than that delineated by the DTM-derived boundary (catchment A). Selection of another DTM-defined catchment by choosing the appropriate grid node shows that the 'missing' part of the user-defined catchment can largely be made up by catchment B. Thus, the user-defined catchment is represented by the combination of two DTM-derived component catchments, A and B.

The catchment descriptor values provided for catchment A need to be adjusted so that they allow for the addition of catchment B. Drainage area can be adjusted by simply adding the area of catchment A to that of B (Table 7.1).

Table 7.1 Addition of component drainage areas

	Catchment A	Catchment B	Combined
Drainage area (km²)	1.920	1.200	3.120
Fraction of combined catchment	0.615	0.385	1.000

7.2.2 Area-weighting method

Many of the catchment descriptors presented on the CD-ROM can be adjusted by a simple area-weighting method, using the fractions presented above. Table 7.2 illustrates this methodology for the most influential descriptors in the statistical procedures for flood frequency estimation (Volume 3) and the rainfall-runoff approach (Volume 4). The Olton Reservoir catchment is again used as an example.

The majority of catchment descriptors provided on the CD-ROM, and listed in the Appendix tables, can be adjusted in this way. However, those descriptors whose derivation demands a contiguous set of drainage paths, connecting all parts of the catchment to a single outlet, cannot use the procedure presented above. *LDP*, *URBCONC* and *URBLOC* are three such descriptors, but since they are

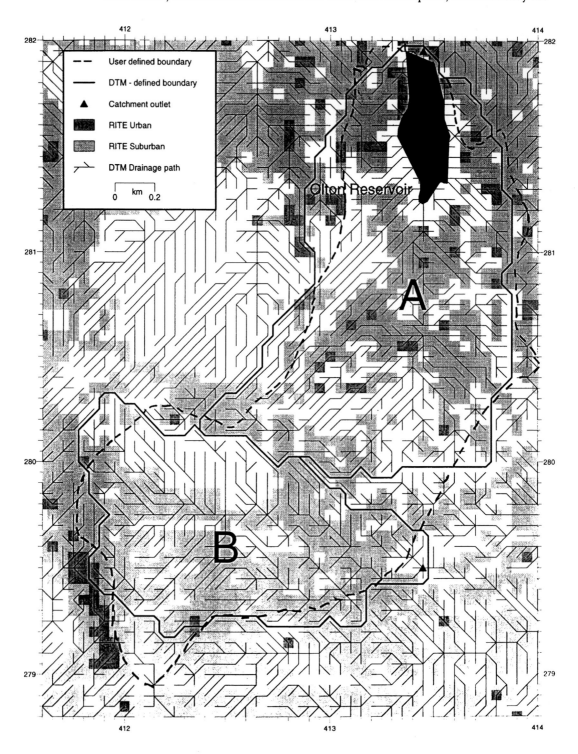

Figure 7.2 *Component DTM-derived drainage areas — Olton Reservoir catchment*

Table 7.2 *Adjustment of catchment descriptor values using area-weighting*

Descriptor	Catchment A weighted average	Catchment B weighted average	Combined catchment average
BFIHOST	0.350 x 0.615 = 0.215	0.325 x 0.385 = 0.125	0.215 + 0.125 = 0.340
DPSBAR (m/km)	17.54 x 0.615 = 10.79	12.40 x 0.385 = 4.77	10.79 + 4.77 = 15.56
PROPWET	0.31 x 0.615 = 0.19	0.27 x 0.385 = 0.10	0.19 + 0.10 = 0.29
SAAR (mm)	720 x 0.615 = 443	727 x 0.385 = 280	443 + 280 = 723
SPRHOST	40.2 x 0.615 = 24.7	39.7 x 0.385 = 15.3	24.7 + 15.3 = 40.0
URBEXT	0.290 x 0.615 = 0.178	0.322 x 0.385 = 0.124	0.178 + 0.124 = 0.302

provided for information only, an adjustment procedure is not strictly necessary. The *FARL* and *DPLBAR* indices too cannot be adjusted using an area-weighting method, but estimates are required of these two descriptors, since they are needed specifically in the derivation of flood estimation parameters.

7.2.3 Adjusting *FARL* values

Flood attenuation attributable to reservoirs and lakes is described by the *FARL* index. The computation of the index is complex and relies on having a contiguous drainage path network from the catchment outlet to each node, without which the software is unable to derive a local attenuation index for each on-line reservoir or lake. Consequently the index cannot be adjusted using an area-weighting method.

The *FARL* index has two main uses in flood estimation procedures: *FARL* values equal to 1.0 indicate no reservoir or lake storage effect, while values significantly less than 1.0 provide a warning that there may be flood attenuation from water bodies in the catchment. In these cases the user is encouraged to obtain more details, particularly where a reservoir is implicated. The index is also required for the estimation of *QMED* (see Volume 3, Chapter 3).

In this example, since the whole catchment is thought to drain to one reservoir, the value of *FARL* for component A overstates the reservoir effect slightly. An estimate of a more appropriate value for the combined catchment is based on a judgement of how the attenuation effect decreases, as the ratio of the surface area of the reservoir to its subcatchment area increases (§4.3.2). Users are encouraged to select familiar examples from the 943 catchment *FARL* values listed, to provide guidance. In this case, an adjustment from a *FARL* value of 0.854, for catchment A, to an estimate of 0.88 is judged to be appropriate.

7.2.4 Adjusting *DPLBAR* values

DPLBAR represents the mean distance between each catchment node and the outlet and, since an unbroken drainage path between these nodal pairs is required to derive the index (§3.2.2), values cannot be adjusted by the area-weighting method. *DPLBAR* is used in the estimation of unit hydrograph time-to-peak Tp(0) in the rainfall-runoff method of flood frequency estimation (4 2.2) and an adjustment procedure is necessary. *DPLBAR* is highly correlated with drainage area and a value for the combined catchment can be estimated by using the combined drainage area in the equation:

$$DPLBAR = AREA^{0.548} \qquad\qquad (7.1)$$

$$[n = 204 \quad r^2 = 0.94 \quad \text{f.s.e.} = 1.22]$$

which is established by regression analysis. The drainage area for the combined catchment in the example above is 3.12 km², which can be used to estimate an adjusted *DPLBAR*. Thus

$$DPLBAR = 3.12^{0.548} = 1.87 \text{ km} \qquad\qquad (7.2)$$

This compares to a *DPLBAR* value of 1.71 km for the DTM-based catchment (i.e. component A).

Acknowledgements

Catchment descriptors are provided on the FEH CD-ROM for all of mainland Britain, Northern Ireland, the Isle of Wight and Anglesey. In Northern Ireland, some of the digital datasets, already held for Great Britain, were completed urgently during the course of the FEH programme so that they were included. Thanks are due to a number of staff at the Department of Agriculture for Northern Ireland for their assistance in obtaining or providing these data: in particular Stephen Dawson, Derrick Pinkerton and Richard Cole at the Rivers Agency and Alex Higgins from the Agricultural and Environmental Science Division. The help given at IH by Beate Gannon (Northern Ireland HOST data) and Becky White (CORINE land cover data) is also gratefully acknowledged.

A catchment boundary defined by the IHDTM is the key component in the automatic production of catchment descriptors. In addition, many of the descriptors themselves, such as catchment mean slope (DPSBAR), are based on the DTM. A special thanks therefore goes to David Morris at IH, for his commitment to producing a high quality DTM and his advice on accessing and manipulating the data.

The Institute of Terrestrial Ecology supplied the urban and suburban land cover data, which after refinement formed the basis of the urban indices. The refinement procedure used settlement polygons licensed from the Ordnance Survey.

The HOST data, made available for use in the FEH, were produced by a collaborative venture between the Institute of Hydrology, the Soil Survey and Land Research Centre, the Macaulay Land Use Research Institute and the Department of Agriculture for Northern Ireland.

References

Bayliss, A.C. 1994. On the variability of flood occurrence. Report to MAFF.

Boorman, D.B., Hollis, J.M. and Lilly, A. 1995. Hydrology of soil types: a hydrologically-based classification of the soils of the United Kingdom. *IH Report No. 126*. Institute of Hydrology, Wallingford.

Brand, M.J.D. and Mitchell, G. 1993. CORINE land cover (Ireland) — the northern perspective. Proceedings of the Association for Geographic Information Conference, Birmingham.

CPRE, 1993. The regional lost land — land use change in England's regions and counties 1945-1990. Report to CPRE prepared by Environment Information Services.

Fisher, N.I. 1993. Statistical analysis of circular data. Cambridge University Press.

Fuller, R.M. and Brown, N. 1996. A CORINE map of Great Britain by automated means. Techniques for automatic generalisation of the Land Cover Map of Great Britain. *Internat. J. Geogr. Information Systems* **10**, 937-953.

Fuller, R.M., Groom, G.B., and Jones, A.R. 1994a. The Land Cover Map of Great Britain: an automated classification of Landsat Thematic Mapper data. *Photogrammetric Engineering and Remote Sensing* **60**, 553-562.

Fuller, R.M., Groom, G.B. and Wallis, S.M. 1994b. The availability of Landsat TM images of Great Britain. *Internat. J. Remote Sens.* **15**, 1357-1362.

Groom, G.B. and Fuller, R.M. 1995. Reclassification of the urban, suburban and tilled land classes in the Land Cover Map of Great Britain using additional spectral bands — a pilot study. Institute of Terrestrial Ecology report to IH.

Higgins, A. 1997. Hydrology Of Soil Types (HOST), In: Cruikshank, J. (ed.), *Soil and Environment: N. Ireland*. Agricultural and Environmental Science Division, Department of Agriculture for Northern Ireland and Agricultural and Environmental Science Department, Queens University Belfast.

Marshall, D.C.W. and Bayliss, A.C. 1994. Flood estimation for small catchments. *IH Report No. 124*. Institute of Hydrology, Wallingford.

Morris, D.G. and Flavin, R.W. 1990. A digital terrain model for hydrology. Proc. 4th International Symposium on Spatial Data Handling, Zürich, **1**, 250-262.

Morris, D.G. and Heerdegen, R.G. 1988. Automatically derived catchment boundaries and channel networks and their hydrological applications. *Geomorphology* **1**, 131-141.

NERC 1975. *Flood Studies Report*. Natural Environment Research Council. 5 Volumes.

Newson, M. 1975. Mapwork for flood studies. Part 1: Selection and derivation of indices. *IH Report No. 25*. Institute of Hydrology, Wallingford.

Newson, M. 1978. Drainage basin characteristics, their selection, derivation and analysis for a flood study of the British Isles. *Earth Surf. Procs.* **3**, 227-293.

Tedd, P., Holton, I.R. and Charles, J.A. 1992. The BRE dams database. Proc. Seventh Conference of the British Dam Society, Stirling, 403-410.

Thompson, N., Barrie, I.A. and Ayles, M. 1981. The Meteorological Office rainfall and evaporation calculation system: MORECS. *Hydrological Memorandum No. 45*.

Appendix

A.1 Introduction

Catchment descriptors were calculated for the 943 gauged sites for which IH hold flood peak data. The accuracy of each IHDTM-derived boundary, used to define a catchment value for all descriptors, was assessed by comparing the DTM-derived drainage area with the catchment area supplied to the National River Flow Archive by the gauging authority (§2.2). Where the ratio of the larger area to smaller area exceeded 1.1, the descriptors defined by these boundaries were deemed unreliable and were not used in the analyses.

A.2 Tables

As a consequence of the validation procedure described above, descriptor values are not given for 57 catchments in the data presented in Tables A.1 and A.2, but the gauge number and name are still listed for these sites in the tables.

Table A.1 gives catchment descriptor values for 943 gauged sites. The descriptors chosen for presentation here are those used in the flood estimation procedures described in Volumes 3 and 4. The values themselves are for information only, but are likely to provide a useful comparison when values are assembled for use at a nearby ungauged site.

Table A.2 lists values for the 943 sites shown in Table A.1, but the descriptors shown are not used specifically in the flood estimation procedures. However, they are tabulated here to provide additional information about the gauged catchments listed. As with those given in Table A.1, they may provide a useful comparison with values assembled for nearby ungauged sites. Preceding each table is a brief description of the variables (§A.3 §A.4).

Table A.3 of Volume 4 summarises the characteristics and derived model parameters of flood events used in the derivation of the new estimation equations for unit hydrograph time-to-peak, and other events stored on the UK Flood Event Archive. Catchment descriptors for those catchments are presented (for information only) in Tables A.3 and A.4. As a consequence of the validation procedure applied to IHDTM-derived boundaries (§A.1) descriptor values are not given for 23 of these sites, although the gauge number and name are still listed.

A.3 Catchment descriptors given in Table A.1

A brief description of each of the variables shown in Table A.1 is given below.

IHDTM NGR — The 12-figure National Grid Reference (Irish Grid Reference in Northern Ireland) of the IHDTM grid point, located nearest the gauging station and on the appropriate DTM drainage path.

AREA — Catchment drainage area using an IHDTM-derived boundary (km^2).

BFIHOST — Base Flow Index derived using the HOST classification.

DPLBAR — Mean of distances between each node (on regular 50 m grid) and the catchment outlet (km). Characterises the catchment size and configuration.

DPSBAR — Mean of all the inter-nodal slopes for the catchment ($m\ km^{-1}$). Characterises the overall steepness.

FARL — Index of flood attenuation attributable to reservoirs and lakes.

PROPWET — Proportion of time when SMD was ≤ 6 mm during 1961-90.

SAAR — Standard period (1961-90) average annual rainfall (mm).

SPRHOST — Standard percentage runoff derived using the HOST classification.

$URBEXT_{1990}$ — Extent of urban and suburban land cover (1990).

Table A.1 Catchment descriptors used in flood estimation procedures — values for 943 gauged catchments

Number	Name	IHDTM NGR	AREA km²	SAAR mm	BFIHOST	SPRHOST	FARL	PROPWET	DPLBAR km	DPSBAR m/km	URBEXT$_{1990}$	Number
2001	Helmsdale at Kilphedir	299650 918250	552.54	1117	0.324	52.9	0.880	0.65	30.05	99.01	0.0000	2001
3001	Shin at Lairg	258050 906350	496.51	1589	0.370	53.3	0.683	0.77	21.92	100.68	0.0001	3001
3002	Carron at Sgodachail	249150 892150	236.99	1785	0.436	49.9	0.978	0.81	15.97	223.90	0.0000	3002
3003	Oykel at Easter Turnaig	240150 900150	331.92	1896	0.359	53.6	0.919	0.81	16.61	151.33	0.0000	3003
3801	Cassley at Duchally	238650 916950	72.29	3035	0.470	51.8	0.867	0.84	9.46	172.42	0.0000	3801
3803	Tirry at Rhian Bridge	255450 916650	62.37	1246	0.273	56.3	0.954	0.84	11.85	71.46	0.0000	3803
4001	Conon at Moy Bridge	248050 854700	962.54	1769	0.363	52.7	0.764	0.75	33.47	203.13	0.0002	4001
4003	Alness at Alness	265450 869650	202.41	1368	0.384	48.2	0.908	0.63	22.55	150.95	0.0005	4003
5001	Beauly at Erchless	242450 840550	855.20	2156	0.400	52.0	0.810	0.74	33.30	269.49	0.0001	5001
6001	Ness at Ness Castle Farm	263750 840950	1811.89	1784	0.414	49.6	0.871	0.72	55.82	184.35	0.0003	6001
6003	Moriston at Invermoriston	241450 816950	397.84	2117	0.362	52.5	0.882	0.74	27.74	213.99	0.0001	6003
6006	Allt Bhlaraidh at Invermoriston	237850 816800	26.23	1549	0.277	56.0	0.757	0.70	6.41	111.47	0.0000	6006
6007	Ness at Ness Side	264400 842550	1839.38	1770	0.417	49.3	0.871	0.71	57.04	182.42	0.0003	6007
6008	Enrick at Mill Of Tore	244900 830100	105.95	1291	0.430	43.6	0.852	0.70	11.23	120.37	0.0002	6008
7001	Findhorn at Shenachie	282550 833550	415.87	1217	0.451	55.8	0.992	0.68	25.63	141.77	0.0002	7001
7002	Findhorn at Forres	301900 858450	781.08	1065	0.434	51.6	0.981	0.56	54.80	119.83	0.0001	7002
7003	Lossie at Sheriffmills	319250 862600	217.07	833	0.577	34.6	0.989	0.42	18.57	80.52	0.0002	7003
8001	Spey at Aberlour	327950 844050	2646.63	1134	0.484	44.5	0.962	0.65	77.40	160.79	0.0006	8001
8002	Spey at Kinrara	288250 808350	1009.45	1316	0.452	49.7	0.938	0.71	37.26	178.84	0.0003	8002
8003	Spey at Ruthven Bridge	276000 799750	532.57	1375	0.424	50.4	0.970	0.73	27.94	181.70	0.0003	8003
8004	Avon at Delnashaugh	318450 835200	540.87	1108	0.451	43.4	0.990	0.63	28.95	181.98	0.0005	8004
8005	Spey at Boat Of Garten	294700 819250	1261.37	1277	0.470	47.6	0.929	0.70	47.51	177.91	0.0005	8005
8006	Spey at Boat O Brig	331850 851850	2861.74	1120	0.485	44.0	0.965	0.63	87.42	160.19	0.0009	8006
8007	Spey at Invertruim	268650 796200	401.84	1431	0.411	51.2	0.990	0.75	21.68	185.06	0.0001	8007
8008	Tromie at Tromie Bridge	279000 799350	131.41	1437	0.447	53.5	0.994	0.72	18.35	216.49	0.0000	8008
8009	Dulnain at Balnaan Bridge	297850 824750	272.27	1011	0.498	46.6	0.997	0.68	21.32	120.43	0.0002	8009
8010	Spey at Grantown	303450 826800	1745.92	1195	0.484	46.4	0.947	0.69	51.33	162.11	0.0005	8010
8011	Livet at Minmore	320050 829250	103.38	1000	0.450	41.9	1.000	0.63	11.64	171.47	0.0012	8011
9001	Deveron at Avochie	353250 846250	444.80	988	0.505	37.3	0.998	0.53	29.06	127.08	0.0017	9001
9002	Deveron at Muiresk	370350 849800	961.17	928	0.511	35.3	0.998	0.46	45.63	103.01	0.0022	9002
9003	Isla at Grange	349250 850650	179.60	900	0.474	36.3	0.994	0.42	14.61	86.52	0.0051	9003
9004	Bogie at Redcraig	352050 837250	182.50	955	0.567	32.6	0.998	0.53	14.36	134.83	0.0012	9004
10001	Ythan at Ardlethen	392400 830950	457.16	830	0.614	28.3	0.993	0.42	24.30	58.25	0.0007	10001
10002	Ugie at Inverugie	410000 848650	325.65	812	0.522	33.0	0.990	0.40	23.47	43.02	0.0029	10002
10003	Ythan at Ellon	394550 830450	532.10	826	0.584	27.8	0.994	0.42	24.90	56.13	0.0013	10003
11001	Don at Parkhill	388850 814150	1269.73	884	0.584	31.3	0.998	0.52	59.85	113.80	0.0028	11001
11002	Don at Haughton	375550 820250	792.76	917	0.573	32.4	0.997	0.55	50.97	140.68	0.0010	11002
11003	Don at Bridge Of Alford	356450 817050	509.42	967	0.565	33.6	0.997	0.56	33.18	164.68	0.0003	11003
11004	Urie at Pitcaple	372250 825950	195.32	870	0.562	31.7	0.996	0.53	15.52	90.27	0.0029	11004
12001	Dee at Woodend	363350 795700	1379.90	1108	0.506	40.3	0.985	0.62	60.29	189.82	0.0005	12001
12002	Dee at Park	379800 798450	1833.30	1080	0.507	39.7	0.987	0.58	67.09	173.10	0.0008	12002
12003	Dee at Polhollick	334300 796350	697.33	1231	0.458	44.9	0.990	0.68	36.92	224.44	0.0001	12003
12004	Girnock Burn at Littlemill	332550 795750	29.79	936	0.466	40.5	1.000	0.68	6.63	165.82	0.0000	12004
12005	Muick at Invermuick	336550 794800	110.25	1240	0.514	42.8	0.961	0.68	15.04	192.23	0.0001	12005
12006	Gairn at Invergairn	335250 796950	145.91	1048	0.452	42.7	0.997	0.64	16.67	184.16	0.0000	12006
12007	Dee at Mar Lodge	309650 789500	292.09	1334	0.400	50.1	0.990	0.69	15.11	240.30	0.0001	12007
12008	Feugh at Heugh Head	368750 792650	232.66	1130	0.426	44.8	0.999	0.54	16.70	149.58	0.0010	12008
13001	Bervie at Inverbervie	382550 773450	124.44	890	0.554	40.2	0.999	0.46	17.86	86.89	0.0022	13001
14001	Eden at Kemback	341450 715650	310.04	799	0.610	29.6	0.989	0.40	19.98	74.26	0.0040	14001
15001	Isla at Forter	318700 764850	71.49	1437	0.432	46.9	1.000	0.68	10.37	251.11	0.0000	15001

Number	Name	IHDTM NGR		AREA km²	SAAR mm	BFIHOST	SPRHOST	FARL	PROPWET	DPLBAR km	DPSBAR m/km	URBEXT$_{1990}$	Number
15002	Newton Burn at Newton	323050	760650	16.55	1201	0.460	39.5	1.000	0.68	7.54	203.62	0.0000	15002
15003	Tay at Caputh	308350	739550	3210.33	1609	0.437	45.4	0.869	0.69	67.66	190.06	0.0007	15003
15004	Inzion at Loch Of Lintrathen	327950	755750	24.20	1082	0.528	35.7	0.999	0.53	6.63	191.83	0.0000	15004
15005	Melgan at Loch Of Lintrathen	327350	755850	42.17	1117	0.478	38.1	0.800	0.56	12.34	169.72	0.0000	15005
15006	Tay at Ballathie	314700	736550	4586.56	1425	0.473	42.9	0.890	0.58	70.30	170.43	0.0014	15006
15007	Tay at Pitnacree	292450	753350	1149.36	1949	0.442	44.6	0.960	0.70	47.58	235.47	0.0005	15007
15008	Dean Water at Cookston	333850	747900	176.90	840	0.622	37.2	0.992	0.38	14.58	60.25	0.0108	15008
15010	Isla at Wester Cardean	329350	746550	363.87	1086	0.532	37.3	0.959	0.51	26.06	154.11	0.0008	15010
15013	Almond at Almondbank	306850	725700	173.30	1393	0.466	42.6	0.996	0.61	29.01	200.93	0.0004	15013
15016	Tay at Kenmore	278350	746800	598.17	2129	0.423	44.8	0.989	0.71	35.55	232.28	0.0002	15016
15017	Braan at Ballinloan	298050	740550	197.01	1345	0.431	40.3	0.960	0.65	14.67	151.34	0.0001	15017
15808	Almond at Almond Intake												15808
15809	Muckle Burn at Eastmill	322300	760550	16.64	1132	0.480	37.6	0.960	0.68	5.65	164.57	0.0000	15809
16001	Earn at Kinkell Bridge	293450	716600	582.19	1509	0.487	41.1	0.952	0.63	31.80	181.41	0.0017	16001
16002	Earn at Aberuchill	275250	721550	176.95	1744	0.447	42.8	0.935	0.66	17.92	241.23	0.0002	16002
16003	Ruchill Water at Cultybraggan	276400	720350	98.58	1901	0.428	44.5	1.000	0.59	12.79	221.20	0.0001	16003
16004	Earn at Forteviot Bridge	304450	718350	781.92	1406	0.510	39.9	0.961	0.59	39.95	158.98	0.0019	16004
17001	Carron at Headswood	283150	681850	121.10	1519	0.377	44.2	0.848	0.59	14.44	100.64	0.0097	17001
17002	Leven at Leven	337050	700450	416.85	947	0.511	34.6	0.832	0.45	27.14	64.02	0.0173	17002
17005	Avon at Polmonthill	295050	679650	190.12	995	0.409	40.2	0.979	0.57	22.34	57.14	0.0172	17005
18001	Allan Water at Kinbuck	279250	705400	160.25	1384	0.507	41.3	0.984	0.59	15.71	94.68	0.0010	18001
18002	Devon at Glenochil	285650	695950	178.71	1331	0.487	40.7	0.942	0.52	25.54	189.75	0.0091	18002
18003	Teith at Bridge Of Teith	272650	701100	516.73	1998	0.459	41.6	0.834	0.67	33.65	238.67	0.0003	18003
18005	Allan Water at Bridge Of Allan	278600	697850	209.87	1337	0.504	42.1	0.983	0.59	22.72	94.09	0.0046	18005
18008	Leny at Anie	258500	709750	191.10	2193	0.462	41.7	0.785	0.75	21.87	312.37	0.0001	18008
19001	Almond at Craigiehall	316500	675350	386.10	892	0.399	44.4	0.969	0.50	24.69	46.62	0.0338	19001
19002	Almond at Almond Weir	300250	665150	44.36	1016	0.364	47.0	0.998	0.57	10.74	37.76	0.0327	19002
19003	Breich Water at Breich Weir	301300	663750	52.83	1012	0.309	47.9	0.998	0.57	11.40	47.29	0.0083	19003
19004	North Esk at Dalmore Weir	325350	661550	79.95	949	0.562	37.2	0.978	0.49	11.52	113.87	0.0186	19004
19005	Almond at Almondell	308600	668450	239.27	963	0.362	46.0	0.957	0.52	16.86	47.69	0.0289	19005
19006	Water Of Leith at Murrayfield	322950	673300	102.56	866	0.429	42.9	0.943	0.49	17.04	73.14	0.1004	19006
19007	Esk at Musselburgh	333900	672450	323.83	836	0.568	34.1	0.952	0.49	24.77	96.50	0.0235	19007
19008	South Esk at Prestonholm	332550	662150	113.03	859	0.593	31.0	0.906	0.49	12.27	95.66	0.0031	19008
19010	Braid Burn at Liberton	327250	670850	15.40	770	0.514	39.6	0.953	0.49	6.28	115.73	0.1545	19010
19011	North Esk at Dalkeith Palace	333250	667950	133.69	906	0.551	37.1	0.967	0.49	22.90	123.49	0.0215	19011
20001	Tyne at East Linton	358950	676650	307.06	713	0.489	35.4	0.991	0.43	25.60	71.45	0.0035	20001
20002	West Peffer Burn at Luffness	348750	681200	26.06	616	0.472	32.1	0.995	0.33	5.76	30.81	0.0000	20002
20003	Tyne at Spilmersford	345500	668800	163.53	724	0.519	33.9	0.993	0.43	10.71	66.78	0.0026	20003
20004	East Peffer Burn at Lochhouses	361150	682450	30.54	618	0.380	36.9	0.980	0.36	7.45	40.83	0.0001	20004
20005	Birns Water at Saltoun Hall	345850	668650	93.43	761	0.534	32.5	0.993	0.43	10.91	77.18	0.0010	20005
20006	Biel Water at Belton House	364350	676650	56.87	743	0.524	34.0	0.992	0.43	10.99	107.14	0.0001	20006
20007	Gifford Water at Lennoxlove	351250	671750	67.66	770	0.527	32.8	0.980	0.43	11.63	114.69	0.0000	20007
21001	Fruid Water at Fruid	308800	620650	22.05	1703	0.392	45.2	0.778	0.72	5.29	225.51	0.0000	21001
21002	Whiteadder Water at Hungry Snout	366150	663200	45.89	909	0.418	44.7	0.930	0.43	7.84	128.93	0.0002	21002
21003	Tweed at Peebles	325550	640150	704.83	1138	0.517	37.2	0.975	0.56	24.64	183.57	0.0019	21003
21005	Tweed at Lyne Ford	320450	639750	378.11	1254	0.507	37.7	0.965	0.66	23.23	206.07	0.0007	21005
21006	Tweed at Boleside	349650	633300	1513.36	1163	0.497	38.3	0.975	0.58	43.68	195.06	0.0020	21006
21007	Ettrick Water at Lindean	348450	631450	501.64	1308	0.442	41.7	0.963	0.67	31.18	194.31	0.0020	21007
21008	Teviot at Ormiston Mill	370350	627950	1120.24	937	0.458	42.9	0.989	0.57	33.19	119.74	0.0025	21008
21009	Tweed at Norham	389650	647700	4407.84	955	0.495	38.9	0.986	0.49	80.67	138.27	0.0024	21009

Number	Name	IHDTM NGR	AREA km²	SAAR mm	BFIHOST	SPRHOST	FARL	PROPWET	DPLBAR km	DPSBAR m/km	URBEXT₁₉₉₀	Number
21010	Tweed at Dryburgh	358650 632050	2101.40	1078	0.514	36.8	0.981	0.51	50.90	174.53	0.0028	21010
21011	Yarrow Water at Philiphaugh	343750 627700	232.13	1348	0.443	42.1	0.952	0.70	24.21	217.95	0.0002	21011
21012	Teviot at Hawick	352050 615750	324.11	1149	0.429	43.6	0.994	0.59	18.44	153.88	0.0060	21012
21013	Gala Water at Galashiels	348050 637250	205.78	929	0.532	34.6	0.999	0.44	23.32	150.77	0.0011	21013
21015	Leader Water at Earlston	356400 638950	240.85	852	0.563	33.4	0.999	0.43	18.34	107.92	0.0012	21015
21016	Eye Water at Eyemouth Mill	394100 663350	122.00	729	0.599	30.2	0.998	0.29	15.33	69.52	0.0001	21016
21017	Ettrick Water at Brockhoperig	323300 613050	38.44	1741	0.421	43.7	1.000	0.72	5.68	247.06	0.0000	21017
21019	Manor Water at Cademuir	321600 637050	58.98	1350	0.481	40.4	0.997	0.72	7.71	279.64	0.0000	21019
21020	Yarrow Water at Gordon Arms	331050 624850	154.08	1496	0.396	46.2	0.821	0.72	12.15	224.64	0.0000	21020
21021	Tweed at Sprouston	375050 635350	3352.30	1014	0.496	38.7	0.984	0.53	63.85	151.48	0.0028	21021
21022	Whiteadder Water at Hutton Castle	388250 655050	499.05	814	0.516	37.6	0.988	0.35	32.15	91.89	0.0009	21022
21023	Leet Water at Coldstream	383750 639700	113.26	671	0.388	37.9	0.999	0.30	16.27	34.42	0.0004	21023
21024	Jed Water at Jedburgh	365550 621350	138.90	915	0.436	44.1	0.996	0.57	18.13	113.72	0.0041	21024
21025	Ale Water at Ancrum	363250 624300	173.84	926	0.391	46.6	0.955	0.58	26.35	88.46	0.0002	21025
21026	Tima Water at Deephope	327800 613750	31.01	1498	0.370	45.1	1.000	0.72	6.44	178.04	0.0000	21026
21027	Blackadder Water at Mouth Bridge	382750 653050	155.58	774	0.519	36.7	0.996	0.41	20.39	57.74	0.0027	21027
21029	Tweed at Glenbreck	306150 621450	34.29	1533	0.353	49.1	1.000	0.72	6.10	168.26	0.0000	21029
21030	Megget Water at Henderland	323100 623050	56.31	1669	0.393	47.7	0.817	0.72	6.46	229.70	0.0000	21030
21031	Till at Etal	392750 639750	634.99	827	0.504	41.5	0.989	0.46	38.24	129.56	0.0011	21031
21032	Glen at Kirknewton	392050 631050	196.11	876	0.455	50.7	0.987	0.46	17.78	197.46	0.0008	21032
21034	Yarrow Water at Craig Douglas	328700 624450	115.99	1556	0.389	47.0	0.769	0.72	10.77	226.24	0.0000	21034
22001	Coquet at Morwick	423250 608450	578.46	850	0.393	42.5	0.985	0.44	44.30	112.10	0.0012	22001
22002	Coquet at Bygate	386850 607850	60.03	1020	0.413	51.1	1.000	0.46	8.50	209.38	0.0000	22002
22003	Usway Burn at Shillmoor	388650 607850	21.94	1057	0.302	56.9	1.000	0.45	8.99	209.21	0.0002	22003
22004	Aln at Hawkhill	421200 612950	202.80	758	0.427	35.7	0.993	0.45	19.14	81.51	0.0046	22004
22006	Blyth at Hartford Bridge	424200 579850	264.88	696	0.334	38.6	0.989	0.43	22.96	32.83	0.0104	22006
22007	Wansbeck at Mitford	417650 585700	282.23	794	0.347	41.7	0.977	0.45	19.62	51.76	0.0006	22007
22008	Alwin at Clennell	392550 606250	27.25	1003	0.382	55.0	1.000	0.45	6.73	249.32	0.0000	22008
23001	Tyne at Bywell	403900 561600	2172.84	1016	0.318	48.2	0.961	0.51	54.89	95.50	0.0020	23001
23002	Derwent at Eddys Bridge	404250 550800	117.97	943	0.316	48.1	0.835	0.59	11.31	98.39	0.0003	23002
23003	North Tyne at Reaverhill	390450 573300	1012.09	1024	0.310	50.7	0.936	0.50	37.37	94.14	0.0005	23003
23004	South Tyne at Haydon Bridge	385750 564700	750.20	1147	0.298	49.2	0.989	0.60	31.94	109.14	0.0013	23004
23005	North Tyne at Tarset	377750 586050	283.49	1230	0.274	54.5	0.815	0.62	21.27	111.01	0.0008	23005
23006	South Tyne at Featherstone	367150 560950	323.09	1332	0.270	52.9	0.995	0.64	19.58	125.70	0.0008	23006
23007	Derwent at Rowlands Gill	416650 558050	243.50	849	0.335	43.8	0.910	0.59	25.85	92.89	0.0176	23007
23008	Rede at Rede Bridge	386950 583350	345.10	941	0.322	49.4	0.978	0.47	25.12	96.26	0.0006	23008
23010	Tarset Burn at Greenhaugh	378800 587750	95.85	993	0.305	52.6	1.000	0.56	9.32	87.00	0.0001	23010
23011	Kielder Burn at Kielder	364400 594600	58.86	1199	0.273	55.0	1.000	0.59	7.42	139.66	0.0000	23011
23012	East Allen at Wide Eals	380250 558300	88.12	1050	0.298	47.6	0.997	0.59	11.85	107.98	0.0017	23012
23013	West Allen at Hindley Wrae	378950 558200	78.14	1157	0.280	51.6	1.000	0.63	9.25	122.08	0.0003	23013
23015	North Tyne at Barrasford	392450 572250	1049.75	1014	0.311	50.4	0.934	0.50	39.10	92.68	0.0005	23015
24001	Wear at Sunderland Bridge	426250 537450	660.96	933	0.342	44.0	0.962	0.47	39.62	98.38	0.0148	24001
24002	Gaunless at Bishop Auckland	421450 530700	92.08	729	0.370	38.1	1.000	0.42	14.98	61.36	0.0351	24002
24003	Wear at Stanhope	398250 539000	173.21	1279	0.300	50.8	0.979	0.59	13.05	133.62	0.0016	24003
24004	Bedburn Beck at Bedburn	411950 532150	74.32	894	0.362	43.8	0.999	0.59	9.62	109.67	0.0007	24004
24005	Browney at Burn Hall	425900 538800	178.35	743	0.331	39.3	1.000	0.41	19.60	77.88	0.0267	24005
24006	Rookhope Burn at Eastgate	395250 539150	36.60	1126	0.293	52.0	0.995	0.59	7.00	122.15	0.0027	24006
24007	Browney at Lanchester	416350 546100	44.65	797	0.333	40.5	1.000	0.59	8.11	75.20	0.0018	24007
24008	Wear at Witton Park	417350 530900	455.06	1034	0.338	46.4	0.958	0.59	27.29	115.35	0.0030	24008
24009	Wear at Chester Le Street	428300 551150	1005.29	855	0.351	41.9	0.974	0.40	60.88	88.29	0.0247	24009

Number	Name	IHDTM NGR	AREA km²	SAAR mm	BFIHOST	SPRHOST	FARL	PROPWET	DPLBAR km	DPSBAR m/km	URBEXT$_{1990}$	Number
24801	Burnhope Burn at Burnhope Reservoir	385650 539400	20.55	1572	0.243	56.4	0.846	0.59	4.81	133.78	0.0000	24801
25001	Tees at Broken Scar	425950 513550	815.69	1140	0.355	47.0	0.943	0.58	46.86	82.63	0.0030	25001
25002	Tees at Dent Bank	393050 525950	218.38	1576	0.277	54.5	0.934	0.60	17.64	101.67	0.0000	25002
25003	Trout Beck at Moor House	375750 533500	11.69	1905	0.227	59.9	1.000	0.64	3.33	87.98	0.0000	25003
25004	Skerne at South Park	428350 513050	255.19	644	0.391	37.4	0.983	0.32	24.75	33.32	0.0604	25004
25005	Leven at Leven Bridge	444500 512100	193.57	726	0.381	40.5	0.998	0.34	25.49	75.96	0.0099	25005
25006	Greta at Rutherford Bridge	403250 512250	86.51	1125	0.242	55.1	0.999	0.62	12.40	67.67	0.0006	25006
25007	Clow Beck at Croft	428050 510000	79.31	719	0.503	35.4	0.985	0.42	16.01	36.72	0.0054	25007
25008	Tees at Barnard Castle	404600 516650	509.48	1308	0.321	50.4	0.912	0.60	26.51	97.57	0.0013	25008
25009	Tees at Low Moor	436250 510650	1267.04	965	0.374	43.6	0.959	0.40	70.20	64.85	0.0169	25009
25010	Baydale Beck at Mowden Bridge	426000 515650	31.08	642	0.342	39.8	1.000	0.32	6.30	28.72	0.0051	25010
25011	Langdon Beck at Langdon	385200 530900	12.73	1463	0.237	58.2	1.000	0.59	4.06	120.61	0.0006	25011
25012	Harwood Beck at Harwood	385050 530900	24.89	1574	0.261	53.5	1.000	0.59	5.41	115.15	0.0000	25012
25018	Tees at Middleton In Teesdale	395150 524850	241.97	1531	0.284	53.8	0.940	0.60	18.96	106.30	0.0002	25018
25019	Leven at Easby	458550 508550	15.06	830	0.525	38.6	1.000	0.37	5.30	130.18	0.0009	25019
25020	Skerne at Preston Le Skerne	429350 523850	153.11	654	0.437	34.8	0.981	0.32	13.64	35.91	0.0382	25020
25021	Skerne at Bradbury	431950 528500	75.43	662	0.471	34.4	0.962	0.32	9.94	40.18	0.0368	25021
25808	Burnt Weir at Moor House											25808
25809	Bog Weir at Moor House	377300 532700	0.05	1757	0.228	59.9	1.000	0.64	0.17	100.40	0.0000	25809
25810	Syke Weir at Moor House	377200 533200	0.04	1757	0.275	55.0	1.000	0.64	0.18	79.91	0.0000	25810
26001	West Beck at Wansford Bridge	503000 456650	193.59	722	0.901	10.2	0.994	0.32	15.57	56.76	0.0077	26001
26002	Hull at Hempholme Lock	508000 449950	389.58	700	0.819	14.9	0.980	0.31	22.75	45.06	0.0097	26002
26003	Foston Beck at Foston Mill											26003
26004	Gypsey Race at Bridlington	516350 467550	256.79	720	0.953	6.3	0.987	0.30	23.31	52.17	0.0037	26004
26007	Catchwater at Withernwick											26007
27001	Nidd at Hunsingore Weir	452900 442650	490.05	965	0.406	39.6	0.954	0.37	36.90	77.27	0.0253	27001
27002	Wharfe at Flint Mill Weir	447400 442050	760.99	1165	0.385	42.8	0.905	0.43	59.40	113.68	0.0103	27002
27004	Calder at Newlands	421850 436450	905.16	1043	0.528	30.0	0.928	0.40	43.10	111.09	0.0856	27004
27006	Don at Hadfields Weir	391150 439150	365.29	1014	0.416	38.4	0.891	0.37	23.40	108.69	0.1078	27006
27007	Ure at Westwick Lock	466950 435500	913.72	1119	0.421	43.6	0.983	0.41	52.58	100.65	0.0039	27007
27008	Swale at Leckby Grange	474850 441350	1350.14	836	0.436	39.9	0.991	0.38	51.33	67.58	0.0091	27008
27009	Ouse at Skelton	455350 456950	3302.12	899	0.439	39.9	0.983	0.37	75.55	70.17	0.0103	27009
27010	Hodge Beck at Bransdale Weir	494350 462800	18.87	987	0.342	50.5	1.000	0.40	5.10	151.64	0.0026	27010
27012	Hebden Water at High Greenwood	430800 397300	36.00	1377	0.265	56.3	0.872	0.57	5.10	115.51	0.0000	27012
27014	Rye at Little Habton	476950 474250	660.30	828	0.538	32.3	0.997	0.35	26.94	100.26	0.0032	27014
27015	Derwent at Stamford Bridge	455850 471450	1637.92	763	0.605	28.4	0.995	0.34	57.84	77.34	0.0071	27015
27021	Don at Doncaster	404150 456950	1253.16	801	0.492	29.9	0.931	0.34	46.85	78.30	0.1181	27021
27022	Don at Rotherham Weir	392950 442700	825.02	863	0.464	32.3	0.914	0.38	28.53	87.04	0.1193	27022
27023	Dearne at Barnsley Weir	407250 435150	117.08	768	0.542	24.9	0.964	0.32	12.83	76.61	0.0557	27023
27024	Swale at Richmond	500600 414750	380.14	1226	0.341	49.3	0.999	0.62	26.07	135.46	0.0004	27024
27025	Rother at Woodhouse Mill	443250 385700	351.55	756	0.494	28.0	0.933	0.38	23.46	70.53	0.1032	27025
27026	Rother at Whittington	439250 374250	167.04	811	0.491	27.9	0.975	0.38	10.10	74.68	0.1061	27026
27027	Wharfe at Ilkley	411050 448150	447.51	1371	0.366	46.6	0.975	0.62	32.71	139.79	0.0018	27027
27028	Aire at Armley	428250 433950	685.49	1048	0.408	38.5	0.963	0.48	44.62	97.15	0.0743	27028
27029	Calder at Elland	412400 422050	340.91	1257	0.455	38.5	0.930	0.57	20.43	142.33	0.0339	27029
27030	Dearne at Adwick	447600 402150	310.93	696	0.533	25.4	0.969	0.32	20.95	62.84	0.0970	27030
27031	Colne at Colne Bridge	417350 419900	244.77	1145	0.607	24.2	0.957	0.52	15.35	124.65	0.0783	27031
27032	Hebden Beck at Hebden	402550 464450	22.25	1434	0.251	57.4	0.997	0.62	6.04	100.30	0.0000	27032
27033	Sea Cut at Scarborough	502650 490750	34.01	753	0.472	32.9	1.000	0.33	6.26	81.54	0.0369	27033
27034	Ure at Kilgram Bridge	418850 486000	511.89	1336	0.386	46.9	0.990	0.63	32.91	132.03	0.0016	27034

Number	Name	IHDTM NGR	AREA km²	SAAR mm	BFIHOST	SPRHOST	FARL	PROPWET	DPLBAR km	DPSBAR m/km	URBEXT₁₉₉₀	Number
27035	Aire at Kildwick Bridge	401400 445750	282.42	1151	0.385	42.5	0.980	0.62	21.08	101.84	0.0086	27035
27036	Derwent at Malton	478750 471450	1405.41	777	0.614	28.4	0.996	0.35	37.66	80.84	0.0075	27036
27038	Costa Beck at Gatehouses											27038
27040	Doe Lea at Staveley	444250 374450	68.14	708	0.433	32.6	0.972	0.38	7.66	63.19	0.0579	27040
27041	Derwent at Buttercrambe	473000 458850	1594.80	765	0.608	28.2	0.995	0.34	54.06	77.96	0.0072	27041
27042	Dove at Kirkby Mills	470450 485350	54.53	915	0.462	39.8	1.000	0.40	14.76	147.69	0.0039	27042
27043	Wharfe at Addingham	409050 449450	432.08	1386	0.366	46.8	0.975	0.62	30.45	140.81	0.0012	27043
27048	Derwent at West Ayton	499000 485150	125.91	842	0.469	37.5	1.000	0.40	16.10	124.50	0.0011	27048
27049	Rye at Ness	469450 479150	239.98	837	0.586	29.8	0.999	0.34	29.57	118.29	0.0017	27049
27051	Crimple at Burn Bridge	428350 451900	8.13	855	0.309	40.8	1.000	0.34	2.52	63.32	0.0015	27051
27052	Whitting at Sheepbridge	437600 374850	54.48	835	0.536	25.2	0.995	0.38	6.34	92.91	0.0891	27052
27053	Nidd at Birstwith	422850 460300	219.30	1218	0.357	45.3	0.916	0.53	20.20	116.32	0.0015	27053
27054	Hodge Beck at Cherry Farm	465050 490350	37.15	947	0.353	48.6	1.000	0.40	7.23	132.27	0.0013	27054
27055	Rye at Broadway Foot	456000 488150	131.37	882	0.422	43.1	0.998	0.34	11.54	145.45	0.0007	27055
27058	Riccal at Crook House Farm	466250 480950	39.96	859	0.511	34.5	1.000	0.38	12.46	94.94	0.0033	27058
27059	Laver at Ripon											27059
27061	Colne at Longroyd Bridge	413450 416100	73.89	1300	0.516	32.3	0.914	0.57	10.83	136.79	0.0642	27061
27811	Aire at Brotherton	449350 424300	1925.26	983	0.475	33.3	0.903	0.38	69.34	94.59	0.1033	27811
27835	Calder at Midland Bridge Dewsbury	424150 421450	715.60	1140	0.519	31.5	0.950	0.51	29.75	125.61	0.0698	27835
27846	Aire at Ash Bridge	447200 426750	1901.01	987	0.472	33.4	0.902	0.39	66.09	95.34	0.1019	27846
27852	Little Don at Langsett Reservoir	421400 400350	21.07	1317	0.318	51.6	0.845	0.42	4.61	125.03	0.0030	27852
28002	Blithe at Hamstall Ridware	410900 319050	162.14	782	0.464	38.2	0.876	0.43	19.83	41.94	0.0213	28002
28003	Tame at Water Orton	417050 291450	405.70	726	0.497	34.2	0.959	0.31	25.14	34.08	0.4027	28003
28004	Tame at Lea Marston	420600 293350	801.81	715	0.470	36.3	0.952	0.30	28.76	31.18	0.2685	28004
28005	Tame at Elford	417350 310350	1492.77	689	0.495	35.5	0.948	0.30	44.95	30.01	0.1743	28005
28006	Trent at Great Haywood	399300 322950	322.43	797	0.474	34.7	0.956	0.44	28.10	58.62	0.1253	28006
28007	Trent at Shardlow	444650 329900	4414.22	751	0.517	33.8	0.959	0.32	85.00	46.96	0.0882	28007
28008	Dove at Rocester Weir	411350 339750	401.51	1020	0.556	24.8	0.997	0.41	28.46	114.32	0.0034	28008
28009	Trent at Colwick	461850 339350	7484.84	760	0.504	34.2	0.926	0.31	94.62	54.71	0.0779	28009
28010	Derwent at Longbridge Weir	435750 336350	1052.27	1012	0.550	26.2	0.953	0.39	52.15	119.65	0.0170	28010
28011	Derwent at Matlock Bath	429700 358450	687.38	1115	0.565	26.1	0.951	0.41	33.60	136.71	0.0074	28011
28012	Trent at Yoxall	413250 317700	1213.94	746	0.518	34.1	0.957	0.35	41.08	42.43	0.0692	28012
28014	Sow at Milford	397350 321500	598.88	713	0.520	34.4	0.975	0.33	24.76	31.48	0.0597	28014
28015	Idle at Mattersey	468900 389650	525.94	650	0.787	18.9	0.920	0.27	38.15	33.39	0.0671	28015
28016	Ryton at Serlby Park	463950 389600	237.57	644	0.760	17.8	0.965	0.30	22.11	31.70	0.0652	28016
28017	Devon at Cotham											28017
28018	Dove at Marston On Dove	423350 328850	883.63	936	0.527	30.2	0.984	0.42	50.28	93.81	0.0094	28018
28019	Trent at Drakelow Park	423750 320300	3085.13	707	0.511	34.8	0.956	0.31	57.49	34.85	0.1161	28019
28020	Churnet at Rocester	410350 338750	234.02	956	0.499	32.7	0.953	0.44	27.94	103.81	0.0144	28020
28021	Derwent at Draycott	444450 332700	1173.67	981	0.550	27.4	0.953	0.38	60.50	111.39	0.0306	28021
28022	Trent at North Muskham	478850 359850	8234.81	746	0.502	34.8	0.912	0.30	126.90	52.50	0.0740	28022
28023	Wye at Ashford	418250 369750	152.17	1165	0.679	14.3	0.984	0.52	16.28	120.15	0.0122	28023
28024	Wreake at Syston Mill	461600 312550	416.83	634	0.403	41.9	0.941	0.28	27.19	41.29	0.0151	28024
28026	Anker at Polesworth	426050 303250	370.40	653	0.445	39.5	0.991	0.30	23.60	27.34	0.0681	28026
28027	Erewash at Stapleford	448150 336550	183.08	709	0.408	35.4	0.915	0.35	16.19	53.52	0.1070	28027
28031	Manifold at Ilam	414050 350700	148.53	1098	0.455	33.3	1.000	0.44	19.11	119.66	0.0023	28031
28032	Meden at Church Warsop	455950 368100	60.41	699	0.821	13.6	0.972	0.38	8.38	42.37	0.0914	28032
28033	Dove at Hollinsclough	406450 366850	7.96	1346	0.403	42.4	1.000	0.52	3.23	173.79	0.0000	28033
28038	Manifold at Hulme End	410600 359350	44.77	1172	0.426	37.7	1.000	0.51	8.44	101.26	0.0016	28038
28039	Rea at Calthorpe Park	407150 284750	74.06	781	0.512	34.9	0.956	0.29	8.12	45.32	0.3305	28039

Number	Name	IHDTM NGR	AREA km²	SAAR mm	BFIHOST	SPRHOST	FARL	PROPWET	DPLBAR km	DPSBAR m/km	URBEXT1990	Number
28040	Trent at Stoke On Trent	389300 346850	53.57	863	0.399	34.2	0.980	0.44	7.27	70.66	0.1380	28040
28041	Hamps at Waterhouses	408100 350350	36.91	1085	0.301	47.2	1.000	0.44	7.68	87.97	0.0033	28041
28043	Derwent at Chatsworth	426050 368450	343.61	1171	0.461	37.5	0.913	0.41	23.76	162.30	0.0023	28043
28045	Meden at Bothamstall	467950 373050	264.86	676	0.832	16.5	0.937	0.28	19.12	37.89	0.0898	28045
28046	Dove at Izaak Walton	414750 351050	85.62	1098	0.652	15.6	1.000	0.46	16.07	144.58	0.0012	28046
28047	Oldcotes Dyke at Blyth	461450 387450	85.83	654	0.713	19.3	0.959	0.34	9.11	35.35	0.0702	28047
28048	Amber at Wingfield Park	437450 352050	128.82	800	0.464	29.6	0.947	0.36	11.96	69.50	0.0417	28048
28049	Ryton at Worksop	457650 379550	75.46	664	0.748	15.8	0.939	0.38	10.88	34.80	0.0656	28049
28052	Sow at Great Bridgford											28052
28053	Penk at Penkridge	392150 314400	283.03	698	0.465	36.7	0.968	0.32	15.67	25.44	0.0888	28053
28054	Sence at Blaby	456750 298400	133.69	641	0.362	43.1	1.000	0.29	13.78	35.92	0.0335	28054
28055	Ecclesbourne at Duffield	431850 344850	50.58	853	0.456	30.3	0.997	0.35	7.55	109.20	0.0129	28055
28056	Rothley Brook at Rothley	458150 312200	91.75	672	0.353	43.2	0.979	0.30	14.73	39.30	0.0612	28056
28058	Henmore Brook at Ashbourne	417500 346150	38.63	895	0.448	31.0	0.977	0.36	8.80	94.48	0.0104	28058
28059	Maun at Mansfield	454800 362450	27.45	717	0.835	15.1	0.914	0.36	5.90	42.89	0.3029	28059
28060	Dover Beck at Lowdham	465450 347850	62.78	683	0.750	24.6	0.959	0.27	8.02	55.04	0.0292	28060
28061	Churnet at Basford Bridge	398250 351850	136.53	976	0.443	35.1	0.931	0.44	11.77	94.30	0.0214	28061
28066	Cole at Coleshill	418300 287550	119.72	722	0.375	39.6	0.981	0.29	13.03	25.90	0.3114	28066
28067	Derwent at Church Wilne	443900 331600	1176.10	980	0.550	27.4	0.953	0.38	62.36	111.18	0.0306	28067
28069	Tame at Tamworth	420550 303800	1423.58	691	0.487	35.9	0.947	0.30	35.35	30.20	0.1798	28069
28070	Burbage Brook at Burbage	425850 380250	8.36	1006	0.427	40.2	1.000	0.38	2.74	87.07	0.0000	28070
28082	Soar at Littlethorpe	454350 297300	180.84	637	0.445	39.9	0.987	0.30	12.51	26.44	0.0364	28082
28804	Trent at Trent Bridge	458250 338550	7469.26	761	0.504	34.3	0.935	0.31	90.47	54.72	0.0772	28804
29001	Waithe Beck at Brigsley	525150 401700	108.28	691	0.883	11.3	0.971	0.29	13.66	53.21	0.0045	29001
29002	Great Eau at Claythorpe Mill	541600 379150	80.69	692	0.712	21.9	0.952	0.28	9.01	53.59	0.0057	29002
29003	Lud at Louth	533550 387800	55.59	698	0.821	24.6	0.962	0.29	7.39	61.13	0.0244	29003
29004	Ancholme at Bishopbridge	503150 390950	58.92	615	0.558	29.4	1.000	0.26	8.39	11.61	0.0036	29004
29005	Rase at Bishopbridge	503200 391050	63.12	641	0.520	38.1	1.000	0.29	12.24	29.40	0.0156	29005
29009	Ancholme at Toft Newton	503250 387550	29.55	616	0.628	25.6	1.000	0.26	5.39	12.42	0.0049	29009
30001	Witham at Claypole Mill	484250 348150	296.04	615	0.592	28.5	0.979	0.27	27.69	30.94	0.0188	30001
30002	Barlings Eau at Langworth Bridge	506750 376450	208.03	609	0.535	30.1	0.984	0.28	11.24	15.16	0.0152	30002
30003	Bain at Fulsby Lock	524350 361250	200.26	667	0.756	22.0	0.969	0.29	20.92	39.93	0.0121	30003
30004	Partney Lymn at Partney Mill	540350 367500	59.94	685	0.570	32.4	0.980	0.29	9.40	54.22	0.0110	30004
30005	Witham at Saltersford Total	492600 333650	124.06	646	0.761	16.6	0.976	0.27	13.40	31.61	0.0036	30005
30006	Slea at Leasingham Mill	508500 347050	52.26	601	0.805	18.9	0.968	0.23	12.62	28.12	0.0300	30006
30011	Bain at Goulceby Bridge	524450 379600	64.02	695	0.843	16.0	0.962	0.29	10.03	45.35	0.0049	30011
30012	Stainfield Beck at Stainfield	512850 374050	37.72	632	0.523	34.3	1.000	0.29	10.44	29.72	0.0141	30012
30013	Heighington Beck at Heighington											30013
30014	Pointon Lode at Pointon	512950 331250	11.09	591	0.340	42.0	1.000	0.22	6.07	29.28	0.0080	30014
30015	Cringle Brook at Stoke Rochford											30015
30017	Witham at Colsterworth	492850 324750	50.23	641	0.657	22.6	1.000	0.27	7.38	22.59	0.0066	30017
31002	Glen at Kates Bridge	510750 315050	338.49	607	0.597	27.0	0.983	0.22	25.04	30.18	0.0065	31002
31004	Welland at Tallington	509650 307650	715.25	631	0.480	37.7	0.926	0.29	43.94	48.41	0.0119	31004
31005	Welland at Tixover	496850 299650	419.59	636	0.377	45.1	0.971	0.30	33.92	51.89	0.0081	31005
31006	Gwash at Belmesthorpe	503800 309550	149.49	630	0.668	23.9	0.758	0.28	22.10	37.30	0.0111	31006
31010	Chater at Fosters Bridge	496100 303100	68.86	640	0.529	33.1	0.998	0.30	10.90	62.65	0.0041	31010
31021	Welland at Ashley	482050 291500	247.19	640	0.326	47.9	0.993	0.30	17.23	48.05	0.0096	31021
31023	West Glen at Easton Wood	496050 325850	4.41	641	0.320	41.3	1.000	0.27	1.95	33.76	0.0000	31023
31025	Gwash South Arm at Manton	496650 305250	24.11	663	0.306	45.1	0.995	0.30	6.94	62.09	0.0030	31025
31026	Egleton Brook at Egleton											31026

Number	Name	IHDTM NGR	AREA km²	SAAR mm	BFIHOST	SPRHOST	FARL	PROPWET	DPLBAR km	DPSBAR m/km	URBEXT1990	Number
32002	Willow Brook at Fotheringhay	506550 293350	94.36	603	0.373	43.2	0.908	0.25	19.92	29.61	0.0641	32002
32003	Harpers Brook at Old Mill Bridge	498450 279850	70.62	621	0.415	40.9	1.000	0.30	12.50	38.28	0.0081	32003
32004	Ise Brook at Harrowden Old Mill	489950 271650	194.93	635	0.542	35.2	0.980	0.29	18.55	40.79	0.0354	32004
32006	Nene/kislingbury at Upton	472250 259100	221.91	651	0.453	42.6	0.986	0.30	19.07	48.17	0.0148	32006
32007	Nene Brampton at St Andrews	474850 261550	232.32	648	0.543	35.2	0.919	0.30	14.88	43.90	0.0182	32007
32008	Nene/kislingbury at Dodford	462850 260550	104.82	660	0.455	42.8	0.982	0.30	10.64	42.38	0.0230	32008
32010	Nene at Wansford	508250 299600	1516.83	620	0.520	36.6	0.928	0.28	71.00	36.83	0.0312	32010
32029	Flore at Experimental Catchment	465950 260950	7.55	625	0.436	41.8	1.000	0.30	1.92	39.57	0.0010	32029
33002	Bedford Ouse at Bedford	505350 249950	1470.12	636	0.453	39.9	0.954	0.30	90.81	31.38	0.0217	33002
33005	Bedford Ouse at Thornborough Mill	473550 235350	387.87	655	0.480	37.3	0.988	0.31	22.25	27.88	0.0092	33005
33006	Wissey at Northwold	576950 296600	259.81	659	0.762	20.2	0.955	0.30	23.18	19.89	0.0136	33006
33007	Nar at Marham	572150 311950	147.29	683	0.803	16.6	0.932	0.26	18.53	23.73	0.0093	33007
33009	Bedford Ouse at Harrold Mill	494950 256400	1323.64	641	0.448	40.1	0.949	0.30	57.65	31.21	0.0202	33009
33011	Little Ouse at County Bridge Euston	589050 280150	130.18	596	0.653	26.0	0.985	0.28	17.49	17.74	0.0086	33011
33012	Kym at Meagre Farm	515450 263250	137.86	585	0.309	49.4	0.992	0.24	16.41	26.58	0.0074	33012
33013	Sapiston at Rectory Bridge	589600 278950	195.93	589	0.610	28.5	0.980	0.28	20.23	18.75	0.0109	33013
33014	Lark at Temple	575650 273100	278.43	593	0.785	18.2	0.955	0.27	17.89	23.65	0.0217	33014
33015	Ouzel at Willen	488250 240650	279.06	638	0.466	41.5	0.979	0.31	26.60	35.49	0.0364	33015
33017	Bedford Ouse at St Ives Staunch	531850 270350	2869.58	604	0.467	40.4	0.962	0.26	95.94	28.93	0.0279	33017
33018	Tove at Cappenham Bridge	471550 248700	133.20	661	0.368	41.2	0.999	0.30	12.23	37.67	0.0065	33018
33019	Thet at Melford Bridge	587850 282850	311.82	620	0.707	23.9	0.957	0.31	27.75	14.16	0.0140	33019
33020	Alconbury Brook at Brampton	520650 271800	212.60	564	0.319	52.3	1.000	0.22	16.09	25.26	0.0108	33020
33021	Rhee at Burnt Mill	541650 252350	308.09	559	0.714	24.0	0.997	0.24	18.49	25.32	0.0143	33021
33022	Ivel at Blunham	515350 251050	539.94	582	0.646	30.2	0.987	0.27	24.49	31.75	0.0440	33022
33023	Lea Brook at Beck Bridge											33023
33024	Cam at Dernford	546750 250450	198.05	589	0.652	26.5	0.995	0.28	20.84	38.68	0.0205	33024
33027	Rhee at Wimpole	533150 248500	125.50	557	0.607	32.0	1.000	0.24	10.80	21.98	0.0069	33027
33028	Flit at Shefford	514300 239300	119.61	598	0.574	37.0	0.991	0.29	14.21	37.30	0.0339	33028
33029	Stringside at White Bridge	571700 300450	97.08	627	0.863	12.4	0.993	0.23	9.56	13.77	0.0073	33029
33030	Clipstone Brook at Clipstone	493300 225650	40.28	640	0.362	47.8	0.983	0.31	6.71	34.61	0.0116	33030
33031	Broughton Brook at Broughton	488900 240650	69.46	629	0.484	40.8	0.985	0.31	10.48	29.57	0.0109	33031
33032	Heacham at Heacham	568350 337550	56.19	687	0.968	6.0	1.000	0.24	11.04	26.26	0.0160	33032
33033	Hiz at Arlesey	518850 237750	108.97	603	0.765	20.8	0.994	0.30	13.22	36.55	0.0566	33033
33034	Little Ouse at Abbey Heath	585200 284550	708.28	607	0.694	24.0	0.973	0.29	29.34	16.57	0.0131	33034
33037	Bedford Ouse at Newport Pagnell	487550 244350	801.81	648	0.437	39.7	0.951	0.30	38.08	30.10	0.0150	33037
33039	Bedford Ouse at Roxton	515850 253400	1662.59	628	0.447	40.9	0.956	0.28	96.38	30.47	0.0258	33039
33044	Thet at Bridgham	595550 285350	275.60	620	0.681	25.6	0.952	0.31	18.55	13.46	0.0131	33044
33045	Wittle at Quidenham	602550 287750	27.65	608	0.535	32.7	0.976	0.31	4.84	15.42	0.0122	33045
33046	Thet at Red Bridge	599550 292200	144.95	624	0.582	32.2	0.956	0.31	10.65	12.73	0.0166	33046
33048	Larling Brook at Stonebridge											33048
33049	Stanford Water at Buckenham Tofts	583000 295250	46.24	645	0.853	16.3	0.923	0.31	9.38	13.18	0.0037	33049
33050	Snail at Fordham	563000 270450	57.91	577	0.738	20.5	1.000	0.26	12.09	28.38	0.0360	33050
33051	Cam at Chesterford	550350 242700	140.25	599	0.576	31.2	0.993	0.29	12.94	41.19	0.0190	33051
33052	Swaffham Lode at Swaffham Bulbeck											33052
33054	Babingley at Castle Rising	568150 325250	48.49	686	0.905	9.7	0.954	0.24	9.40	29.03	0.0087	33054
33055	Granta at Babraham	551100 250250	101.29	580	0.636	27.1	1.000	0.26	12.32	36.35	0.0115	33055
33057	Ouzel at Leighton Buzzard	491700 223950	221.21	643	0.525	37.5	0.999	0.31	9.45	33.81	0.0141	33057
33058	Ouzel at Bletchley	488450 232050	103.56	641	0.481	40.2	0.994	0.31	19.03	36.45	0.0231	33058
33063	Little Ouse at Knettishall	595300 280800		595	0.596	29.1	0.982	0.28	11.88	17.49	0.0102	33063
33805	Beechamwell Brook at Beechamwell	573950 303550	34.50	656	0.966	5.9	0.999	0.23	7.65	17.06	0.0114	33805

Number	Name	IHDTM NGR	AREA km²	SAAR mm	BFIHOST	SPRHOST	FARL	PROPWET	DPLBAR km	DPSBAR m/km	URBEXT$_{1990}$	Number
33809	Bury Brook at Bury Weir	528600 283850	61.97	547	0.414	47.4	0.970	0.22	11.45	16.52	0.0116	33809
33813	Mel at Meldreth											33813
34001	Yare at Colney	618250 308350	227.90	635	0.529	35.3	0.965	0.31	23.05	18.78	0.0213	34001
34002	Tas at Shotesham	622450 299300	150.95	610	0.436	37.3	0.994	0.29	13.01	19.74	0.0197	34002
34003	Bure at Ingworth	619050 329750	168.09	669	0.779	20.8	0.977	0.31	12.53	23.62	0.0121	34003
34004	Wensum at Costessey Mill	617550 312950	560.95	672	0.689	26.1	0.958	0.30	43.05	20.88	0.0176	34004
34005	Tud at Costessey Park	617150 311150	72.02	649	0.600	32.6	0.983	0.31	14.46	20.56	0.0303	34005
34006	Waveney at Needham Mill	622750 280950	379.26	594	0.422	36.6	0.999	0.28	20.52	16.14	0.0128	34006
34007	Dove at Oakley Park	617400 277050	140.10	585	0.427	37.3	0.997	0.28	14.16	15.43	0.0101	34007
34008	Ant at Honing Lock											34008
34010	Waveney at Billingford Bridge	616650 278250	152.63	603	0.439	35.1	1.000	0.29	11.94	15.49	0.0191	34010
34011	Wensum at Fakenham	591850 329300	162.10	698	0.857	14.4	0.997	0.29	14.39	17.09	0.0146	34011
34012	Burn at Burnham Overy	584550 342650	81.33	669	0.966	6.2	1.000	0.30	8.53	27.60	0.0116	34012
34018	Stiffkey at Warham All Saints	594550 341450	86.33	662	0.787	17.2	0.997	0.31	12.44	26.87	0.0139	34018
35001	Gipping at Constantine Weir	615250 244250	315.02	578	0.477	37.7	0.934	0.28	24.57	28.53	0.0281	35001
35003	Alde at Farnham	636000 259950	62.95	592	0.366	41.6	0.990	0.26	11.43	26.51	0.0024	35003
35004	Ore at Beversham Bridge	635750 258150	56.12	596	0.454	38.1	0.989	0.26	11.01	23.33	0.0083	35004
35008	Gipping at Stowmarket	605950 257850	127.43	577	0.401	43.4	0.998	0.28	8.80	25.05	0.0201	35008
35010	Gipping at Bramford	612700 246400	297.50	578	0.458	38.6	0.943	0.28	19.66	28.31	0.0168	35010
35011	Belstead Brook at Belstead	614150 242100	43.69	566	0.517	36.5	0.993	0.28	8.99	32.20	0.0268	35011
35014	Bucklesham Mill at Newbourn											35014
36001	Stour at Stratford St Mary	603900 233850	837.33	578	0.511	38.1	0.972	0.25	39.17	33.36	0.0125	36001
36002	Glem at Glemsford	584450 247050	86.09	598	0.403	43.6	0.987	0.26	11.71	38.40	0.0100	36002
36003	Box at Polstead	598350 237850	56.63	566	0.555	37.8	0.994	0.26	8.57	26.95	0.0091	36003
36004	Chad Brook at Long Melford	586950 245900	50.07	589	0.440	40.5	1.000	0.28	9.16	28.94	0.0052	36004
36005	Brett at Hadleigh	602400 242900	155.98	580	0.428	43.6	0.994	0.28	15.34	30.30	0.0076	36005
36006	Stour at Langham	602150 234550	571.79	580	0.509	37.8	0.962	0.25	43.07	34.33	0.0139	36006
36007	Belchamp Brook at Bardfield Bridge	584850 242200	58.56	560	0.525	36.1	0.997	0.25	7.25	26.56	0.0057	36007
36008	Stour at Westmill	582850 246450	223.63	589	0.414	42.9	0.986	0.26	21.94	33.94	0.0151	36008
36009	Brett at Cockfield	591400 252550	25.70	598	0.396	46.7	1.000	0.28	5.35	18.71	0.0046	36009
36010	Bumpstead Brook at Broad Green	569050 241800	28.03	588	0.387	44.6	1.000	0.27	4.63	34.85	0.0055	36010
36011	Stour Brook at Sturmer	569700 244000	34.56	592	0.382	44.6	1.000	0.26	6.65	34.10	0.0554	36011
36012	Stour at Kedington	570850 245150	76.79	599	0.396	44.0	0.990	0.26	11.00	30.65	0.0088	36012
36015	Stour at Lamarsh	589650 235750	481.44	583	0.474	39.4	0.970	0.26	30.19	33.54	0.0152	36015
37001	Roding at Redbridge	541500 188250	301.20	607	0.331	46.6	0.985	0.29	33.67	30.40	0.0495	37001
37003	Ter at Crabbs Bridge	578500 210750	77.81	570	0.461	41.8	0.977	0.31	13.33	18.89	0.0075	37003
37005	Colne at Lexden	596350 226000	236.04	566	0.537	38.1	0.950	0.25	24.85	30.98	0.0140	37005
37006	Can at Beach's Mill	569150 207200	228.28	589	0.317	46.9	0.993	0.28	14.57	25.41	0.0343	37006
37007	Wid at Writtle	568450 206050	135.73	592	0.244	47.6	0.996	0.28	15.72	27.90	0.0462	37007
37008	Chelmer at Springfield	571150 206950	190.13	584	0.492	39.3	0.976	0.31	25.63	28.28	0.0234	37008
37009	Brain at Guithavon Valley	581750 214700	60.22	572	0.535	36.4	1.000	0.30	13.74	24.64	0.0580	37009
37010	Blackwater at Appleford Bridge	584550 215900	246.98	572	0.476	40.1	0.989	0.26	27.93	26.21	0.0206	37010
37011	Chelmer at Churchend	562750 223400	72.94	591	0.447	41.2	0.993	0.31	9.29	32.39	0.0085	37011
37012	Colne at Poolstreet	577250 236350	64.68	574	0.403	43.9	0.992	0.29	8.15	26.81	0.0063	37012
37013	Sandon Brook at Sandon Bridge	575550 205500	75.05	575	0.277	46.6	0.852	0.28	8.86	24.71	0.0182	37013
37014	Roding at High Ongar	556050 203850	93.08	598	0.403	46.5	0.986	0.31	15.59	18.83	0.0092	37014
37016	Pant at Copford Hall	566800 231450	63.64	588	0.404	43.6	0.998	0.30	9.83	29.23	0.0114	37016
37017	Blackwater at Stisted	579150 224350	140.34	579	0.493	39.1	0.986	0.31	21.63	30.06	0.0217	37017
37018	Ingrebourne at Gaynes Park	555150 186100	44.78	594	0.283	45.4	0.987	0.27	9.33	43.99	0.1161	37018
37019	Beam at Bretons Farm	551650 185450	50.21	588	0.363	41.4	0.982	0.27	7.84	28.77	0.2713	37019

Number	Name	IHDTM NGR	AREA km²	SAAR mm	BFIHOST	SPRHOST	FARL	PROPWET	DPLBAR km	DPSBAR m/km	URBEXT1990	Number
37020	Chelmer at Felsted	567100 219450	133.70	588	0.467	40.2	0.970	0.31	12.81	30.12	0.0122	37020
37021	Roman at Bounstead Bridge	598600 220550	52.56	560	0.602	40.6	0.988	0.23	8.63	21.26	0.0384	37021
37031	Crouch at Wickford	574850 193350	70.37	572	0.218	49.2	0.975	0.27	8.18	30.11	0.1426	37031
37033	Eastwood Brook at Eastwood	586050 188900	9.93	555	0.342	45.1	1.000	0.21	3.90	29.97	0.3038	37033
38001	Lea at Feildes Weir	539050 209200	1040.78	630	0.565	34.0	0.954	0.29	29.64	37.10	0.0579	38001
38002	Ash at Mardock	539300 214650	78.23	619	0.505	35.8	1.000	0.31	12.81	35.04	0.0134	38002
38003	Mimram at Panshanger Park	528350 213150	130.53	656	0.720	27.4	0.986	0.30	16.74	45.03	0.0424	38003
38004	Rib at Wadesmill	536150 217300	136.55	625	0.469	38.0	0.999	0.30	18.64	39.03	0.0126	38004
38007	Canons Brook at Elizabeth Way	543200 210550	20.80	601	0.355	45.8	0.990	0.31	4.39	29.84	0.1736	38007
38011	Mimram at Fulling Mill	522550 217000	98.90	658	0.741	25.9	0.982	0.30	11.56	43.88	0.0287	38011
38013	Upper Lee at Luton Hoo	511750 218550	70.67	660	0.869	13.8	0.948	0.30	10.89	40.48	0.2785	38013
38018	Upper Lee at Water Hall	529800 209750	157.21	663	0.688	27.3	0.946	0.30	22.92	41.30	0.1636	38018
38020	Cobbins Brook at Sewardstone Road	538700 200050	38.81	617	0.223	49.5	0.997	0.29	7.09	45.36	0.0376	38020
38021	Turkey Brook at Albany Park	536050 198500	41.55	666	0.243	47.9	0.950	0.29	9.32	56.33	0.0439	38021
38022	Pymmes Brook at Edmonton Silver Street	534150 192500	40.71	672	0.243	48.0	0.982	0.29	8.08	41.15	0.4239	38022
38026	Pincey Brook at Sheering Hall	549450 212750	52.71	599	0.388	46.9	0.984	0.31	10.23	24.43	0.0131	38026
39001	Thames at Kingston	517750 169650	9950.95	706	0.653	27.0	0.913	0.30	140.81	42.78	0.0429	39001
39002	Thames at Days Weir	456850 193650	3483.91	690	0.650	27.0	0.944	0.31	79.76	37.80	0.0265	39002
39003	Wandle at Connollys Mill											39003
39004	Wandle at Beddington Park	529450 165450	118.34	763	0.845	16.6	0.994	0.33	13.89	76.65	0.1432	39004
39005	Beverley Brook at Wimbledon Common	521700 171850	39.71	630	0.477	33.9	1.000	0.29	7.30	27.16	0.3766	39005
39006	Windrush at Newbridge	440200 201750	362.05	744	0.790	17.2	0.909	0.33	42.71	61.59	0.0152	39006
39007	Blackwater at Swallowfield	473200 164650	360.37	708	0.630	26.8	0.895	0.32	19.37	32.80	0.0664	39007
39008	Thames at Eynsham	444350 208650	1623.06	730	0.686	24.1	0.924	0.32	57.68	39.90	0.0243	39008
39010	Colne at Denham	505300 186250	733.19	703	0.623	31.9	0.786	0.29	37.23	43.67	0.0754	39010
39011	Wey at Tilford	487550 143250	391.08	855	0.795	18.3	0.969	0.35	24.31	60.16	0.0236	39011
39012	Hogsmill at Kingston Upon Thames	518350 168700	72.89	671	0.599	27.2	0.993	0.30	10.99	32.76	0.2064	39012
39014	Ver at Hansteads	514950 201750	135.10	699	0.676	32.1	0.946	0.30	18.81	39.30	0.0713	39014
39015	Whitewater at Lodge Farm	473000 152150	45.35	781	0.922	7.5	1.000	0.35	7.11	49.13	0.0081	39015
39016	Kennet at Theale	464750 170650	1032.62	759	0.767	18.7	0.956	0.31	45.86	56.15	0.0137	39016
39017	Ray at Grendon Underwood											39017
39018	Ock at Abingdon	448450 196900	248.23	637	0.635	29.1	0.984	0.31	16.57	23.97	0.0193	39018
39019	Lambourn at Shaw	446850 168300	235.09	736	0.839	16.1	0.983	0.32	19.21	60.48	0.0046	39019
39020	Coln at Bibury	412250 206350	107.29	821	0.858	12.2	0.963	0.33	19.37	78.39	0.0100	39020
39021	Cherwell at Enslow Mill	448350 213350	557.53	664	0.590	31.4	0.983	0.30	37.32	47.64	0.0234	39021
39022	Loddon at Sheepbridge	471850 165050	176.49	735	0.594	26.4	0.931	0.33	19.24	33.54	0.0454	39022
39023	Wye at Hedsor	489550 186550	134.24	755	0.797	19.6	0.983	0.36	16.95	89.70	0.0702	39023
39024	Gatwick Stream at Gatwick	528700 140350	30.50	835	0.609	34.1	0.951	0.36	7.57	51.14	0.0766	39024
39025	Enborne at Brimpton	456800 164950	142.13	789	0.500	32.8	0.985	0.32	14.15	54.61	0.0094	39025
39026	Cherwell at Banbury	445650 241250	204.60	664	0.416	42.4	0.971	0.30	15.48	43.52	0.0153	39026
39027	Pang at Pangbourne	463500 176450	175.49	694	0.720	22.0	0.994	0.31	20.68	53.85	0.0045	39027
39028	Dun at Hungerford	432250 168550	100.36	786	0.768	21.3	0.990	0.31	10.07	47.16	0.0123	39028
39029	Tillingbourne at Shalford	499950 147950	58.87	810	0.885	14.9	0.896	0.36	11.69	95.47	0.0083	39029
39031	Lambourn at Welford											39031
39032	Lambourn at East Shefford	439150 174500	144.99	746	0.896	11.5	0.994	0.32	11.50	68.95	0.0039	39032
39033	Winterbourne at St Bagnor	445250 169350	45.46	717	0.766	22.4	1.000	0.32	10.39	46.47	0.0018	39033
39034	Evenlode at Cassington Mill	444950 209850	427.35	691	0.699	24.1	0.967	0.32	33.95	47.34	0.0182	39034
39035	Churn at Cerney Wick											39035
39036	Law Brook at Albury	504600 146900	16.00	819	0.888	15.1	0.961	0.36	4.85	87.35	0.0010	39036
39037	Kennet at Marlborough	418800 168750	136.49	772	0.959	5.1	1.000	0.34	14.84	52.50	0.0102	39037

Number	URBEXT₁₉₉₀	DPSBAR m/km	DPLBAR km	PROPWET	FARL	SPRHOST	BFIHOST	SAAR mm	AREA km²	IHDTM NGR	Number	Name
39038	0.0235	35.71	24.87	0.31	0.983	37.2	0.499	647	443.86	466650 205600	39038	Thame at Shabbington
39040											39040	Thames at West Mill Cricklade
39042	0.0075	37.36	18.95	0.33	0.980	12.2	0.865	736	77.44	422850 199350	39042	Leach at Priory Mill Lechlade
39044	0.0367	32.68	11.34	0.35	0.942	30.0	0.589	707	83.72	475350 159350	39044	Hart at Bramshill House
39049	0.2978	41.58	5.33	0.29	0.973	50.3	0.182	686	28.24	521550 189650	39049	Silk Stream at Colindeep Lane
39052	0.1182	25.36	7.62	0.29	0.942	41.6	0.354	676	50.20	485300 171400	39052	The Cut at Binfield
39053	0.0913	34.90	10.52	0.36	0.947	40.3	0.463	812	91.59	527050 143250	39053	Mole at Horley
39055	0.3849	15.73	6.11	0.29	1.000	50.1	0.172	656	17.71	508400 184600	39055	Yeading Bk West at Yeading West
39056	0.2565	49.07	11.49	0.28	0.993	22.3	0.715	714	127.88	537250 173050	39056	Ravensbourne at Catford Hill
39057											39057	Crane at Cranford Park
39058	0.4322	30.90	6.48	0.29	0.985	32.4	0.529	664	38.33	537200 172600	39058	Pool at Winsford Road
39069	0.0738	30.17	13.41	0.36	0.956	41.5	0.445	795	146.03	526200 146050	39069	Mole at Kinnersley Manor
39081	0.0187	24.09	16.07	0.31	0.984	29.2	0.633	638	245.85	448100 196450	39081	Ock at Abingdon
39086	0.0765	48.61	8.75	0.36	0.954	34.7	0.593	830	32.42	528400 141850	39086	Gatwick Stream at Gatwick Link
39088	0.0315	60.42	17.54	0.30	0.960	30.3	0.693	753	97.23	506550 194550	39088	Chess at Rickmansworth
39089	0.0326	64.36	8.02	0.31	0.979	29.4	0.700	723	46.26	505400 207550	39089	Gade at Bury Mill
39090	0.0568	29.80	15.84	0.31	0.970	34.3	0.530	682	140.01	420850 196900	39090	Cole at Inglesham
39092	0.2525	50.48	6.33	0.29	0.990	50.5	0.178	689	23.76	524050 189350	39092	Dollis Bk at Hendon Lane Bridge
39093	0.3973	37.87	9.22	0.29	0.937	49.7	0.197	672	115.85	520150 184850	39093	Brent at Monks Park
39095	0.3740	37.11	7.34	0.27	1.000	28.9	0.609	643	33.93	539350 174700	39095	Quaggy at Manor House Gardens
39096	0.4228	26.15	4.41	0.29	1.000	50.6	0.175	664	23.26	519100 186350	39096	Wealdstone Brook at Wembley
39813	0.1219	43.95	2.89	0.36	0.889	29.1	0.684	827	13.13	524500 136250	39813	Mole at Ifield Weir
39824	0.3562	25.52	3.66	0.27	1.000	24.6	0.692	680	10.18	540350 168550	39824	Ravensbourne East at Bromley South
39827	0.4316	31.00	5.90	0.29	0.985	32.3	0.530	664	37.77	536900 172050	39827	Pool at Selworthy Road
39830											39830	Beck at Rectory Road
39831											39831	Chaffinch Brook at Beckenham
39834											39834	Brent at Hanwell
40003	0.0186	54.68	35.73	0.35	0.949	41.4	0.439	744	1258.80	570650 152850	40003	Medway at Teston
40004	0.0078	94.28	17.22	0.35	0.975	44.4	0.388	857	205.36	577450 124650	40004	Rother at Udiam
40005	0.0062	27.95	19.45	0.34	0.994	44.6	0.353	691	278.14	575950 147800	40005	Beult at Stile Bridge
40006	0.0241	65.44	8.34	0.36	0.969	29.5	0.628	719	50.21	563200 149550	40006	Bourne at Hadlow
40007	0.0200	83.94	14.54	0.35	0.939	42.3	0.441	830	252.40	551600 140650	40007	Medway at Chafford Weir
40008	0.0307	39.87	18.97	0.34	0.984	28.0	0.658	741	226.07	605050 147150	40008	Great Stour at Wye
40009	0.0050	79.96	12.69	0.36	0.905	42.6	0.443	812	134.43	571850 140050	40009	Teise at Stone Bridge
40010	0.0161	48.03	20.01	0.35	0.925	41.2	0.425	742	224.88	552150 143850	40010	Eden at Penshurst
40011	0.0227	51.95	26.92	0.34	0.982	25.4	0.706	747	341.29	611750 155550	40011	Great Stour at Horton
40012	0.0416	72.72	18.86	0.29	0.882	16.1	0.832	729	187.41	555250 171950	40012	Darent at Hawley
40016	0.1784	46.26	12.73	0.27	0.946	14.6	0.857	692	125.52	551200 174450	40016	Cray at Crayford
40017	0.0052	106.58	6.40	0.35	0.994	43.9	0.432	887	26.43	568050 124150	40017	Dudwell at Burwash
40018	0.0366	75.23	13.78	0.33	0.888	17.0	0.814	763	117.11	552950 164200	40018	Darent at Lullingstone
40020	0.0256	90.75	8.70	0.36	0.974	42.4	0.453	866	53.20	552050 136650	40020	Eridge Stream at Hendal Bridge
40022	0.0135	41.65	12.56	0.34	0.973	23.3	0.744	726	66.92	599350 142400	40022	Great Stour at Chart Leacon
40809	0.0017	94.35	6.52	0.36	0.915	42.6	0.412	860	23.97	547800 134350	40809	Pippingford Brook at Paygate
41003	0.0216	51.54	14.71	0.34	0.989	43.2	0.409	814	135.45	553250 105250	41003	Cuckmere at Sherman Bridge
41005	0.0223	74.92	15.30	0.35	0.924	40.9	0.493	835	182.26	542750 121500	41005	Ouse at Gold Bridge
41006	0.0234	73.27	10.62	0.35	0.983	43.2	0.431	822	87.84	545900 118950	41006	Uck at Isfield
41007	0.0186	49.83	28.09	0.35	0.975	43.4	0.388	806	401.33	503700 121400	41007	Arun at Park Mound
41011	0.0119	76.62	13.72	0.35	0.974	26.8	0.675	921	157.02	485050 122850	41011	Rother at Iping Mill
41012	0.0596	49.23	12.27	0.34	0.964	43.8	0.376	829	93.97	521950 119150	41012	Adur E Branch at Sakeham
41014	0.0191	50.49	26.30	0.35	0.973	43.3	0.389	805	383.59	504550 122950	41014	Arun at Pallingham Quay

Number	Name	IHDTM NGR	AREA km²	SAAR mm	BFIHOST	SPRHOST	FARL	PROPWET	DPLBAR km	DPSBAR m/km	URBEXT_1990	Number
41015	Ems at Westbourne	475450 107250	57.93	899	0.904	9.3	0.981	0.34	9.46	82.87	0.0087	41015
41016	Cuckmere at Cowbeech	561150 115150	18.54	856	0.476	41.9	0.966	0.34	4.84	80.90	0.0134	41016
41018	Kird at Tanyards	504350 125750	67.14	820	0.360	45.7	0.967	0.35	10.94	41.95	0.0008	41018
41020	Bevern Stream at Clappers Bridge	542150 116450	35.23	886	0.355	43.2	0.987	0.34	7.85	47.69	0.0121	41020
41021	Clayhill Stream at Old Ship	544850 115300	7.09	805	0.252	48.3	1.000	0.34	2.84	27.65	0.0000	41021
41022	Lod at Halfway Bridge	493250 122350	52.22	857	0.478	38.8	0.951	0.35	9.31	80.67	0.0022	41022
41023	Lavant at Graylingwell	487250 106350	86.63	921	0.935	7.3	1.000	0.34	12.06	103.82	0.0061	41023
41025	Loxwood Stream at Drungewick	505850 130750	93.81	812	0.320	46.5	0.982	0.35	14.96	57.52	0.0062	41025
41026	Cockhaise Brook at Holywell	537650 126250	36.10	851	0.441	42.8	0.894	0.35	5.82	99.86	0.0056	41026
41027	Rother at Princes Marsh	477150 127050	37.57	908	0.665	26.6	0.973	0.35	5.14	80.48	0.0135	41027
41028	Chess Stream at Chess Bridge	521850 117400	24.96	850	0.499	35.9	0.984	0.34	6.42	48.40	0.0118	41028
41801	Hollington Stream at Hollington	578800 110050	3.47	781	0.366	46.2	1.000	0.34	2.17	85.21	0.4334	41801
41806	North End Stream at Allington	538400 113800	2.32	929	0.647	25.2	1.000	0.34	1.23	131.73	0.0000	41806
41807	Bevern Stream at East Chiltington	536650 115200	5.95	939	0.533	32.6	0.989	0.34	2.37	97.89	0.0092	41807
42001	Wallington at North Fareham	458700 107650	112.18	819	0.641	24.1	0.981	0.34	12.91	47.76	0.0386	42001
42005	Wallop Brook at Broughton	431100 132900	53.61	770	0.955	6.0	1.000	0.34	6.91	43.44	0.0056	42005
42006	Meon at Mislingford	459050 114150	72.75	899	0.961	5.0	0.980	0.34	13.41	87.95	0.0033	42006
42007	Alre at Drove Lane	457550 132600	57.40	857	0.964	4.8	0.881	0.34	7.04	51.58	0.0068	42007
42008	Cheriton Stream at Sewards Bridge	457250 132350	74.28	885	0.940	6.9	0.998	0.34	10.40	55.34	0.0042	42008
42009	Candover Stream at Borough Bridge	456950 132450	71.99	819	0.951	6.1	0.934	0.34	15.20	53.34	0.0021	42009
42010	Itchen at Highbridge	446800 121150	342.26	832	0.938	6.7	0.943	0.34	27.66	54.77	0.0146	42010
42011	Hamble at Frog Mill	452150 114900	56.33	838	0.749	17.9	0.991	0.33	8.13	53.15	0.0143	42011
42012	Anton at Fullerton	437900 139450	186.13	773	0.931	8.1	0.949	0.34	16.52	40.95	0.0244	42012
42014	Blackwater at Ower	432850 117250	102.51	837	0.442	34.2	0.985	0.33	11.26	45.17	0.0089	42014
42017	Hermitage at Havant	471100 106900	16.93	786	0.243	46.1	0.992	0.34	3.96	33.68	0.1646	42017
43001	Avon at Ringwood	414050 105250	1616.64	809	0.877	11.2	0.984	0.34	59.46	63.92	0.0145	43001
43002	Stour at Ensbury	408950 96250	1052.35	861	0.663	25.7	0.989	0.35	57.51	55.57	0.0148	43002
43003	Avon at East Mills Flume	416250 115250	1455.28	807	0.894	10.2	0.987	0.34	49.63	55.63	0.0150	43003
43004	Bourne at Laverstock Mill	415750 130550	165.03	768	0.952	5.9	1.000	0.34	26.23	51.83	0.0209	43004
43005	Avon at Amesbury	415050 141450	326.46	744	0.903	10.7	1.000	0.34	26.40	51.56	0.0154	43005
43006	Nadder at Wilton Park	409950 130850	215.69	875	0.763	19.6	0.979	0.35	21.01	80.13	0.0056	43006
43007	Stour at Throop Mill	411750 95850	1063.99	861	0.664	25.6	0.990	0.35	61.51	55.12	0.0170	43007
43008	Wylye at South Newton	408450 134450	447.95	830	0.937	6.9	0.977	0.35	25.16	71.53	0.0103	43008
43009	Stour at Hammoon	382050 114550	519.04	849	0.442	40.0	0.993	0.36	25.79	50.93	0.0095	43009
43010	Allen at Loverley Mill	400750 108550	84.86	872	0.944	6.3	0.979	0.35	11.71	66.17	0.0033	43010
43012	Wylye at Norton Bavant	390750 142950	114.07	925	0.885	11.2	0.978	0.35	12.44	75.48	0.0187	43012
43014	East Avon at Upavon	413350 156000	85.82	759	0.838	17.6	1.000	0.32	9.96	55.83	0.0156	43014
43017	West Avon at Upavon											43017
43018	Allen at Walford Mill	400950 100650	171.64	860	0.913	8.3	0.976	0.35	17.81	52.79	0.0036	43018
44002	Piddle at Baggs Mill	391200 87750	183.76	942	0.859	12.9	0.972	0.36	22.67	81.41	0.0032	44002
44003	Asker at Bridport	346850 92650	48.69	923	0.696	26.5	0.994	0.38	7.34	140.69	0.0116	44003
44004	Frome at Dorchester Total	370950 90300	197.61	1012	0.773	20.7	0.973	0.38	17.33	104.39	0.0091	44004
44006	Sydling Water at Sydling St Nicholas	363300 99550	12.16	1030	0.880	13.3	0.971	0.38	3.41	131.57	0.0020	44006
44008	Sth Winterbourne at W'bourne Steepleton	362850 89850	19.89	1012	0.809	19.7	1.000	0.38	4.92	95.62	0.0021	44008
44009	Wey at Broadwey											44009
45001	Exe at Thorverton	293600 101750	600.03	1253	0.525	36.1	0.985	0.46	38.11	140.72	0.0025	45001
45002	Exe at Stoodleigh	294250 117650	420.87	1360	0.495	38.0	0.980	0.48	26.49	145.44	0.0004	45002
45003	Culm at Wood Mill	302100 105950	228.69	971	0.585	31.8	0.996	0.40	15.23	72.19	0.0038	45003
45004	Axe at Whitford	326250 95400	288.58	994	0.498	38.8	0.992	0.39	18.70	92.15	0.0046	45004
45005	Otter at Dotton	308700 88550	202.52	970	0.548	34.4	0.998	0.40	19.42	86.88	0.0079	45005

Number	Name	IHDTM NGR	AREA km²	SAAR mm	BFIHOST	SPRHOST	FARL	PROPWET	DPLBAR km	DPSBAR m/km	URBEXT₁₉₉₀	Number
45006	Quarme at Enterwell	135450	20.25	1420	0.514	37.0	1.000	0.54	5.51	157.32	0.0005	45006
45008	Otter at Fenny Bridges	98750	110.20	1035	0.486	38.3	0.996	0.40	12.52	94.58	0.0089	45008
45009	Exe at Pixton	126150	147.81	1375	0.548	34.6	0.950	0.51	14.77	157.11	0.0001	45009
45011	Barle at Brushford	125850	128.01	1585	0.449	42.8	0.999	0.54	21.81	139.27	0.0004	45011
45012	Creedy at Cowley	96850	263.55	909	0.577	32.0	0.995	0.46	15.81	113.61	0.0023	45012
45801	Back Brook at Hawkerland	88650	2.45	860	0.577	28.0	1.000	0.40	1.36	66.91	0.0000	45801
46002	Teign at Preston	74450	377.61	1230	0.585	25.6	0.984	0.46	22.48	134.31	0.0027	46002
46003	Dart at Austins Bridge	66050	248.90	1771	0.523	32.8	0.996	0.47	19.82	124.02	0.0036	46003
46005	East Dart at Bellever	77650	22.29	2096	0.362	47.5	1.000	0.46	6.22	96.98	0.0000	46005
46006	Erme at Ermington	53350	43.69	1713	0.472	38.3	1.000	0.47	10.11	103.20	0.0167	46006
46007	West Dart at Dunnabridge	74250	47.47	1987	0.368	47.7	1.000	0.47	7.73	88.54	0.0022	46007
46008	Avon at Loddiswell	47750	102.73	1553	0.553	32.9	1.000	0.47	14.98	126.81	0.0035	46008
46801	Erme at Erme Intake	63300	14.64	2112	0.258	57.6	1.000	0.47	3.95	76.36	0.0000	46801
46806	Avon at Avon Intake	64250	14.21	2154	0.371	46.4	1.000	0.47	4.63	91.62	0.0000	46806
47001	Tamar at Gunnislake	72450	920.07	1215	0.481	37.0	0.994	0.49	39.43	88.17	0.0034	47001
47004	Lynher at Pillaton Mill	62500	135.37	1422	0.549	33.8	0.997	0.48	17.85	109.31	0.0080	47004
47005	Ottery at Werrington Park	86700	121.51	1200	0.450	38.9	0.999	0.49	15.27	72.68	0.0027	47005
47006	Lyd at Lifton Park	84350	220.33	1228	0.485	36.3	0.997	0.50	13.14	106.81	0.0003	47006
47007	Yealm at Puslinch	51200	56.42	1427	0.549	33.2	0.992	0.47	9.97	106.67	0.0118	47007
47008	Thrushel at Tinhay	85550	112.71	1144	0.422	39.1	1.000	0.50	10.78	91.19	0.0000	47008
47009	Tiddy at Tideford	59550	37.37	1276	0.591	30.8	1.000	0.48	8.00	123.50	0.0073	47009
47010	Tamar at Crowford Bridge	99250	77.47	1181	0.386	41.6	0.947	0.50	13.39	54.13	0.0038	47010
47011	Plym at Carn Wood	61400	79.56	1618	0.481	38.3	0.952	0.48	11.21	106.07	0.0076	47011
47014	Walkham at Horrabridge	69800	44.01	1665	0.585	26.1	1.000	0.48	7.43	111.41	0.0102	47014
48001	Fowey at Trekeivesteps	69650	36.78	1637	0.445	40.5	0.938	0.47	7.07	94.40	0.0007	48001
48002	Fowey at Restormel	61150	171.12	1431	0.524	35.2	0.921	0.46	18.41	116.29	0.0022	48002
48003	Fal at Tregony	44850	89.08	1211	0.546	34.6	0.988	0.45	13.93	80.74	0.0175	48003
48004	Warleggan at Trengoffe	67250	25.21	1445	0.500	35.7	0.973	0.45	6.09	96.09	0.0013	48004
48005	Kenwyn at Truro	44950	19.09	1100	0.601	32.6	0.988	0.42	4.98	92.38	0.0312	48005
48006	Cober at Helston	27400	40.27	1209	0.672	17.2	0.984	0.44	7.62	76.15	0.0168	48006
48007	Kennall at Ponsanooth	37700	26.65	1294	0.736	8.5	0.867	0.44	6.10	66.60	0.0142	48007
48009	St Neot at Craigshill Wood	66200	22.86	1512	0.463	40.0	0.635	0.45	7.12	79.52	0.0034	48009
48010	Seaton at Trebrownbridge	59650	38.49	1326	0.590	30.7	0.989	0.48	6.92	109.26	0.0155	48010
48011	Fowey at Restormel Ii	62350	167.36	1435	0.522	35.2	0.920	0.46	17.16	115.66	0.0022	48011
49001	Camel at Denby	68050	209.76	1338	0.555	34.6	0.993	0.45	15.65	89.89	0.0120	49001
49002	Hayle at St Erth	34350	48.77	1076	0.643	25.5	0.970	0.44	7.95	62.59	0.0141	49002
49003	De Lank at De Lank	76550	21.70	1627	0.379	47.8	0.995	0.45	4.73	78.05	0.0000	49003
49004	Gannel at Gwills	59250	40.56	1046	0.617	32.1	1.000	0.45	5.78	72.95	0.0121	49004
50001	Taw at Umberleigh	123550	832.32	1153	0.472	37.8	0.997	0.48	34.61	106.94	0.0007	50001
50002	Torridge at Torrington	118350	664.15	1185	0.425	40.5	0.998	0.49	40.87	82.68	0.0013	50002
50005	West Okement at Vellake	90200	13.30	2067	0.350	49.3	0.983	0.49	4.90	164.50	0.0000	50005
50006	Mole at Woodleigh	120950	327.64	1306	0.502	36.8	0.999	0.54	19.15	127.29	0.0010	50006
50007	Taw at Taw Bridge	106650	72.13	1226	0.490	35.0	0.989	0.46	12.97	99.09	0.0011	50007
50810	Little Dart at Dart Bridge	113750	125.96	1073	0.386	41.0	0.992	0.46	16.47	86.38	0.0005	50810
51001	Doniford Stream at Swill Bridge	142900	74.38	911	0.630	27.6	0.990	0.35	8.57	132.43	0.0077	51001
51002	Horner Water at West Luccombe	145950	20.49	1484	0.540	29.7	0.978	0.54	6.31	216.92	0.0000	51002
51003	Washford at Beggearn Huish	139350	36.43	1153	0.586	31.5	0.992	0.38	6.63	198.75	0.0021	51003
52003	Halse Water at Bishops Hull	125400	93.55	851	0.622	30.6	0.990	0.35	9.43	87.52	0.0055	52003
52004	Isle at Ashford Mill	118850	87.42	891	0.499	39.8	0.980	0.40	10.28	65.80	0.0100	52004
52005	Tone at Bishops Hull	125050	203.63	964	0.562	32.9	0.979	0.36	17.70	99.88	0.0068	52005

Number	Name	IHDTM NGR	AREA km²	SAAR mm	BFIHOST	SPRHOST	FARL	PROPWET	DPLBAR km	DPSBAR m/km	URBEXT1990	Number
52006	Yeo at Pen Mill	357350 116050	216.17	865	0.569	34.3	0.965	0.38	14.01	64.79	0.0193	52006
52007	Parrett at Chiselborough	346000 114550	74.43	886	0.537	36.8	1.000	0.38	7.35	69.82	0.0119	52007
52009	Sheppey at Fenny Castle	349650 143950	58.61	973	0.687	20.2	0.998	0.37	11.55	80.23	0.0288	52009
52010	Brue at Lovington	359150 131800	139.52	867	0.524	36.4	1.000	0.37	13.46	72.51	0.0065	52010
52011	Cary at Somerton	349900 129050	84.83	716	0.533	37.9	1.000	0.37	11.57	30.87	0.0127	52011
52014	Tone at Greenham	307800 120050	57.34	1101	0.553	33.3	0.937	0.35	11.41	147.89	0.0001	52014
52015	Land Yeo at Wraxall Bridge											52015
52016	Currypool Stream at Currypool Farm	322000 138200	15.72	934	0.586	29.2	1.000	0.35	4.65	136.25	0.0000	52016
52017	Congresbury Yeo at Iwood	345050 163100	60.64	984	0.602	25.5	0.890	0.35	7.35	92.26	0.0106	52017
52020	Gallica Stream at Gallica Bridge	357050 109850	16.44	950	0.388	45.3	0.971	0.38	3.82	88.31	0.0000	52020
52801	Tone at Wadhams Farm	305650 126650	31.17	1163	0.580	32.1	0.887	0.35	6.98	145.19	0.0000	52801
53001	Avon at Melksham	390400 164150	668.05	763	0.552	32.6	0.990	0.34	37.82	34.57	0.0179	53001
53002	Semington Brook at Semington	390550 160600	153.62	712	0.564	33.0	0.991	0.34	13.00	48.91	0.0261	53002
53003	Avon at Bath St James	375400 164650	1611.04	817	0.575	31.2	0.988	0.33	47.90	52.65	0.0235	53003
53004	Chew at Compton Dando	364900 164850	129.10	987	0.590	28.9	0.843	0.35	15.42	72.28	0.0089	53004
53005	Midford Brook at Midford	376350 161150	147.40	965	0.625	29.1	0.993	0.36	13.76	81.94	0.0301	53005
53006	Frome(bristol) at Frenchay	363850 177200	150.61	792	0.362	43.5	0.995	0.35	13.17	29.23	0.0713	53006
53007	Frome(somerset) at Tellisford	380650 156250	261.85	965	0.565	29.8	0.967	0.36	20.50	61.77	0.0163	53007
53008	Avon at Great Somerford	396450 183200	305.11	804	0.622	28.0	0.989	0.34	18.39	29.17	0.0077	53008
53009	Wellow Brook at Wellow	374000 157950	73.47	999	0.643	27.3	0.987	0.37	10.35	70.05	0.0383	53009
53013	Marden at Stanley	395650 172750	99.28	724	0.560	32.4	0.980	0.34	10.02	51.67	0.0234	53013
53017	Boyd at Bitton	368000 169650	47.88	806	0.498	37.5	0.999	0.35	9.11	64.00	0.0126	53017
53018	Avon at Bathford	378550 167000	1567.16	817	0.575	31.1	0.988	0.34	43.69	50.02	0.0230	53018
53019	Woodbridge Brook at Crab Mill	394750 186600	46.57	744	0.330	45.5	0.982	0.34	7.43	31.16	0.0049	53019
53020	Gauze Brook at Rodbourne											53020
53023	Sherston Avon at Fosseway											53023
53025	Mells at Vallis	375850 149100	118.04	1056	0.656	19.9	0.951	0.37	11.94	61.74	0.0110	53025
54001	Severn at Bewdley	378050 276300	4330.14	912	0.541	33.7	0.975	0.38	117.76	90.63	0.0117	54001
54002	Avon at Evesham	404000 243650	2200.66	654	0.401	43.1	0.977	0.29	64.86	38.50	0.0416	54002
54003	Vyrnwy at Vyrnwy Reservoir											54003
54004	Sowe at Stoneleigh	433200 273250	263.29	667	0.509	35.8	0.982	0.30	16.99	28.39	0.1348	54004
54005	Severn at Montford	341050 314500	2035.27	1145	0.472	38.4	0.980	0.50	64.71	136.38	0.0026	54005
54006	Stour at Kidderminster	383050 276750	311.45	693	0.666	26.5	0.986	0.30	22.30	62.20	0.1527	54006
54007	Arrow at Broom	408700 253450	312.20	689	0.376	41.2	0.964	0.28	20.98	46.50	0.0363	54007
54008	Teme at Tenbury	359800 268500	1123.29	841	0.612	28.5	0.995	0.36	44.00	118.66	0.0062	54008
54010	Stour at Alscot Park	420650 250850	316.96	659	0.385	44.8	0.995	0.30	25.70	58.65	0.0150	54010
54011	Salwarpe at Harford Mill	386850 261950	186.20	666	0.523	35.2	0.992	0.28	13.43	42.82	0.0496	54011
54012	Tern at Walcot	359050 312200	851.85	694	0.616	28.6	0.960	0.34	29.32	28.79	0.0199	54012
54013	Clywedog at Cribynau	294350 285550	57.00	1868	0.445	42.6	0.805	0.66	11.34	168.03	0.0000	54013
54014	Severn at Abermule	316550 295850	574.09	1257	0.449	39.7	0.975	0.52	31.20	149.56	0.0031	54014
54016	Roden at Rodington	358900 314250	261.90	693	0.616	27.5	0.984	0.34	28.81	22.76	0.0104	54016
54017	Leadon at Wedderburn Bridge											54017
54018	Rea Brook at Hookagate	346750 309350	170.09	755	0.504	32.0	1.000	0.42	16.02	89.55	0.0049	54018
54019	Avon at Stareton	433150 271500	346.32	654	0.424	42.5	0.954	0.29	37.53	30.75	0.0349	54019
54020	Perry at Yeaton	343250 319200	183.18	739	0.648	26.6	0.965	0.40	19.03	29.91	0.0082	54020
54022	Severn at Plynlimon Flume	285300 287200	8.68	2482	0.323	52.7	1.000	0.66	2.91	184.94	0.0000	54022
54023	Badsey Brook at Offenham	406150 245050	94.26	652	0.332	47.7	0.992	0.29	8.48	43.74	0.0349	54023
54024	Worfe at Burcote	374750 295150	258.46	688	0.639	30.7	0.954	0.34	18.00	40.56	0.0347	54024
54025	Dulas at Rhos-y-pentref	295100 282400	52.78	1267	0.439	40.2	1.000	0.59	7.54	165.21	0.0000	54025
54026	Chelt at Slate Mill											54026

Number	Name	IHDTM NGR	AREA km²	SAAR mm	BFIHOST	SPRHOST	FARL	PROPWET	DPLBAR km	DPSBAR m/km	$URBEXT_{1990}$	Number
54027	Frome at Ebley Mill	383000 204550	197.11	827	0.738	20.5	0.951	0.32	12.50	126.79	0.0239	54027
54028	Vyrnwy at Llanymynech	325050 319600	780.29	1337	0.439	41.1	0.971	0.51	34.54	164.90	0.0007	54028
54029	Teme at Knightsford Bridge	373400 255850	1482.28	818	0.600	30.8	0.995	0.35	68.40	112.35	0.0064	54029
54032	Severn at Saxons Lode	386350 239150	6853.22	855	0.562	32.7	0.982	0.35	134.88	90.35	0.0213	54032
54034	Dowles Brook at Dowles	376650 276500	42.07	715	0.632	19.2	0.999	0.32	7.49	93.30	0.0045	54034
54036	Isbourne at Hinton On The Green	402400 240650	92.82	702	0.479	39.2	0.991	0.32	12.26	79.20	0.0174	54036
54038	Tanat at Llanyblodwel	325050 322550	229.86	1294	0.473	38.9	0.996	0.51	19.63	209.74	0.0006	54038
54040	Meese at Tibberton	367850 320550	160.42	700	0.588	30.2	0.935	0.34	18.97	30.68	0.0068	54040
54041	Tern at Eaton On Tern	364850 323150	195.63	718	0.645	27.5	0.968	0.34	19.22	36.44	0.0108	54041
54043	Severn at Upton On Severn	386350 240050	6850.07	855	0.562	32.7	0.982	0.35	134.00	90.39	0.0213	54043
54044	Tern at Ternhill	363050 331450	95.70	739	0.698	25.1	0.953	0.34	15.83	45.01	0.0136	54044
54052	Bailey Brook at Ternhill	362950 331750	37.41	707	0.576	30.8	0.983	0.34	7.76	22.46	0.0092	54052
54057	Severn at Haw Bridge	385250 227750	9884.28	793	0.513	35.9	0.977	0.32	133.04	75.00	0.0263	54057
54058	Stoke Park Brook at Stoke Park	364500 326150	14.46	692	0.575	30.9	0.987	0.34	4.01	28.16	0.0086	54058
54059	Allford Brook at Allford	365550 322400	10.23	672	0.788	19.5	1.000	0.34	3.13	16.79	0.0021	54059
54060	Potford Brook at Potford											54060
54061	Hodnet Brook at Hodnet											54061
54062	Stoke Brook at Stoke											54062
54065	Roden at Stanton	356350 324100	212.50	703	0.614	27.3	0.981	0.34	18.15	23.29	0.0091	54065
54088	Little Avon at Berkeley Kennels	368150 198800	133.45	806	0.521	33.5	0.987	0.35	14.20	80.33	0.0108	54088
54090	Tanllwyth at Tanllwyth Flume											54090
54091	Severn at Hafren Flume	284350 287650	3.48	2511	0.304	54.1	1.000	0.66	2.34	162.83	0.0000	54091
54092	Hore at Hore Flume	284550 287250	3.19	2531	0.330	52.1	1.000	0.66	2.16	220.51	0.0000	54092
55001	Wye at Cadora	353450 209150	4046.38	1009	0.544	35.4	1.000	0.37	130.94	118.64	0.0069	55001
55002	Wye at Belmont	348350 238750	1918.89	1223	0.473	39.7	0.968	0.49	95.12	136.61	0.0021	55002
55003	Lugg at Lugwardine	354950 239900	879.60	814	0.587	33.8	0.982	0.35	48.93	96.87	0.0075	55003
55004	Irfon at Abernant	289050 246000	73.08	1845	0.402	46.2	1.000	0.65	11.47	192.28	0.0009	55004
55005	Wye at Rhayader	297050 267550	165.00	1656	0.419	43.7	0.997	0.59	17.93	187.09	0.0009	55005
55007	Wye at Erwood	307450 244600	1283.61	1386	0.426	42.2	0.960	0.53	42.28	155.55	0.0011	55007
55008	Wye at Cefn Brwyn	282800 283700	10.56	2458	0.377	48.5	1.000	0.66	3.11	196.23	0.0000	55008
55009	Monnow at Kentchurch	341750 224950	355.11	956	0.583	35.3	0.997	0.41	19.55	132.98	0.0034	55009
55010	Wye at Pant Mawr	284300 282550	27.22	2342	0.386	47.8	1.000	0.66	4.73	215.74	0.0001	55010
55011	Ithon at Llandewi	310500 268250	110.47	1086	0.395	44.0	0.998	0.48	15.88	130.73	0.0003	55011
55012	Irfon at Cilmery	299450 250550	246.41	1627	0.431	42.8	0.998	0.65	19.91	161.90	0.0004	55012
55013	Arrow at Titley Mill	332950 258500	125.83	962	0.553	34.3	0.999	0.49	14.40	132.58	0.0030	55013
55014	Lugg at Byton	336550 264850	202.85	977	0.593	31.4	0.997	0.49	17.31	161.66	0.0023	55014
55015	Honddu at Tafolog	327700 229250	24.97	1314	0.573	27.0	1.000	0.54	5.44	263.49	0.0000	55015
55016	Ithon at Disserth	302550 257750	358.64	1066	0.427	40.3	0.998	0.49	31.99	134.94	0.0018	55016
55017	Chwefru at Carreg-y-wen	299800 252950	29.01	1487	0.400	43.9	1.000	0.65	7.07	158.63	0.0001	55017
55018	Frome at Yarkhill	361350 242700	143.85	706	0.567	39.2	0.997	0.32	17.25	69.24	0.0105	55018
55021	Lugg at Butts Bridge	350350 258900	365.13	877	0.610	30.3	0.994	0.37	26.86	128.15	0.0053	55021
55022	Trothy at Mitchel Troy	350150 211250	142.41	887	0.572	36.9	0.998	0.36	17.89	101.32	0.0014	55022
55023	Wye at Redbrook	352750 211150	4016.49	1010	0.542	35.6	0.979	0.38	128.38	118.51	0.0067	55023
55025	Llynfi at Three Cocks	316550 237450	131.48	999	0.575	30.6	0.951	0.54	11.48	107.22	0.0017	55025
55026	Wye at Ddol Farm	297450 267450	172.68	1635	0.423	43.4	0.997	0.59	18.01	183.92	0.0015	55026
55029	Monnow at Grosmont	341650 224900	355.14	956	0.583	35.3	0.997	0.41	19.67	132.98	0.0034	55029
55030	Clearwyn at Dol Y Mynach	291150 262150	94.32	1880	0.332	51.9	0.850	0.65	10.04	133.57	0.0000	55030
55033	Wye at Gwy Flume	282450 285350	3.80	2576	0.329	52.2	1.000	0.66	2.05	205.72	0.0000	55033
55034	Cyff at Cyff Flume	282250 284200	3.11	2417	0.395	47.1	1.000	0.66	1.90	186.13	0.0000	55034
55035	Iago at Iago Flume	282500 285400	1.07	2467	0.334	51.9	1.000	0.66	1.14	188.54	0.0000	55035

Number	Name	IHDTM NGR		AREA km²	SAAR mm	BFIHOST	SPRHOST	FARL	PROPWET	DPLBAR km	DPSBAR m/km	URBEXT1990	Number
56001	Usk at Chain Bridge	334650	205600	925.30	1368	0.596	29.0	0.982	0.56	53.03	162.81	0.0045	56001
56002	Ebbw at Rhiwderyn	325900	188750	212.29	1454	0.538	29.8	0.977	0.49	22.10	185.89	0.0507	56002
56003	Honddu at The Forge Brecon	305000	229850	62.53	1171	0.528	35.2	1.000	0.53	10.46	123.81	0.0002	56003
56004	Usk at Llandetty	312700	220450	556.56	1479	0.545	35.2	0.976	0.57	30.02	151.12	0.0019	56004
56005	Lwyd at Ponthir	332850	192400	98.33	1394	0.525	33.1	0.979	0.49	15.59	147.06	0.0783	56005
56006	Usk at Trallong	294550	229650	193.99	1666	0.475	40.7	0.966	0.62	12.78	138.64	0.0008	56006
56007	Senni at Pont Hen Hafod	292950	225600	19.51	1972	0.496	38.9	1.000	0.62	5.61	202.14	0.0000	56007
56011	Sirhowy at Wattsville	320450	191150	76.26	1482	0.524	30.4	0.974	0.49	18.02	140.80	0.0456	56011
56012	Grwyne at Millbrook	324050	217750	82.50	1242	0.647	18.1	0.988	0.54	11.44	246.28	0.0001	56012
56013	Yscir at Pontaryscir	300300	230550	63.31	1300	0.494	38.3	1.000	0.61	11.55	140.79	0.0000	56013
56015	Olway Brook at Olway Inn	338550	201150	111.27	948	0.598	30.4	1.000	0.34	10.35	99.85	0.0034	56015
56019	Ebbw at Aberbeeg	320950	201350	71.82	1481	0.490	34.2	0.960	0.54	9.38	191.87	0.0626	56019
57003	Taff at Tongwynlais	313150	181900	486.89	1801	0.420	42.2	0.955	0.50	31.88	165.71	0.0419	57003
57004	Cynon at Abercynon	308050	195600	103.54	1772	0.422	40.1	0.980	0.53	15.18	145.76	0.0388	57004
57005	Taff at Pontypridd	308050	189650	451.99	1832	0.409	43.3	0.951	0.50	22.62	167.05	0.0406	57005
57006	Rhondda at Trehafod	305250	191000	102.57	2183	0.365	47.8	0.985	0.49	14.06	214.98	0.0593	57006
57007	Taff at Fiddlers Elbow	308750	195150	194.06	1719	0.402	44.7	0.908	0.52	20.79	156.40	0.0300	57007
57008	Rhymney at Llanedeyrn	322500	182250	184.64	1411	0.521	33.1	0.983	0.48	27.23	128.84	0.0478	57008
57009	Ely at St Fagans	311950	177000	145.67	1351	0.575	34.3	0.987	0.47	17.02	83.60	0.0288	57009
57010	Ely at Lanelay	303400	182550	38.99	1619	0.456	39.0	1.000	0.47	6.71	120.35	0.0223	57010
57015	Taff at Merthyr Tydfil	304150	206800	111.28	1858	0.352	49.9	0.851	0.55	10.81	159.91	0.0088	57015
57803	Clun at Cross Inn	305450	182500	26.40	1379	0.415	40.5	1.000	0.47	4.95	88.34	0.0541	57803
58001	Ogmore at Bridgend	290300	179350	157.97	1774	0.478	36.4	0.998	0.52	13.86	174.78	0.0396	58001
58002	Neath at Resolven	281450	201650	190.93	1946	0.347	47.7	0.987	0.52	17.58	149.90	0.0073	58002
58003	Ewenny at Ewenny Priory	291550	178100	63.85	1321	0.557	29.0	1.000	0.52	8.19	76.40	0.0377	58003
58004	Afan at Cwmavon	278200	192000	85.69	2066	0.444	41.0	1.000	0.53	11.93	215.19	0.0108	58004
58005	Ogmore at Brynmenyn	290350	184350	74.32	1976	0.492	35.7	0.999	0.52	9.13	226.51	0.0215	58005
58006	Mellte at Pontneddfechan	291350	208100	65.18	1981	0.322	51.3	0.975	0.62	10.44	134.91	0.0003	58006
58007	Llynfi at Coytrahen	289250	185650	50.82	1778	0.474	37.0	0.997	0.52	7.92	161.98	0.0374	58007
58008	Dulais at Cilfrew	277900	200950	43.36	1807	0.377	45.3	1.000	0.62	8.30	145.77	0.0095	58008
58009	Ewenny at Keepers Lodge	292150	178250	63.25	1323	0.556	29.1	0.934	0.52	7.60	76.94	0.0371	58009
58010	Hepste at Esgair Carnau	296900	213250	10.86	2075	0.261	57.4	0.995	0.62	3.52	79.73	0.0000	58010
58011	Thaw at Gigman Bridge	301750	171600	49.20	1132	0.740	18.7	0.983	0.47	8.85	69.00	0.0138	58011
59001	Tawe at Ynystanglws	268500	199900	227.71	1890	0.407	42.5	0.997	0.62	20.82	146.45	0.0167	59001
59002	Loughor at Tir-y-dail	262300	212650	46.52	1497	0.465	35.5	0.999	0.58	6.36	103.91	0.0128	59002
60002	Cothi at Felin Mynachdy	250850	222500	298.54	1551	0.500	37.9	0.998	0.56	27.72	177.03	0.0002	60002
60003	Taf at Clog-y-fran	223950	215850	216.73	1420	0.553	34.0	0.999	0.46	17.13	104.81	0.0017	60003
60004	Dewi Fawr at Glasfryn Ford	228950	217350	36.77	1476	0.569	33.3	0.999	0.52	9.19	126.07	0.0001	60004
60005	Bran at Llandovery	277100	234300	63.78	1489	0.485	39.3	0.997	0.63	10.82	189.06	0.0003	60005
60006	Gwili at Glangwili	242950	222050	130.98	1603	0.536	35.1	1.000	0.52	15.84	154.11	0.0008	60006
60007	Tywi at Dolau Hirion	276200	236050	220.53	1685	0.432	43.8	0.934	0.64	21.33	189.18	0.0001	60007
60009	Sawdde at Felin-y-cwm	271100	226750	79.10	1792	0.448	39.8	0.995	0.62	8.85	171.14	0.0000	60009
60010	Tywi at Nantgaredig	248950	220400	1079.79	1535	0.478	38.9	0.983	0.59	43.46	160.61	0.0008	60010
60012	Twrch at Ddol Las	265100	243900	19.78	1531	0.420	42.9	1.000	0.65	6.18	163.71	0.0000	60012
60013	Cothi at Pont Ynys Brechfa	253550	230000	242.98	1538	0.493	38.5	0.998	0.57	21.02	172.63	0.0002	60013
61001	Western Cleddau at Prendergast Mill	195250	217850	197.76	1276	0.560	32.6	0.997	0.44	15.65	69.42	0.0012	61001
61002	Eastern Cleddau at Canaston Bridge	207050	215250	181.98	1436	0.538	35.3	0.966	0.44	15.27	98.32	0.0008	61002
61003	Gwaun at Cilrhedyn Bridge	200400	235000	31.29	1550	0.495	39.1	1.000	0.44	5.21	122.07	0.0000	61003
62001	Teifi at Glan Teifi	224550	241550	897.27	1380	0.507	37.0	0.995	0.52	45.90	112.35	0.0017	62001
62002	Teifi at Llanfair	243450	240450	517.05	1392	0.484	39.0	0.993	0.54	36.83	108.39	0.0014	62002

Number	Name	IHDTM NGR	AREA km²	SAAR mm	BFIHOST	SPRHOST	FARL	PROPWET	DPLBAR km	DPSBAR m/km	URBEXT₁₉₉₀	Number
63001	Ystwyth at Pont Llolwyn	259250 277250	170.26	1456	0.488	39.2	0.990	0.63	19.21	163.33	0.0006	63001
63002	Rheidol at Llanbadarn Fawr	260250 280450	182.90	1752	0.436	43.9	0.902	0.66	26.16	198.23	0.0005	63002
63003	Wyre at Llanrhystyd	254350 269750	40.70	1183	0.471	38.1	1.000	0.53	7.75	113.11	0.0001	63003
64001	Dyfi at Dyfi Bridge	274350 301900	464.56	1835	0.478	39.8	0.995	0.66	20.06	276.17	0.0004	64001
64002	Dysynni at Pont-y-garth	263100 306550	75.20	2163	0.449	42.8	0.952	0.66	9.64	329.55	0.0002	64002
64005	Wnion at Dolgellau	272850 317950	109.22	2105	0.399	48.4	0.996	0.68	10.04	200.81	0.0010	64005
64006	Leri at Dolybont	263500 288050	47.24	1494	0.504	38.4	0.983	0.66	9.05	208.01	0.0012	64006
65001	Glaslyn at Beddgelert	259200 347650	67.23	2808	0.406	45.1	0.909	0.62	7.54	323.20	0.0003	65001
65002	Dwyryd at Maentwrog	267050 341400	78.15	2212	0.378	47.2	0.938	0.71	6.58	204.97	0.0057	65002
65004	Gwyrfai at Bontnewydd	248250 359900	46.17	2150	0.412	45.2	0.868	0.54	10.63	218.18	0.0009	65004
65005	Erch at Pencaenewydd	240000 340550	19.47	1479	0.440	39.2	0.991	0.56	6.77	99.06	0.0000	65005
65006	Seiont at Peblig Mill	249450 362300	80.15	2255	0.499	39.4	0.854	0.49	13.70	268.29	0.0051	65006
65007	Dwyfawr at Garndolbenmaen	249750 342800	52.01	2056	0.404	45.8	0.969	0.56	7.96	198.17	0.0000	65007
66001	Clwyd at Pont-y-cambwll	307050 370950	404.60	910	0.589	32.1	0.996	0.41	19.51	120.16	0.0036	66001
66002	Elwy at Pant Yr Onen	302150 370300	218.63	1145	0.483	38.8	0.980	0.58	22.65	132.40	0.0004	66002
66003	Aled at Bryn Aled	295850 370150	69.99	1161	0.476	40.3	0.951	0.60	9.66	133.51	0.0003	66003
66004	Wheeler at Bodfari	310600 371550	62.94	863	0.696	25.2	0.995	0.38	7.52	110.18	0.0021	66004
66005	Clwyd at Ruthin Weir	312100 359050	96.12	958	0.518	35.0	0.993	0.51	12.29	117.17	0.0034	66005
66006	Elwy at Pont-y-gwyddel	295350 371950	191.40	1185	0.476	39.5	0.981	0.60	14.39	131.55	0.0004	66006
66011	Conwy at Cwm Llanerch	280300 358250	339.86	2041	0.363	48.9	0.980	0.70	16.42	173.11	0.0005	66011
66801	Upperconway at Blaen Y Coed	335850 341250	1028.67	1356	0.430	42.6	0.937	0.55	56.16	156.03	0.0024	66801
67002	Dee at Erbistock Rectory	297500 354050	22.17	1317	0.319	53.0	0.595	0.70	3.75	73.08	0.0000	67002
67003	Brenig at Llyn Brenig Outflow	329650 337250	111.94	1197	0.462	40.8	1.000	0.51	17.58	189.84	0.0018	67003
67005	Ceiriog at Brynkinalt Weir	304050 343600	185.40	1306	0.403	44.1	0.903	0.62	16.22	122.98	0.0004	67005
67006	Alwen at Druid	315350 342850	729.08	1491	0.405	44.5	0.914	0.59	33.47	152.39	0.0008	67006
67007	Dee at Glyndyfrdwy	333450 353950	227.16	916	0.592	29.8	0.991	0.41	24.06	110.27	0.0209	67007
67008	Alyn at Pont-y-capel	320450 366550	82.50	967	0.616	27.7	0.988	0.41	13.94	144.88	0.0016	67008
67009	Alyn at Rhydymwyn	284350 341950	12.89	2001	0.252	58.3	0.969	0.71	3.40	131.11	0.0000	67009
67010	Gelyn at Cynefail	294750 335050	32.58	1754	0.415	45.0	1.000	0.71	6.23	227.74	0.0001	67010
67013	Hirnant at Plas Rhiwedog											67013
67014	Dee at Corwen	306750 343150	656.90	1540	0.394	45.3	0.905	0.60	24.89	151.44	0.0006	67014
67015	Dee at Manley Hall	334950 341350	1008.78	1368	0.431	42.7	0.936	0.55	56.05	158.12	0.0025	67015
67018	Dee at New Inn	287450 330850	54.30	2016	0.312	51.9	1.000	0.71	7.04	152.19	0.0001	67018
67019	Tryweryn at Weir X	293200 335900	111.33	1838	0.313	51.3	0.851	0.71	12.67	141.31	0.0001	67019
67020	Dee at Chester Weir	341650 366400	1801.07	1110	0.471	38.9	0.961	0.43	80.63	115.15	0.0117	67020
67025	Clywedog at Bowling Bank	339450 348350	103.02	852	0.528	35.4	0.990	0.51	12.93	62.63	0.0684	67025
68001	Weaver at Ashbrook	366950 363150	622.68	731	0.513	32.7	0.984	0.34	29.62	30.60	0.0232	68001
68002	Gowy at Picton	344150 371500	152.04	728	0.535	32.4	0.995	0.35	14.21	34.51	0.0122	68002
68003	Dane at Rudheath	366950 371700	414.20	853	0.461	35.4	0.977	0.40	32.66	61.59	0.0359	68003
68004	Wistaston Brook at Marshfield Bridge	367550 355250	94.85	732	0.545	31.6	0.985	0.35	11.01	34.53	0.0818	68004
68005	Weaver at Audlem	365300 343250	202.54	719	0.502	34.3	0.992	0.34	13.89	28.28	0.0053	68005
68006	Dane at Hulme Walfield	384600 364250	151.10	1020	0.417	39.1	0.983	0.50	18.90	117.90	0.0252	68006
68007	Wincham Brook at Lostock Gralam	369550 375650	147.62	818	0.508	32.7	0.958	0.39	13.65	23.41	0.0113	68007
68010	Fender at Ford	327950 388150	17.59	774	0.429	37.2	1.000	0.38	4.08	30.53	0.2038	68010
68011	Arley Brook at Gore Farm	369750 379900	34.79	831	0.435	35.7	1.000	0.37	7.16	12.83	0.0107	68011
68014	Sandersons Brook at Sandbach	349850 362250	49.47	731	0.525	31.7	0.993	0.34	9.11	38.06	0.0092	68014
68015	Gowy at Huxley	385950 363300	144.15	1030	0.411	39.5	0.982	0.50	16.91	120.84	0.0192	68015
68018	Dane at Congleton Park	344650 371200	150.57	729	0.536	32.3	0.995	0.35	13.71	34.80	0.0121	68018
68020	Gowy at Bridge Trafford											68020
69001	Mersey at Irlam Weir	376800 393850	673.90	1122	0.415	38.3	0.923	0.52	42.43	114.21	0.0979	69001

Number	Name	IHDTM NGR	AREA km²	SAAR mm	BFIHOST	SPRHOST	FARL	PROPWET	DPLBAR km	DPSBAR m/km	URBEXT₁₉₉₀	Number
69002	Irwell at Adelphi Weir	382450 398850	553.61	1259	0.428	37.4	0.929	0.54	39.05	93.12	0.1134	69002
69003	Irk at Scotland Weir	384250 399200	73.18	1025	0.508	31.8	0.964	0.57	11.85	46.76	0.2878	69003
69006	Bollin at Dunham Massey	372850 387450	257.22	881	0.505	32.7	0.956	0.43	23.78	58.24	0.0466	69006
69007	Mersey at Ashton Weir	377350 393450	673.48	1122	0.415	38.3	0.923	0.52	41.68	114.29	0.0979	69007
69008	Dean at Stanneylands											69008
69011	Micker Brook at Cheadle											69011
69012	Bollin at Wilmslow	384850 381550	67.89	933	0.539	31.4	0.965	0.52	13.79	84.51	0.0755	69012
69013	Sinderland Brook at Partington	372700 390500	45.08	827	0.480	32.8	0.989	0.39	7.58	12.69	0.2034	69013
69015	Etherow at Compstall	396050 390800	149.55	1321	0.367	44.3	0.838	0.53	17.40	158.34	0.0207	69015
69017	Goyt at Marple Bridge	396400 389650	183.83	1153	0.482	32.5	0.930	0.52	17.30	155.75	0.0136	69017
69018	Newton Brook at Newton Le Willows	358400 393300	32.25	916	0.480	34.7	0.942	0.38	7.98	24.15	0.1467	69018
69019	Worsley Brook at Eccles	375350 397850	23.74	955	0.349	37.6	0.969	0.43	5.25	22.55	0.2507	69019
69020	Medlock at London Road	384750 397550	52.72	1036	0.388	35.3	0.993	0.55	12.30	64.75	0.2518	69020
69023	Roch at Blackford Bridge	380800 407850	187.63	1248	0.492	33.4	0.921	0.57	19.66	97.38	0.1083	69023
69024	Croal at Farnworth Weir	374450 406950	142.80	1287	0.330	44.4	0.879	0.51	12.87	82.64	0.1217	69024
69025	Irwell at Manchester Racecourse	382150 400250	551.78	1260	0.428	37.4	0.929	0.54	36.89	93.32	0.1121	69025
69027	Tame at Portwood	390450 391900	146.60	1212	0.365	42.6	0.926	0.54	26.46	124.05	0.1062	69027
69034	Musbury Brook at Helmshore	377400 421300	3.14	1453	0.344	49.1	1.000	0.51	1.65	163.95	0.0000	69034
69035	Irwell at Bury Bridge	379800 411050	156.03	1353	0.425	37.4	0.958	0.54	17.52	116.47	0.0606	69035
69040	Irwell at Stubbins	379150 418650	104.78	1391	0.450	36.4	0.946	0.54	10.62	122.32	0.0461	69040
69041	Tame at Broomstair Bridge	393750 395450	115.71	1289	0.368	43.7	0.908	0.55	18.48	140.04	0.0791	69041
69802	Etherow at Woodhead											69802
70002	Douglas at Wanes Blades Bridge											70002
70003	Douglas at Central Park Wigan											70003
70004	Yarrow at Croston Mill											70004
70005	Lostock at Littlewood Bridge	349550 419650	55.02	1023	0.478	37.9	0.977	0.51	12.62	39.20	0.1065	70005
70006	Tawd at Newburgh	346900 410850	28.32	946	0.604	23.2	1.000	0.51	6.42	34.08	0.1171	70006
71001	Ribble at Samlesbury	358950 430550	1146.10	1350	0.371	42.1	0.980	0.56	51.24	97.98	0.0247	71001
71003	Croasdale at Croasdale Flume	370600 454750	10.66	1886	0.275	54.6	1.000	0.60	3.28	163.71	0.0000	71003
71004	Calder at Whalley Weir	373050 436000	317.11	1232	0.395	38.4	0.957	0.55	22.08	97.34	0.0729	71004
71005	Bottoms Beck at Bottoms Beck Flume	374500 456500	10.64	1511	0.281	48.4	1.000	0.60	3.38	96.16	0.0000	71005
71006	Ribble at Henthorn	372100 439050	448.05	1342	0.367	43.4	0.999	0.61	33.48	90.24	0.0074	71006
71007	Ribble at Hodderfoot	370950 437750	716.09	1434	0.354	44.4	0.987	0.60	31.89	103.31	0.0050	71007
71008	Hodder at Hodder Place	370950 439950	258.09	1602	0.330	46.2	0.969	0.60	23.54	127.28	0.0007	71008
71009	Ribble at Jumbles Rock	370050 437750	1049.08	1368	0.367	42.4	0.978	0.57	31.62	100.92	0.0259	71009
71010	Pendle Water at Barden Lane	383600 435250	110.00	1250	0.388	39.4	0.969	0.58	12.33	102.53	0.0558	71010
71011	Ribble at Arnford	384050 455600	203.87	1445	0.382	46.1	1.000	0.61	20.53	105.82	0.0027	71011
71013	Darwen at Ewood Bridge	367650 426350	39.19	1339	0.423	36.7	0.964	0.51	6.11	98.53	0.0945	71013
71014	Darwen at Blue Bridge	356650 427700	135.51	1198	0.410	38.7	0.958	0.51	17.53	79.33	0.0993	71014
71802	Ribble at Halton West	385100 455200	206.68	1441	0.387	45.7	1.000	0.61	21.55	104.93	0.0027	71802
71803	Hodder at Higher Hodder Bridge	369750 440950	254.97	1607	0.329	46.3	0.969	0.60	21.87	127.82	0.0007	71803
72001	Lune at Halton	350250 464700	993.39	1519	0.405	43.6	0.993	0.64	42.34	141.20	0.0017	72001
72002	Wyre at St Michaels	346450 441050	276.56	1253	0.369	44.2	0.950	0.56	17.60	74.53	0.0057	72002
72004	Lune at Caton	352950 465450	984.20	1522	0.404	43.7	0.993	0.64	38.73	141.67	0.0016	72004
72005	Lune at Killington New Bridge	362250 490850	219.03	1670	0.438	40.9	0.999	0.71	20.94	179.51	0.0008	72005
72006	Lune at Kirkby Lonsdale	361500 477950	510.31	1652	0.424	43.0	0.999	0.71	31.65	174.59	0.0010	72006
72009	Wenning at Wennington Road Bridge	361350 470200	140.12	1306	0.371	44.8	0.997	0.60	17.35	93.58	0.0018	72009
72011	Rawthey at Brigg Flatts	363750 491150	195.88	1748	0.350	48.2	1.000	0.71	14.07	185.99	0.0009	72011
72013	Borrowbeck at Borrow Bridge Weir	360750 501450	26.10	2027	0.378	48.2	1.000	0.71	8.50	222.51	0.0000	72013
72014	Conder at Galgate	348250 455350	28.56	1188	0.442	36.0	1.000	0.60	6.95	97.28	0.0017	72014

Number	Name	IHDTM NGR	AREA km²	SAAR mm	BFIHOST	SPRHOST	FARL	PROPWET	DPLBAR km	DPSBAR m/km	URBEXT$_{1990}$	Number
72015	Lune at Lunes Bridge	361300 502750	141.01	1629	0.440	39.5	0.998	0.71	10.36	150.10	0.0011	72015
72016	Wyre at Scorton Weir	349950 450100	88.44	1473	0.317	50.0	0.905	0.60	12.83	105.99	0.0002	72016
72803	Lune at Halton Upper Weir	351450 464900	991.03	1519	0.405	43.6	0.993	0.64	41.07	141.32	0.0016	72803
72804	Lune at Broadraine	362150 489950	219.91	1669	0.439	40.8	0.999	0.71	21.87	179.24	0.0008	72804
72807	Wenning at Hornby	358450 468400	230.27	1387	0.350	46.4	0.998	0.60	17.60	101.18	0.0013	72807
73001	Leven at Newby Bridge	337200 486450	241.44	2191	0.440	46.7	0.921	0.71	21.34	227.89	0.0046	73001
73002	Crake at Low Nibthwaite	329450 488300	73.13	2147	0.362	50.4	0.737	0.71	9.17	203.14	0.0010	73002
73005	Kent at Sedgwick	350900 487550	212.38	1725	0.514	38.1	0.984	0.71	18.92	158.65	0.0117	73005
73008	Bela at Beetham	349600 480450	132.15	1290	0.535	32.5	0.965	0.68	13.43	89.32	0.0026	73008
73009	Sprint at Sprint Mill	351300 495950	34.46	2000	0.448	44.3	1.000	0.71	10.03	228.47	0.0002	73009
73011	Mint at Mint Bridge	352350 494400	65.72	1598	0.513	36.8	1.000	0.71	10.23	142.24	0.0004	73011
73013	Rothay at Miller Bridge House	337100 504050	59.92	2394	0.410	51.2	0.867	0.71	8.08	313.76	0.0027	73013
73014	Brathay at Jeffy Knotts	336150 503400	56.69	2751	0.436	49.3	0.922	0.71	9.21	306.27	0.0012	73014
73015	Keer at High Keer Weir											73015
73803	Winster at Lobby Bridge	342300 488550	22.20	1508	0.539	35.2	0.998	0.71	4.71	122.26	0.0002	73803
73805	Kent at Kendal (nether Bridge)	351700 492050	193.31	1765	0.506	39.0	0.982	0.71	14.11	166.46	0.0089	73805
74001	Duddon at Duddon Hall	319550 489550	85.69	2265	0.337	53.7	0.986	0.71	10.78	215.66	0.0002	74001
74002	Irt at Galesyke	313450 503850	43.94	2613	0.368	52.2	0.924	0.71	9.76	392.06	0.0003	74002
74005	Ehen at Braystones	300850 506250	128.52	1757	0.496	35.4	0.899	0.69	19.15	170.96	0.0119	74005
74006	Calder at Calder Hall	303450 504350	43.10	1832	0.424	47.3	1.000	0.71	9.83	166.22	0.0006	74006
75002	Derwent at Camerton	303650 530450	659.37	1810	0.437	42.0	0.844	0.63	36.63	214.53	0.0030	75002
75004	Cocker at Southwaite Bridge	313250 527950	116.78	1974	0.483	40.1	0.832	0.63	14.08	296.54	0.0004	75004
75005	Derwent at Portinscale	325250 523800	235.85	2241	0.406	47.8	0.852	0.64	16.38	253.45	0.0022	75005
75006	Newlands Beck at Braithwaite	323950 524050	33.81	2372	0.459	41.8	1.000	0.64	6.86	384.63	0.0008	75006
75007	Glenderamackin at Threlkeld	332150 524800	62.99	1732	0.389	45.5	1.000	0.62	8.76	188.73	0.0003	75007
75009	Greta at Low Briery	328450 524100	145.56	2027	0.397	47.5	0.919	0.63	13.24	234.88	0.0001	75009
75010	Marron at Ullock	307400 523900	26.85	1514	0.540	32.8	0.973	0.63	5.15	125.26	0.0008	75010
75017	Ellen at Bullgill	309750 538550	102.25	1107	0.488	34.4	0.984	0.62	14.93	80.63	0.0037	75017
76002	Eden at Warwick Bridge	347100 556550	1375.72	1273	0.509	36.9	0.957	0.65	62.23	128.02	0.0028	76002
76003	Eamont at Udford	357650 530450	407.92	1768	0.453	42.6	0.865	0.66	27.64	192.50	0.0051	76003
76004	Lowther at Eamont Bridge	352550 528600	155.74	1830	0.404	45.8	0.906	0.69	19.28	157.72	0.0012	76004
76005	Eden at Temple Sowerby	360400 528150	618.58	1143	0.475	37.0	1.000	0.66	29.65	101.55	0.0020	76005
76007	Eden at Sheepmount	338850 557100	2272.48	1183	0.489	37.8	0.973	0.64	61.43	106.21	0.0053	76007
76008	Irthing at Greenholme	348500 558000	333.75	1073	0.359	46.5	0.996	0.62	26.39	78.28	0.0015	76008
76009	Caldew at Holm Hill	337650 546750	147.80	1402	0.408	40.9	0.999	0.62	18.75	136.41	0.0004	76009
76010	Petteril at Harraby Green	341200 554350	161.48	942	0.587	30.6	0.994	0.64	25.46	52.80	0.0049	76010
76011	Coal Burn at Coalburn	369450 577850	1.55	1097	0.196	58.9	1.000	0.62	1.03	49.93	0.0000	76011
76014	Eden at Kirkby Stephen	377250 509850	68.18	1484	0.413	45.5	1.000	0.69	9.95	153.37	0.0031	76014
77001	Esk at Netherby	339150 571900	848.51	1359	0.371	45.4	0.997	0.61	35.46	149.93	0.0006	77001
77002	Esk at Canonbie	339700 575250	495.86	1423	0.405	44.3	0.994	0.61	33.00	168.74	0.0007	77002
77003	Liddel Water at Rowanburnfoot	341400 575850	318.90	1291	0.314	48.0	1.000	0.62	27.11	131.25	0.0006	77003
77005	Lyne at Cliff Bridge	341350 566200	209.61	1134	0.315	49.2	0.999	0.62	20.91	73.34	0.0001	77005
78003	Annan at Brydekirk	319150 570350	924.96	1350	0.486	39.0	0.992	0.62	43.77	128.21	0.0014	78003
78004	Kinnel Water at Redhall	307700 586950	76.12	1466	0.431	43.9	0.999	0.62	15.94	100.57	0.0001	78004
78005	Kinnel Water at Bridgemuir	309050 584650	229.21	1397	0.434	43.8	0.997	0.62	21.19	112.77	0.0002	78005
79002	Nith at Friars Carse	292450 585100	797.72	1460	0.433	42.2	0.994	0.67	40.71	160.83	0.0013	79002
79003	Nith at Hall Bridge	268450 612950	155.68	1513	0.357	45.5	0.986	0.63	15.69	124.17	0.0016	79003
79004	Scar Water at Capenoch	284400 594100	142.47	1627	0.446	42.0	0.999	0.66	13.49	199.76	0.0001	79004
79005	Cluden Water at Fiddlers Ford	292950 579600	237.44	1422	0.497	37.3	0.991	0.64	23.44	132.40	0.0004	79005
79006	Nith at Drumlanrig	285750 599250	469.18	1485	0.386	44.5	0.995	0.68	32.16	156.90	0.0015	79006

Number	Name	IHDTM NGR	AREA km²	SAAR mm	BFIHOST	SPRHOST	FARL	PROPWET	DPLBAR km	DPSBAR m/km	URBEXT₁₉₉₀	Number
80001	Urr at Dalbeattie	282150 560850	196.94	1340	0.376	48.4	0.969	0.64	20.38	81.17	0.0004	80001
80003	White Laggan Burn at Loch Dee	246800 578000	5.71	2469	0.385	49.1	0.996	0.69	2.03	252.37	0.0000	80003
80801	Pullaugh Burn at Diversion Works	254400 574100	18.22	2261	0.352	50.2	0.773	0.69	5.31	141.37	0.0000	80801
81002	Cree at Newton Stewart	241300 565150	367.00	1756	0.342	50.8	0.944	0.69	23.97	120.88	0.0011	81002
81003	Luce at Airyhemming	218150 559800	170.89	1503	0.296	54.8	0.978	0.58	16.21	73.02	0.0000	81003
82001	Girvan at Robstone	221550 599550	243.98	1368	0.401	42.2	0.956	0.60	26.38	107.78	0.0022	82001
82003	Stinchar at Balnowlart	210650 583200	324.48	1507	0.392	45.1	0.989	0.63	24.72	112.51	0.0000	82003
83002	Garnock at Dalry	229300 648950	90.77	1717	0.369	43.9	0.966	0.61	10.20	96.61	0.0134	83002
83003	Ayr at Catrine	252650 625800	166.90	1292	0.327	48.4	0.992	0.67	21.83	91.20	0.0012	83003
83004	Lugar at Langholm											83004
83005	Irvine at Shewalton	334350 636950	368.45	1228	0.340	42.4	0.982	0.60	27.65	56.36	0.0240	83005
83006	Ayr at Mainholm	336250 621550	579.01	1213	0.330	46.1	0.994	0.62	41.32	75.23	0.0033	83006
83802	Irvine at Kilmarnock	343000 636750	212.38	1221	0.349	41.7	0.988	0.59	20.36	64.79	0.0164	83802
84001	Kelvin at Killermont	255650 670600	321.31	1273	0.411	40.7	0.975	0.58	20.38	81.78	0.0591	84001
84002	Calder at Muirshiel	230900 663650	12.27	2316	0.273	58.0	0.987	0.61	4.51	97.90	0.0000	84002
84003	Clyde at Hazelbank	283600 645200	1093.20	1165	0.450	41.7	0.981	0.60	48.12	118.65	0.0019	84003
84004	Clyde at Sills	292750 642550	741.89	1224	0.458	42.6	0.976	0.60	42.74	137.96	0.0011	84004
84005	Clyde at Blairston	270250 657950	1700.10	1139	0.422	41.9	0.968	0.59	57.62	99.19	0.0131	84005
84006	Kelvin at Bridgend	267350 675000	69.39	1328	0.431	41.4	0.962	0.57	8.18	94.98	0.0256	84006
84007	South Calder Water at Forgewood	275000 658650	92.88	928	0.330	41.6	0.989	0.58	16.05	48.25	0.0621	84007
84008	Rotten Calder Water at Redlees	267950 660250	54.84	1217	0.314	42.2	0.998	0.58	12.85	53.81	0.0621	84008
84009	Nethan at Kirkmuirhill	281050 642750	66.88	1194	0.410	45.1	0.976	0.66	11.89	89.53	0.0029	84009
84011	Gryfe at Craigend											84011
84012	White Cart Water at Hawkhead	250050 662900	229.68	1308	0.413	38.0	0.947	0.60	20.70	64.71	0.1270	84012
84013	Clyde at Daldowie	267050 661750	1901.66	1128	0.412	41.8	0.966	0.59	60.77	94.13	0.0220	84013
84014	Avon Water at Fairholm	275350 651900	263.25	1264	0.376	44.0	0.989	0.59	23.41	62.94	0.0057	84014
84015	Kelvin at Dryfield	263650 673850	223.36	1278	0.397	41.5	0.981	0.58	12.35	86.19	0.0456	84015
84016	Luggie Water at Condorrat	273950 672550	35.30	1089	0.327	41.4	0.998	0.58	5.77	56.92	0.0363	84016
84017	Black Cart Water at Milliken Park	241000 661900	103.20	1790	0.445	42.4	0.793	0.61	12.06	90.93	0.0093	84017
84018	Clyde at Tulliford Mill	289250 640400	938.79	1204	0.452	42.3	0.979	0.61	42.86	128.79	0.0013	84018
84019	North Calder Water at Calderpark	268150 662350	129.15	973	0.326	41.5	0.930	0.58	19.34	50.85	0.1048	84019
84020	Glazert Water at Milton Of Campsie	265600 676300	51.88	1560	0.414	45.2	0.995	0.59	8.10	146.49	0.0089	84020
84023	Bothlin Burn at Auchengeich											84023
84025	Luggie Water at Oxgang											84025
84026	Allander Water at Milngavie	255800 673650	30.29	1423	0.369	44.2	0.935	0.61	8.07	103.35	0.0371	84026
84806	Clyde at Cambusnethan	278750 652300	1262.66	1142	0.441	41.7	0.981	0.59	54.92	113.27	0.0030	84806
85001	Leven at Linnbrane	239450 680400	783.04	2025	0.437	44.0	0.689	0.71	31.35	183.20	0.0022	85001
85002	Endrick Water at Gaidrew	248350 686700	219.14	1484	0.454	41.6	0.984	0.65	16.89	110.97	0.0000	85002
85003	Falloch at Glen Falloch	232100 719550	80.13	2846	0.379	49.3	0.993	0.78	7.37	260.78	0.0000	85003
86001	Little Eachaig at Dalinlongart	214150 681950	31.77	2342	0.392	47.2	1.000	0.71	4.93	282.88	0.0000	86001
86002	Bachaig at Eckford	214150 684200	139.47	2469	0.380	48.8	0.836	0.75	15.75	308.36	0.0000	86002
87801	Allt Uaine at Intake	226200 711350	2.88	3473	0.358	53.5	1.000	0.74	1.38	378.89	0.0000	87801
89804	Strae at Duiletter	214750 729550	37.34	2765	0.362	52.0	0.999	0.79	7.01	330.53	0.0000	89804
90801	Nevis at Achreoch											90801
91002	Lochy at Camisky	214650 780650	1255.51	2188	0.386	51.1	0.868	0.83	44.41	249.63	0.0003	91002
91802	Allt Leachdach at Intake	226200 778050	6.51	2556	0.397	53.3	0.993	0.83	2.61	415.21	0.0000	91802
93001	Carron at New Kelso	194100 843050	138.96	2616	0.406	49.1	0.884	0.83	14.96	297.66	0.0001	93001
94001	Ewe at Poolewe	186000 880350	441.14	2273	0.365	50.1	0.670	0.83	25.92	226.53	0.0001	94001
95801	Little Gruinard at Little Gruinard	194550 889850	81.87	2053	0.371	48.4	0.557	0.80	15.19	208.92	0.0000	95801
95803	Abhain Cuileg at Braemore	219350 879050	66.81	2114	0.357	53.7	0.869	0.83	9.19	217.27	0.0000	95803

Number	Name	IHDTM NGR	AREA km²	SAAR mm	BFIHOST	SPRHOST	FARL	PROPWET	DPLBAR km	DPSBAR m/km	URBEXT₁₉₉₀	Number
96001	Halladale at Halladale	289050 956250	194.04	1096	0.298	55.6	0.969	0.69	13.37	56.31	0.0000	96001
96002	Naver at Apigill	271350 956950	474.79	1383	0.338	52.3	0.843	0.73	35.25	113.93	0.0001	96002
97002	Thurso at Halkirk	312950 959500	414.26	1058	0.291	55.2	0.872	0.58	29.34	38.32	0.0001	97002
201002	Fairy Water at Dudgeon Bridge	240750 375850	160.99	1282	0.419	38.8	0.999	0.62	15.32	75.54	0.0043	201002
201005	Camowen at Camowen Terrace	246150 373100	276.27	1144	0.514	33.9	0.991	0.64	21.90	65.22	0.0222	201005
201006	Drumragh at Campsie Bridge	245850 372350	314.89	1163	0.441	35.9	0.998	0.60	23.22	64.88	0.0074	201006
201007	Burn Dennet at Burndennett Bridge	237350 404800	147.05	1186	0.454	40.7	1.000	0.61	16.38	100.58	0.0044	201007
201008	Derg at Castlederg	226450 384250	335.74	1558	0.504	35.4	0.917	0.62	20.25	69.29	0.0033	201008
201009	Owenkillen at Crosh	241700 386450	440.85	1366	0.355	48.2	0.998	0.64	25.74	117.92	0.0016	201009
201010	Mourne at Drumnabuoy House	234800 396150	1838.57	1288	0.448	38.9	0.979	0.62	47.57	81.21	0.0121	201010
202001	Roe at Ardnargle	267250 424750	365.61	1250	0.403	42.0	0.993	0.61	22.37	91.34	0.0148	202001
202002	Faughan at Drumahoe	246250 414950	272.87	1220	0.426	41.1	1.000	0.61	19.15	101.09	0.0100	202002
203010	Blackwater at Maydown Bridge	281850 351950	971.30	1008	0.395	37.4	0.983	0.58	41.84	77.37	0.0105	203010
203011	Main at Dromona	305100 408750	242.95	1206	0.492	34.8	0.993	0.61	18.10	59.09	0.0062	203011
203012	Ballinderry at Ballinderry Bridge	292550 380050	426.42	1079	0.523	34.3	1.000	0.56	26.10	62.61	0.0227	203012
203017	Upper Bann at Dynes Bridge	304250 351050	316.13	1023	0.448	35.5	0.981	0.53	33.40	88.50	0.0238	203017
203018	Six Mile Water at Antrim	314750 386600	277.71	1075	0.425	35.1	0.993	0.52	20.05	54.23	0.0302	203018
203019	Claudy at Glenone Bridge	296350 403850	126.36	1131	0.463	35.1	0.994	0.60	16.03	49.46	0.0205	203019
203020	Moyola at Moyola New Bridge	295550 390350	304.32	1224	0.454	39.4	0.999	0.55	26.68	76.16	0.0229	203020
203021	Kells Water at Currys Bridge	310450 397100	126.29	1188	0.346	44.6	0.992	0.54	18.62	65.73	0.0044	203021
203022	Blackwater at Derrymeen Bridge	262350 353100	183.45	1143	0.460	37.2	0.984	0.58	15.91	79.60	0.0056	203022
203024	Cusher at Gamble's Bridge	304750 347250	170.81	995	0.365	38.2	0.994	0.53	20.98	78.41	0.0099	203024
203025	Callan at Callan New Bridge	289200 352300	166.79	933	0.386	38.2	0.959	0.53	20.84	73.23	0.0281	203025
203026	Glenavy at Glenavy	314750 372650	44.35	987	0.376	36.8	0.980	0.52	11.71	51.11	0.0171	203026
203027	Braid at Ballee	309800 401550	182.85	1203	0.498	32.6	0.994	0.61	15.79	62.48	0.0329	203027
203028	Agivey at White Hill	288150 419300	100.19	1271	0.404	41.8	1.000	0.61	15.41	60.79	0.0139	203028
203033	Upper Bann at Bannfield	323400 334050	101.68	1261	0.470	36.9	0.951	0.53	9.83	120.95	0.0049	203033
203039	Clogh at Tullynewey											203039
203042	Crumlin at Cidercourt Bridge	313650 376650	54.42	991	0.338	39.6	1.000	0.52	10.60	42.50	0.0227	203042
203043	Oonawater at Sharmoy U/s	278050 355700	95.62	999	0.399	36.0	0.984	0.59	13.11	80.04	0.0088	203043
203046	Rathmore at Rathmore Bridge											203046
203049	Clady at Clady Bridge	319950 383750	29.42	1079	0.367	40.6	1.000	0.52	7.97	59.27	0.0000	203049
203092	Maine at Dunminning	305250 411200	219.82	1216	0.497	34.6	0.994	0.61	16.14	61.01	0.0069	203092
203093	Maine at Shanes Viaduct	308500 389750	705.35	1154	0.459	35.7	0.995	0.57	34.96	56.73	0.0242	203093
204001	Bush at Seneirl	294150 436350	299.79	1116	0.561	29.3	0.993	0.61	23.40	44.53	0.0084	204001
205003	Lagan at Dunmurry	329750 367900	448.27	912	0.450	39.0	0.985	0.52	33.08	60.71	0.0373	205003
205004	Lagan at Newforge	332750 369350	492.56	916	0.458	38.8	0.986	0.52	37.64	60.94	0.0377	205004
205005	Ravernet at Ravernet	326850 361300	73.54	947	0.422	44.9	0.949	0.52	10.31	56.82	0.0000	205005
205008	Lagan at Drummiller	323650 352550	84.78	1016	0.403	44.9	0.992	0.53	11.73	88.13	0.0135	205008
205010	Lagan at Banoge	312300 354150	178.90	927	0.423	41.0	0.992	0.53	19.94	76.85	0.0225	205010
205011	Annacloy at Kilmore	344800 350750	186.41	968	0.440	44.6	0.984	0.53	15.27	67.55	0.0235	205011
205020	Enler at Comber	345750 369850	60.92	934	0.438	37.2	1.000	0.52	7.81	65.93	0.0407	205020
205101	Blackstaff at Easons											205101
206001	Clanrye at Mount Mill Bridge											206001
206002	Jerretspass at Jerretspass	306350 333350	105.20	891	0.388	38.3	0.977	0.53	11.26	84.07	0.0119	206002
206004	Bessbrook at Carnbane	307350 329350	24.98	1036	0.604	19.1	1.000	0.53	5.12	93.13	0.0571	206004
206006	Annalong at Recorder	334800 323350	13.74	1719	0.336	51.7	1.000	0.53	3.18	281.24	0.0000	206006
206999	Woodburn at Control Area											206999
236005	Colebrooke at Ballindarragh Bridge	233250 336050	311.86	1157	0.421	39.0	0.994	0.58	24.35	76.16	0.0067	236005
236007	Sillees at Drumrainey Bridge	220500 340000	167.62	1330	0.495	31.3	0.892	0.60	24.03	104.91	0.0020	236007

A.4 Catchment descriptors given in Table A.2

A brief description of each of the variables shown in Table A.2 is given below.

ALTBAR   Mean altitude of the catchment (metres above sea level).

ASPBAR   Mean direction of all the inter-nodal slopes in the catchment (bearing in degrees, where north is zero). Represents the dominant aspect of catchment slopes.

ASPVAR   Invariability of slope directions, where values near to zero indicate that there is considerable variability in the aspect of catchment slopes. Values approaching one indicate that catchment slopes tend to face in one particular direction.

LDP   Longest drainage path (km), defined by recording the greatest distance from a catchment node to the defined outlet. Principally a measure of catchment size but also reflects the catchment configuration.

RMED-1D   Median annual maximum 1-day rainfall (mm).

RMED-2D   Median annual maximum 2-day rainfall (mm).

RMED-1H   Median annual maximum 1-hour rainfall (mm).

$SAAR_{4170}$ Standard period (1941-70) average annual rainfall (mm).

SMDBAR   Mean SMD for the period 1961-90 calculated from MORECS month-end values (mm).

URBCONC   Concentration of urban and suburban land cover. High index values (approaching one) indicate concentrated urban and/or suburban land cover. Not defined when URBEXT < 0.005 or in Northern Ireland where the resolution of CORINE land cover data is too coarse.

URBLOC   Location of urban and suburban land cover. Low index values indicate that development is near the catchment outlet. Not defined when URB_{EXT} < 0.005.

Table A.2 *Catchment descriptors provided for information only — values for 943 gauged catchments*

Number	Name	IHDTM NGR		AREA km²	ALTBAR m	ASPBAR degrees	ASPVAR	LDP km	RMED-1D mm	RMED-2D mm	RMED-1H mm	$SAAR_{4170}$ mm	SMDBAR mm	URBCONC	URBLOC	Number
2001	Helmsdale at Kilphedir	299650	918250	552.54	213.4	204.8	0.045	56.31	33.0	43.7	8.3	1102	8.50			2001
3001	Shin at Lairg	258050	906350	496.51	239.4	173.9	0.141	46.04	44.0	64.7	9.2	1584	4.15			3001
3002	Carron at Sgodachail	249150	892150	236.99	440.2	46.8	0.061	31.85	43.7	65.4	9.2	2025	3.65			3002
3003	Oykel at Easter Turnaig	240150	900150	331.92	296.9	62.5	0.065	31.02	45.4	65.2	9.4	1962	3.65			3003
3801	Cassley at Duchally	238650	916950	72.29	393.9	104.7	0.189	18.83	67.2	104.5	11.5	2749	3.23			3801
3803	Tirry at Rhian Bridge	255450	916650	62.37	245.3	202.8	0.285	21.39	42.3	61.0	9.0	1314	3.10			3803
4001	Conon at Moy Bridge	248050	854700	962.54	377.4	123.2	0.044	61.25	44.4	66.4	9.2	1766	5.31			4001
4003	Alness at Alness	265450	869650	202.41	395.5	124.3	0.109	43.04	40.0	56.5	9.3	1473	7.92			4003
5001	Beauly at Erchless	242450	840550	855.20	470.9	99.3	0.097	61.30	49.7	73.9	10.3	2169	5.33			5001
6001	Ness at Ness Castle Farm	263750	840950	1811.89	377.9	11.5	0.044	106.25	48.1	68.6	10.7	1829	6.50			6001
6003	Moriston at Invermoriston	241450	816950	397.84	407.8	135.3	0.105	49.47	55.4	81.5	11.2	2148	5.57			6003
6006	Allt Bhlaraidh at Invermoriston	237850	816800	26.23	471.0	151.7	0.328	11.85	38.0	53.9	9.9	1576	7.68			6006
6007	Ness at Ness Side	264400	842550	1839.38	374.9	9.4	0.048	108.24	47.9	68.2	10.7	1814	6.61			6007
6008	Enrick at Mill Of Tore	244900	830100	105.95	347.4	353.1	0.139	25.04	35.5	51.2	9.2	1342	7.68			6008
7001	Findhorn at Shenachie	282550	833550	415.87	559.9	22.9	0.106	50.98	39.4	56.9	10.3	1429	9.36			7001
7002	Findhorn at Forres	301900	858450	781.08	443.2	10.8	0.158	50.13	39.1	54.2	10.0	1207	12.73			7002
7003	Lossie at Sheriffmills	319250	862600	217.07	192.6	2.8	0.349	39.36	37.5	48.1	9.1	890	24.79			7003
8001	Spey at Aberlour	327950	844050	2646.63	474.1	14.7	0.060	147.58	36.7	51.7	9.3	1195	9.61			8001
8002	Spey at Kinrara	288250	808350	1009.45	534.1	8.2	0.024	71.35	36.5	52.7	9.6	1340	6.73			8002
8003	Spey at Ruthven Bridge	276000	799750	532.57	512.3	140.1	0.008	52.44	38.0	53.8	9.8	1392	5.88			8003
8004	Avon at Delnashaugh	318450	835200	540.87	525.2	10.3	0.099	65.00	39.9	55.5	9.3	1234	10.93			8004
8005	Spey at Boat Of Garten	294700	819250	1261.37	522.1	347.4	0.044	88.62	36.4	52.5	9.5	1307	7.25			8005
8006	Spey at Boat O Brig	331850	851850	2852.74	460.4	16.6	0.063	162.67	36.8	51.6	9.2	1184	10.26			8006
8007	Spey at Invertruim	268650	796200	401.84	517.9	308.0	0.031	41.47	39.5	55.6	10.0	1446	5.20			8007
8008	Tromie at Tromie Bridge	279000	799350	131.41	622.3	8.9	0.103	29.15	38.0	56.8	10.1	1452	7.00			8008
8009	Dulnain at Balnaan Bridge	297850	824750	272.27	461.0	94.0	0.193	44.28	33.1	46.8	9.1	1056	9.38			8009
8010	Spey at Grantown	303450	826800	1745.92	495.2	12.7	0.047	102.80	35.6	51.1	9.3	1235	7.98			8010
8011	Livet at Minmore	320050	829250	103.38	443.8	334.5	0.171	22.54	37.0	50.4	9.0	1140	10.95			8011
9001	Deveron at Avochie	353250	846250	444.80	328.7	55.7	0.127	54.11	36.2	51.8	8.6	1078	16.28			9001
9002	Deveron at Muiresk	370350	849800	961.17	243.7	73.1	0.093	84.40	34.8	48.6	8.3	994	20.64			9002
9003	Isla at Grange	349250	850650	179.60	208.1	98.9	0.105	27.64	36.3	48.9	8.5	957	24.82	0.680	0.747	9003
9004	Bogie at Redcraig	352050	837250	182.50	297.3	71.9	0.117	29.82	35.4	51.6	8.4	1045	17.45			9004
10001	Ythan at Ardlethen	392400	830950	457.16	111.3	115.5	0.138	52.06	33.7	44.3	8.3	861	24.14			10001
10002	Ugie at Inverugie	410000	848650	325.65	86.7	86.3	0.170	41.37	34.0	44.6	8.2	876	29.19			10002
10003	Ythan at Ellon	394550	830450	532.10	107.5	104.3	0.145	54.95	33.6	44.3	8.3	857	24.23			10003
11001	Don at Parkhill	388850	814150	1269.73	262.0	95.9	0.107	127.27	34.4	47.2	8.3	964	16.87			11001
11002	Don at Haughton	375550	820250	792.76	331.5	83.3	0.114	102.37	34.9	47.6	8.4	1025	15.23			11002
11003	Don at Bridge Of Alford	356450	817050	509.42	408.2	75.7	0.109	68.66	35.7	49.2	8.6	1081	14.00			11003
11004	Urie at Pitcaple	372250	825950	195.32	206.1	91.5	0.160	26.37	33.5	45.5	8.1	882	17.45			11004
12001	Dee at Woodend	363350	795700	1379.90	512.0	93.3	0.066	107.34	38.0	53.3	8.5	1193	10.31			12001
12002	Dee at Park	379800	798450	1833.30	446.5	82.4	0.070	127.83	38.5	53.6	8.5	1162	11.73			12002
12003	Dee at Polhollick	334300	796350	697.33	621.2	94.0	0.035	62.68	39.0	55.0	8.7	1342	7.78			12003
12004	Girnock Burn at Littlemill	332550	795750	29.79	411.0	27.2	0.201	12.42	33.5	46.0	8.1	1098	7.89			12004
12005	Muick at Invermuick	336550	794800	110.25	589.8	8.5	0.146	28.96	43.8	59.5	9.0	1350	7.89			12005
12006	Gairn at Invergairn	335250	796950	145.91	556.6	132.3	0.168	34.12	35.9	50.1	8.4	1036	9.95			12006
12007	Dee at Mar Lodge	309650	789500	292.09	682.7	117.1	0.088	28.62	42.0	60.5	9.1	1492	7.59			12007
12008	Feugh at Heugh Head	368750	792650	232.66	329.8	39.0	0.157	30.17	44.0	59.7	8.8	1186	15.65			12008
13001	Bervie at Inverbervie	382550	773450	124.44	149.4	148.6	0.143	33.25	40.7	51.7	8.7	929	18.59			13001
14001	Eden at Kemback	341450	715650	310.04	108.5	73.5	0.110	40.54	34.5	45.4	8.4	830	24.66			14001
15001	Isla at Forter	318700	764850	71.49	644.5	186.9	0.207	19.33	46.7	65.9	9.4	1467	7.89			15001

Number	Name	IHDTM NGR	AREA km²	ALTBAR m	ASPBAR degrees	ASPVAR	LDP km	RMED-1D mm	RMED-2D mm	RMED-1H mm	SAAR4170 mm	SMDBAR mm	URBCONC	URBLOC	Number
15002	Newton Burn at Newton	323050 760650	16.55	462.0	178.1	0.230	14.28	44.3	59.6	8.8	1238	7.89			15002
15003	Tay at Caputh	308350 739550	3210.33	459.7	119.0	0.053	118.10	43.4	61.1	9.9	1611	7.43			15003
15004	Inzion at Loch Of Lintrathen	327950 755750	24.20	371.6	172.8	0.268	11.30	44.3	56.7	8.8	1105	13.25			15004
15005	Melgan at Loch Of Lintrathen	327350 755850	42.17	399.2	189.9	0.187	20.93	43.8	57.7	8.7	1136	11.56			15005
15006	Tay at Ballathie	314700 736500	4586.56	410.5	133.7	0.062	130.95	41.6	57.6	9.4	1442	10.46			15006
15007	Tay at Pitnacree	292450 753350	1149.36	466.4	80.9	0.058	89.00	49.4	69.9	10.4	1898	7.20			15007
15008	Dean Water at Cookston	333850 747900	176.90	139.5	16.9	0.125	26.29	37.1	48.3	8.2	874	26.44	0.748	1.096	15008
15010	Isla at Wester Cardean	329350 746550	363.87	362.1	161.6	0.246	52.95	40.5	53.8	8.5	1116	14.99			15010
15013	Almond at Almondbank	306450 725700	173.30	407.7	126.8	0.171	51.49	44.8	61.0	9.8	1459	11.36			15013
15016	Tay at Kenmore	278350 746800	598.17	446.1	78.6	0.063	69.01	52.9	75.1	10.7	2068	6.54			15016
15017	Braan at Ballinloan	298050 740550	197.01	418.3	77.8	0.066	31.44	39.9	53.6	9.3	1512	10.19			15017
15808	Almond at Almond Intake														15808
15809	Muckle Burn at Eastmill	322300 760550	16.64	414.9	164.8	0.314	11.09	41.9	56.6	8.5	1149	7.89			15809
16001	Earn at Kinkell Bridge	293450 716600	582.19	316.3	147.5	0.101	60.17	46.0	63.5	9.8	1535	10.66			16001
16002	Earn at Aberuchill	275250 721550	176.95	383.5	120.9	0.028	33.16	48.4	68.1	10.3	1743	9.14			16002
16003	Ruchill Water at Cultybraggan	276400 720350	98.58	401.0	55.1	0.138	22.58	52.5	73.3	10.8	1940	13.21			16003
16004	Earn at Forteviot Bridge	304450 718350	781.92	274.4	84.7	0.060	75.98	43.8	60.4	9.5	1420	11.93			16004
17001	Carron at Headswood	283150 681850	121.10	243.9	77.9	0.243	27.92	43.9	62.1	10.3	1473	13.35	0.716	0.252	17001
17002	Leven at Leven	337050 700450	416.85	151.4	123.2	0.222	48.95	35.5	47.1	8.8	951	22.66	0.752	0.738	17002
17005	Avon at Polmonthill	295050 679650	190.12	160.5	23.3	0.121	41.97	35.4	46.7	8.8	995	15.56	0.657	0.775	17005
18001	Allan Water at Kinbuck	279250 705400	160.25	244.8	105.3	0.046	25.89	42.9	57.2	9.5	1331	13.35			18001
18002	Devon at Glenochil	285650 695950	178.71	287.2	167.5	0.108	49.88	40.8	54.8	9.3	1397	15.27	0.689	0.391	18002
18003	Teith at Bridge Of Teith	272650 701100	516.73	338.0	158.5	0.105	60.09	50.6	72.2	10.7	2009	8.19			18003
18005	Allan Water at Bridge Of Allan	278600 697850	209.87	231.5	192.7	0.050	37.15	41.5	55.6	9.4	1290	13.35			18005
18008	Leny at Anie	258500 709750	191.10	421.0	115.7	0.100	38.85	56.0	82.2	11.3	2259	6.21			18008
19001	Almond at Craigiehall	316500 675350	386.10	176.6	20.9	0.245	46.91	35.0	46.1	8.6	905	18.71	0.730	0.768	19001
19002	Almond at Almond Weir	300250 665150	44.36	202.8	39.5	0.268	19.46	34.0	46.1	8.6	1022	15.39	0.697	0.696	19002
19003	Breich Water at Breich Weir	301300 663750	52.83	247.3	7.5	0.243	19.37	34.0	47.0	8.6	1030	15.49	0.563	0.752	19003
19004	North Esk at Dalmore Weir	325350 661550	79.95	298.6	93.0	0.265	21.50	38.3	52.3	8.7	970	20.33	0.643	0.360	19004
19005	Almond at Almondell	308600 668450	239.27	219.4	6.0	0.262	31.88	35.4	47.8	8.7	977	17.79	0.709	0.598	19005
19006	Water Of Leith at Murrayfield	322950 673300	102.56	228.0	348.4	0.462	32.54	38.0	49.5	8.9	901	20.33	0.867	0.291	19006
19007	Esk at Musselburgh	333900 672450	323.83	238.4	26.3	0.233	44.54	35.9	49.8	8.6	852	20.33	0.737	0.628	19007
19008	South Esk at Prestonholm	332550 662150	113.03	287.2	353.1	0.352	23.55	37.2	50.8	8.9	884	20.33			19008
19010	Braid Burn at Liberton	327250 670850	15.40	189.9	1.8	0.469	12.17	35.4	47.9	8.8	767	20.33	0.818	0.755	19010
19011	North Esk at Dalkeith Palace	333250 667950	133.69	272.2	84.1	0.247	37.15	38.0	52.1	8.7	920	20.33	0.676	0.625	19011
20001	Tyne at East Linton	358950 676650	307.06	174.1	3.0	0.253	43.29	34.7	48.9	8.5	735	24.69			20001
20002	West Peffer Burn at Luffness	348750 681200	26.06	31.7	317.6	0.170	10.23	33.0	42.7	8.2	644	32.34			20002
20003	Tyne at Spilmersford	345500 668800	163.53	195.1	4.2	0.264	22.57	32.7	48.7	8.4	758	24.05			20003
20004	East Peffer Burn at Lochhouses	361150 682450	30.54	40.9	63.4	0.204	14.41	34.8	44.5	8.3	609	29.30			20004
20005	Birns Water at Saltoun Hall	345850 668650	93.43	231.2	347.4	0.360	22.16	34.2	44.9	8.6	799	25.18			20005
20006	Biel Water at Belton House	364350 676650	56.87	179.0	341.0	0.386	20.51	43.6	54.8	9.3	745	25.41			20006
20007	Gifford Water at Lennoxlove	351750 671750	67.66	221.5	344.7	0.391	20.62	40.3	53.1	9.0	790	25.41			20007
21001	Fruid Water at Fruid	308800 620650	22.05	474.4	333.5	0.296	10.21	46.2	64.1	11.0	1741	6.82			21001
21002	Whiteadder Water at Hungry Snout	366150 663200	45.89	363.6	67.9	0.183	15.11	49.9	62.5	10.2	991	25.41			21002
21003	Tweed at Peebles	325550 640150	704.83	354.7	26.0	0.046	48.98	37.7	49.6	9.4	1198	12.39			21003
21005	Tweed at Lyne Ford	320450 639750	378.11	378.4	340.3	0.082	42.01	39.9	52.7	9.9	1308	8.10			21005
21006	Tweed at Boleside	349650 633300	1513.36	358.4	75.6	0.071	83.26	38.3	50.6	9.6	1231	11.06			21006
21007	Ettrick Water at Lindean	348450 631450	501.64	373.2	90.9	0.137	53.66	41.3	55.5	9.6	1413	8.04			21007
21008	Teviot at Ormiston Mill	370350 627950	1120.24	238.9	31.7	0.128	61.34	34.2	44.5	9.6	1007	14.32			21008
21009	Tweed at Norham	389650 647700	4407.84	264.2	67.0	0.096	152.50	35.7	46.8	9.3	1009	16.63			21009

Number	Name	IHDTM NGR		AREA km²	ALTBAR m	ASPBAR degrees	ASPVAR	LDP km	RMED-1D mm	RMED-2D mm	RMED-1H mm	SAAR₄₁₇₀ mm	SMDBAR mm	URBCONC	URBLOC	Number
21010	Tweed at Dryburgh	358650	632050	2101.40	338.1	94.4	0.091	98.79	37.3	49.2	9.5	1138	14.25			21010
21011	Yarrow Water at Philiphaugh	343750	627700	232.13	410.8	99.4	0.153	41.66	41.2	55.7	10.1	1389	7.35			21011
21012	Teviot at Hawick	352050	615750	324.11	283.1	57.9	0.129	32.31	38.7	50.1	10.4	1204	12.53	0.753	0.170	21012
21013	Gala Water at Galashiels	348050	637250	205.78	339.0	79.4	0.150	41.91	36.2	48.2	9.3	994	22.94			21013
21015	Leader Water at Earlston	356400	638950	240.85	291.8	139.4	0.198	30.59	35.7	47.7	9.1	893	25.16			21015
21016	Eye Water at Eyemouth Mill	394100	663350	122.00	148.3	112.5	0.122	36.73	33.3	44.6	8.7	748	39.35			21016
21017	Ettrick Water at Brockhoperig	323300	613050	38.44	470.3	80.0	0.118	11.62	49.9	67.2	11.6	1940	6.82			21017
21019	Manor Water at Cademuir	321600	637050	58.98	461.6	8.6	0.178	14.16	40.7	52.8	10.0	1480	6.82			21019
21020	Yarrow Water at Gordon Arms	331050	624850	154.08	451.7	99.4	0.169	23.67	44.6	60.2	10.6	1545	6.82			21020
21021	Tweed at Sprouston	375050	635350	3352.30	295.8	66.5	0.091	124.43	35.9	47.1	9.5	1077	14.32			21021
21022	Whiteadder Water at Hutton Castle	388250	655050	499.05	236.3	120.5	0.216	57.70	37.9	50.8	9.0	861	28.09			21022
21023	Leet Water at Coldstream	383750	639700	113.26	87.6	118.0	0.320	27.94	31.5	41.4	8.3	714	31.79			21023
21024	Jed Water at Jedburgh	365550	621350	138.90	253.6	5.2	0.250	32.68	32.7	43.3	9.5	972	15.29			21024
21025	Ale Water at Ancrum	363250	624300	173.84	241.5	83.2	0.170	47.53	32.7	42.6	9.3	996	13.65			21025
21026	Tima Water at Deephope	327800	613750	31.01	389.6	67.1	0.112	12.16	48.5	63.4	11.4	1818	6.82			21026
21027	Blackadder Water at Mouth Bridge	382750	653050	155.58	195.4	138.9	0.296	37.45	33.1	45.7	8.6	803	26.35			21027
21029	Tweed at Glenbreck	306150	621450	34.29	420.2	6.6	0.077	11.93	43.7	61.2	10.8	1721	6.82			21029
21030	Megget Water at Henderland	323100	623050	56.31	509.8	105.1	0.197	13.30	48.6	65.5	11.1	1638	6.82			21030
21031	Till at Etal	392750	639750	634.99	209.2	45.4	0.120	74.54	37.9	49.7	9.2	850	21.53			21031
21032	Glen at Kirknewton	392050	631050	196.11	272.4	355.9	0.127	36.43	38.4	51.7	9.5	926	21.35			21032
21034	Yarrow Water at Craig Douglas	328700	624450	115.99	460.4	96.8	0.167	20.34	46.5	62.7	10.8	1596	6.82			21034
22001	Coquet at Morwick	423250	604450	578.46	225.0	109.8	0.191	81.24	34.4	44.7	9.1	885	22.22			22001
22002	Coquet at Bygate	386850	608400	60.03	407.2	120.8	0.185	15.61	36.0	48.7	9.8	1071	20.76			22002
22003	Usway Burn at Shillmoor	388650	607850	21.94	444.9	191.3	0.235	15.79	40.5	54.6	9.8	1054	21.61			22003
22004	Aln at Hawkhill	421200	612950	202.80	134.3	103.6	0.152	32.93	35.8	44.3	9.0	753	21.73			22004
22006	Blyth at Hartford Bridge	424200	579850	264.88	117.1	93.2	0.245	43.53	33.2	42.8	9.4	727	23.35	0.736	0.864	22006
22007	Wansbeck at Mitford	417650	585700	282.23	181.9	111.9	0.262	37.71	34.0	44.6	9.5	848	22.58			22007
22008	Alwin at Clennell	392550	606250	27.25	391.8	175.7	0.275	11.07	35.6	46.1	9.3	1005	21.61			22008
23001	Tyne at Bywell	403900	561600	2172.84	286.0	82.4	0.091	93.54	35.6	47.7	9.9	1082	15.58			23001
23002	Derwent at Eddys Bridge	404250	550800	117.97	362.8	48.1	0.284	23.07	41.2	52.1	10.4	958	13.15			23002
23003	North Tyne at Reaverhill	390450	573300	1012.09	278.7	125.5	0.140	65.07	34.7	46.3	9.8	1093	16.50			23003
23004	South Tyne at Haydon Bridge	385750	564700	750.20	350.3	22.3	0.146	59.67	38.3	52.4	10.3	1236	12.05			23004
23005	North Tyne at Tarset	377750	586050	283.49	325.0	114.5	0.135	31.58	39.0	51.2	10.5	1321	11.98			23005
23006	South Tyne at Featherstone	367150	560950	323.09	429.8	12.3	0.198	35.48	41.5	56.8	10.7	1470	10.84			23006
23007	Derwent at Rowlands Gill	416650	558050	245.50	281.4	50.4	0.240	49.03	39.1	49.9	10.1	867	13.15	0.606	0.479	23007
23008	Rede at Rede Bridge	386950	583350	345.10	285.0	128.5	0.109	47.67	32.7	44.0	9.4	1024	20.08			23008
23010	Tarset Burn at Greenhaugh	378800	587750	95.85	300.0	148.7	0.258	17.49	34.1	45.0	9.7	1064	13.51			23010
23011	Kielder Burn at Kielder	364400	594600	58.86	407.9	192.6	0.148	12.29	38.3	50.9	10.6	1401	12.96			23011
23012	East Allen at Wide Eals	380250	558300	88.12	385.6	16.4	0.240	22.50	40.2	53.6	10.3	1154	13.09			23012
23013	West Allen at Hindley Wrae	378950	558200	78.14	402.0	35.6	0.270	17.60	39.2	54.2	10.3	1253	11.13			23013
23015	North Tyne at Barrasford	392450	572250	1049.75	275.0	128.3	0.145	67.93	34.6	46.1	9.8	1082	16.72			23015
24001	Wear at Sunderland Bridge	426250	537450	660.96	301.0	94.8	0.205	71.27	35.8	46.9	10.1	967	15.87	0.606	0.500	24001
24002	Gaunless at Bishop Auckland	421450	530700	92.08	189.3	101.9	0.197	31.58	30.8	39.6	10.0	788	18.45	0.670	0.497	24002
24003	Wear at Stanhope	398250	539000	173.21	471.0	72.1	0.173	23.28	42.4	55.3	10.4	1307	13.09			24003
24004	Bedburn Beck at Bedburn	411950	532150	74.32	315.9	94.7	0.342	17.05	34.8	45.1	10.0	949	13.15			24004
24005	Browney at Burn Hall	425900	538800	178.35	197.5	90.2	0.257	34.10	33.3	43.0	9.2	751	18.61	0.650	0.804	24005
24006	Rookhope Burn at Eastgate	395250	539150	36.60	451.3	114.1	0.192	14.12	39.8	50.8	10.2	1223	13.15			24006
24007	Browney at Lanchester	416350	546100	44.65	252.3	73.2	0.389	14.45	34.8	44.8	10.1	795	13.15			24007
24008	Wear at Witton Park	417350	530900	455.06	364.8	90.7	0.207	50.24	38.2	50.1	10.2	1068	13.13			24008
24009	Wear at Chester Le Street	428300	551150	1005.29	249.2	90.1	0.179	103.28	34.5	45.0	9.9	882	19.57	0.658	0.653	24009

Number	Name	IHDTM NGR	AREA km²	ALTBAR m	ASPBAR degrees	ASPVAR	LDP km	RMED-1D mm	RMED-2D mm	RMED-1H mm	SAAR$_{4170}$ mm	SMDBAR mm	URBCONC	URBLOC	Number
24801	Burnhope Burn at Burnhope Reservoir	385650	20.55	550.8	70.8	0.373	8.34	49.5	66.8	11.1	1569	12.76			24801
25001	Tees at Broken Scar	425950	815.69	370.3	98.3	0.215	84.50	40.0	52.7	10.5	1245	13.00			25001
25002	Tees at Dent Bank	393050	218.38	543.3	103.6	0.150	34.26	48.6	66.4	11.1	1753	12.17			25002
25003	Trout Beck at Moor House	375750	11.69	656.5	45.1	0.572	5.94	53.1	75.8	11.7	2028	10.80			25003
25004	Skerne at South Park	428350	255.19	100.1	154.0	0.266	48.20	28.9	37.2	9.9	682	34.71	0.722	0.719	25004
25005	Leven at Leven Bridge	444500	193.57	126.6	300.6	0.244	42.34	33.3	43.6	10.1	726	32.71	0.573	0.948	25005
25006	Greta at Rutherford Bridge	403250	86.73	402.1	55.6	0.311	23.52	40.3	54.4	10.7	1263	11.77			25006
25007	Clow Beck at Croft	428050	79.31	134.9	55.0	0.374	33.66	31.7	40.2	10.4	763	18.37	0.367	1.029	25007
25008	Tees at Barnard Castle	404600	509.48	451.8	106.8	0.199	53.83	43.4	57.7	10.7	1441	12.38			25008
25009	Tees at Low Moor	436250	1267.04	271.3	105.6	0.197	121.08	36.2	47.2	10.3	1045	19.56	0.672	0.677	25009
25010	Baydale Beck at Mowden Bridge	426000	31.08	96.3	171.5	0.569	13.16	28.5	36.6	10.3	677	33.07	0.527	0.396	25010
25011	Langdon Beck at Langdon	385200	12.73	543.8	208.6	0.401	6.64	44.2	59.5	10.7	1454	13.15			25011
25012	Harwood Beck at Harwood	385050	24.89	537.5	143.2	0.257	9.62	49.3	68.7	11.1	1736	12.76			25012
25018	Tees at Middleton In Teesdale	395150	241.97	531.4	109.3	0.149	37.10	47.8	65.1	10.5	1699	12.26			25018
25019	Leven at Easby	458550	15.06	215.9	255.9	0.049	9.21	37.8	52.0	10.5	854	28.73			25019
25020	Skerne at Preston Le Skerne	429350	153.11	112.5	144.9	0.218	28.97	29.0	37.7	9.8	696	35.33	0.647	1.109	25020
25021	Skerne at Bradbury	431950	75.43	114.9	165.3	0.221	21.36	29.9	38.6	9.8	692	35.33	0.631	0.994	25021
25808	Burnt Weir at Moor House														25808
25809	Bog Weir at Moor House	377300	0.05	529.9	109.5	0.724	0.36	55.5	79.9	11.8	1997	10.80			25809
25810	Syke Weir at Moor House	377200	0.04	534.2	88.0	0.778	0.33	55.4	79.8	11.8	1995	10.80			25810
26001	West Beck at Wansford Bridge	503000	193.59	106.3	108.4	0.315	31.86	33.8	42.9	11.1	768	39.79	0.491	0.524	26001
26002	Hull at Hempholme Lock	508000	389.58	79.8	124.3	0.272	45.39	32.7	41.6	10.7	733	40.54	0.580	0.748	26002
26003	Foston Beck at Foston Mill														26003
26004	Gypsey Race at Bridlington	516350	256.79	104.9	136.2	0.101	42.39	31.8	40.4	10.4	749	40.78			26004
26007	Catchwater at Witherwick														26007
27001	Nidd at Hunsingore Weir	442650	490.05	196.5	93.8	0.225	74.93	38.6	48.9	11.4	970	27.30	0.784	0.600	27001
27002	Wharfe at Flint Mill Weir	442050	760.99	273.4	135.9	0.130	109.13	40.7	53.5	11.0	1171	17.93	0.644	0.543	27002
27004	Calder at Newlands	421850	905.16	213.5	88.4	0.166	74.14	39.9	53.9	10.9	1043	21.58	0.731	0.713	27004
27006	Don at Hadfields Weir	391150	365.29	261.7	73.4	0.286	50.59	40.7	54.2	10.6	1012	30.06	0.790	0.459	27006
27007	Ure at Westwick Lock	466950	913.72	272.6	84.8	0.208	101.91	41.8	53.8	11.2	1119	19.50			27007
27008	Swale at Leckby Grange	441350	1350.14	183.0	117.1	0.105	110.57	34.5	43.7	10.8	873	24.62	0.552	0.686	27008
27009	Ouse at Skelton	456950	3302.12	184.8	100.9	0.133	149.96	36.5	46.4	11.0	918	25.80	0.621	0.749	27009
27010	Hodge Beck at Bransdale Weir	462800	18.87	322.1	161.2	0.234	9.86	36.0	47.4	10.4	1040	27.10			27010
27012	Hebden Water at High Greenwood	397300	36.00	374.5	150.2	0.195	9.71	43.2	60.0	11.4	1396	15.36			27012
27014	Rye at Little Habton	474250	660.30	184.1	154.2	0.249	55.48	32.5	43.1	10.4	854	30.90			27014
27015	Derwent at Stamford Bridge	471450	1637.92	126.1	163.4	0.148	101.46	32.2	42.2	10.6	782	33.16	0.541	0.889	27015
27021	Don at Doncaster	456950	1253.16	154.0	76.8	0.199	82.40	35.9	47.2	10.5	801	32.89	0.753	0.848	27021
27022	Don at Rotherham Weir	442700	825.20	185.7	74.8	0.212	56.35	37.2	48.3	10.6	861	30.65	0.771	0.697	27022
27023	Dearne at Barnsley Weir	435150	117.08	147.9	78.7	0.256	25.11	37.2	49.2	10.2	766	39.02	0.703	0.654	27023
27024	Swale at Richmond	414750	380.14	411.4	85.5	0.161	48.50	42.9	55.6	11.0	1306	11.77			27024
27025	Rother at Woodhouse Mill	443250	351.55	134.0	76.6	0.165	39.35	34.4	43.0	10.5	761	31.11	0.755	0.882	27025
27026	Rother at Whittington	439250	167.04	163.9	77.0	0.227	18.17	35.2	43.6	10.4	796	31.11	0.742	0.733	27026
27027	Wharfe at Ilkley	411050	447.51	354.6	162.8	0.128	63.57	43.5	58.0	11.1	1382	12.26			27027
27028	Aire at Armley	428250	685.93	219.1	121.4	0.110	79.71	37.8	50.5	10.5	1038	15.53	0.772	0.551	27028
27029	Calder at Elland	412400	340.91	291.3	103.3	0.147	35.14	43.2	58.6	11.2	1262	15.36	0.658	0.560	27029
27030	Dearne at Adwick	447600	310.93	105.7	85.4	0.199	44.48	33.8	45.7	10.3	707	38.74	0.715	0.822	27030
27031	Colne at Colne Bridge	417350	244.77	246.2	53.9	0.240	27.75	44.4	60.1	11.1	1134	16.75	0.701	0.573	27031
27032	Hebden Beck at Hebden	402550	22.25	454.0	178.9	0.409	12.63	42.0	54.9	11.5	1454	12.29			27032
27033	Sea Cut at Scarborough	502650	34.01	94.7	124.5	0.207	13.03	34.3	44.2	10.7	769	33.67	0.662	0.510	27033
27034	Ure at Kilgram Bridge	418850	511.89	364.9	84.1	0.143	60.08	45.3	59.7	11.1	1342	11.67			27034

Number	Name	IHDTM NGR		AREA km²	ALTBAR m	ASPBAR degrees	ASPVAR	LDP km	RMED-1D mm	RMED-2D mm	RMED-1H mm	SAAR$_{4170}$ mm	SMDBAR mm	URBCONC	URBLOC	Number
27035	Aire at Kildwick Bridge	401400	445750	282.42	231.2	169.8	0.125	37.61	39.3	52.8	10.5	1135	12.29	0.604	0.605	27035
27036	Derwent at Malton	478750	471450	1405.41	136.5	161.7	0.168	74.79	32.5	42.6	10.5	796	32.08	0.549	0.750	27036
27038	Costa Beck at Gatehouses															27038
27040	Doe Lea at Staveley	444250	374450	68.14	113.5	21.6	0.128	17.42	34.1	41.6	10.7	717	31.11	0.687	0.726	27040
27041	Derwent at Buttercrambe	473000	458850	1594.80	127.7	160.8	0.149	96.33	32.2	42.2	10.6	784	32.98	0.542	0.866	27041
27042	Dove at Kirkby Mills	470450	485350	54.53	228.8	173.7	0.238	24.85	34.0	45.8	10.1	964	27.05			27042
27043	Wharfe at Addingham	409050	449450	432.08	359.9	166.7	0.139	60.25	43.8	58.4	11.2	1401	12.26			27043
27048	Derwent at West Ayton	499000	485150	125.91	169.5	150.1	0.226	28.01	36.1	47.5	10.9	849	27.07			27048
27049	Rye at Ness	469450	479150	239.98	221.6	133.8	0.186	48.23	34.4	45.2	10.6	877	32.77			27049
27051	Crimple at Burn Bridge	428350	451900	8.13	174.8	86.2	0.416	5.03	37.8	45.7	12.8	864	37.97			27051
27052	Whitting at Sheepbridge	437600	374600	54.48	182.5	113.2	0.269	12.02	34.9	44.3	10.5	824	31.11	0.750	0.895	27052
27053	Nidd at Birstwith	422850	460300	219.30	320.3	98.8	0.231	39.25	42.3	54.8	11.3	1209	14.13			27053
27054	Hodge Beck at Cherry Farm	465050	490350	37.15	282.5	174.5	0.272	15.02	34.5	45.6	10.3	988	27.07			27054
27055	Rye at Broadway Foot	456000	488150	131.37	268.3	189.3	0.166	21.17	35.7	47.2	10.4	940	33.19			27055
27058	Riccal at Crook House Farm	466250	480950	39.96	198.6	169.1	0.420	21.85	32.5	42.8	10.3	854	28.21			27058
27059	Laver at Ripon															27059
27061	Colne at Longroyd Bridge	413450	416100	73.89	299.9	80.8	0.236	19.68	47.3	63.6	11.6	1301	15.36	0.592	0.374	27061
27811	Aire at Brotherton	449350	424300	1925.26	190.9	99.3	0.141	115.54	38.0	50.6	10.7	978	22.46	0.769	0.735	27811
27835	Calder at Midland Bridge Dewsbury	424150	421450	715.60	248.6	88.4	0.171	53.23	42.1	57.1	11.0	1142	16.82	0.704	0.636	27835
27846	Aire at Ash Bridge	447200	426750	1901.01	192.8	100.7	0.140	111.46	38.1	50.8	10.7	983	22.24	0.765	0.728	27846
27852	Little Don at Langsett Reservoir	421400	400350	21.07	390.1	38.3	0.488	9.44	47.2	60.5	11.1	1326	21.77	0.709	1.511	27852
28002	Blithe at Hamstall Ridware	410900	319050	162.14	149.9	143.0	0.197	41.46	32.2	40.0	10.9	779	25.74	0.870	0.993	28002
28003	Tame at Water Orton	417050	291450	405.70	144.0	96.1	0.144	45.02	33.7	41.4	11.0	731	38.22	0.861	1.080	28003
28004	Tame at Lea Marston	420600	293350	801.81	131.9	80.2	0.112	53.40	32.8	40.8	10.8	722	39.75	0.842	1.177	28004
28005	Tame at Elford	417350	310350	1492.77	118.7	76.7	0.053	78.80	32.5	40.3	10.7	702	40.17	0.799	1.311	28005
28006	Trent at Great Haywood	399300	322950	322.43	146.1	208.8	0.181	51.28	31.6	39.8	10.2	808	25.51	0.811	1.169	28006
28007	Trent at Shardlow	444650	329900	4414.22	135.7	140.9	0.066	131.47	32.2	40.0	10.5	761	33.62			28007
28008	Dove at Rocester Weir	411150	339750	401.51	268.6	149.9	0.136	51.76	35.8	45.3	10.4	1020	25.29			28008
28009	Trent at Colwick	461850	339350	7484.84	142.1	135.7	0.063	157.86	32.5	41.1	10.6	771	34.26	0.801	1.049	28009
28010	Derwent at Longbridge Weir	435750	336350	1052.27	258.8	131.4	0.127	90.05	36.3	48.2	10.2	1017	27.41	0.613	0.626	28010
28011	Derwent at Matlock Bath	429700	358450	687.38	311.3	127.7	0.121	57.93	37.5	51.1	10.0	1127	24.21	0.502	0.767	28011
28012	Trent at Yoxall	413250	317700	1213.94	129.1	182.6	0.068	71.58	31.2	38.9	10.5	761	30.13	0.779	1.248	28012
28014	Sow at Milford	397350	321500	598.88	117.4	229.2	0.018	43.49	30.5	38.0	10.4	736	33.11	0.776	1.142	28014
28015	Idle at Mattersey	468900	389650	525.94	77.3	68.6	0.203	60.82	32.3	41.4	11.4	651	41.03	0.747	1.173	28015
28016	Ryton at Serlby Park	463950	389600	237.57	68.9	79.0	0.251	44.66	31.6	41.7	11.4	626	36.11	0.763	1.116	28016
28017	Devon at Cotham															28017
28018	Dove at Marston On Dove	423350	328850	883.63	216.5	156.6	0.137	83.93	34.3	43.1	10.4	934	25.25	0.612	0.880	28018
28019	Trent at Drakelow Park	423750	320300	3085.13	119.6	128.3	0.040	96.08	31.8	39.4	10.6	722	35.96	0.821	1.199	28019
28020	Churnet at Rocester	410350	338750	234.02	224.1	216.3	0.145	46.93	34.5	42.4	10.3	949	24.65	0.653	1.083	28020
28021	Derwent at Draycott	444450	332700	1173.67	241.2	134.5	0.137	103.44	35.8	47.3	10.3	984	28.07	0.718	0.487	28021
28022	Trent at North Muskham	478850	359850	8234.81	133.9	124.1	0.061	199.57	32.3	40.9	10.6	756	35.31	0.795	1.075	28022
28023	Wye at Ashford	418250	369750	152.17	339.7	122.4	0.124	26.29	37.4	51.1	10.0	1201	19.73	0.556	1.208	28023
28024	Wreake at Syston Mill	461600	312550	416.83	117.1	239.4	0.030	53.34	30.7	40.5	11.1	648	42.97	0.681	0.674	28024
28026	Anker at Polesworth	426250	303250	370.40	107.8	255.4	0.089	39.70	31.7	39.5	10.7	680	41.81	0.759	1.074	28026
28027	Erewash at Stapleford	448150	336550	183.00	100.6	161.8	0.138	32.47	31.4	39.6	10.6	721	33.82	0.756	0.901	28027
28031	Manifold at Ilam	414050	350700	148.53	307.7	98.2	0.185	33.52	36.3	46.4	10.1	1085	23.72			28031
28032	Meden at Church Warsop	455950	368100	60.41	125.3	82.9	0.325	16.74	33.0	40.8	10.9	710	31.20	0.738	1.004	28032
28033	Dove at Hollinsclough	406450	366850	7.96	407.9	110.9	0.223	6.12	41.6	55.6	10.5	1363	19.73			28033
28038	Manifold at Hulme End	410600	359350	44.77	328.9	92.8	0.249	16.37	38.7	50.7	10.2	1197	19.86			28038
28039	Rea at Calthorpe Park	407150	284750	74.06	167.7	77.9	0.240	16.88	34.5	44.0	11.1	792	40.29	0.831	0.958	28039

Number	Name	IHDTM NGR	AREA km²	ALTBAR m	ASPBAR degrees	ASPVAR	LDP km	RMED-1D mm	RMED-2D mm	RMED-1H mm	SAAR$_{4170}$ mm	SMDBAR mm	URBCONC	URBLOC	Number
28040	Trent at Stoke On Trent	389300 346850	53.57	185.7	235.7	0.199	14.83	32.3	41.5	9.9	882	25.51	0.786	0.785	28040
28041	Hamps at Waterhouses	408100 350350	36.91	327.9	110.8	0.228	15.61	35.4	44.5	10.1	1064	25.45			28041
28043	Derwent at Chatsworth	426050 368450	343.61	335.0	139.1	0.129	42.35	38.5	54.0	9.9	1181	24.61			28043
28045	Meden at Bothamstall	467950 373050	264.86	98.9	72.6	0.249	32.47	32.4	41.4	11.2	680	38.68	0.781	1.190	28045
28046	Dove at Izaak Walton	414750 351050	85.62	317.1	185.4	0.092	30.74	36.3	47.4	10.2	1154	22.25			28046
28047	Oldcotes Dyke at Blyth	461450 387450	85.83	73.8	87.9	0.362	18.54	31.8	42.5	11.4	614	32.67	0.712	1.227	28047
28048	Amber at Wingfield Park	437450 352050	128.82	158.0	135.6	0.160	23.61	34.0	42.7	10.7	782	32.75	0.710	0.925	28048
28049	Ryton at Worksop	457650 379550	75.46	97.0	89.7	0.240	20.04	32.4	42.0	11.3	649	31.11	0.772	0.956	28049
28052	Sow at Great Bridgford														28052
28053	Penk at Penkridge	392150 314400	283.03	120.6	354.3	0.037	28.40	30.4	37.9	10.6	709	37.06	0.800	1.302	28053
28054	Sence at Blaby	456750 298400	133.69	120.1	288.1	0.157	27.24	32.8	40.8	11.9	665	41.63	0.775	0.490	28054
28055	Ecclesbourne at Duffield	431850 344850	50.58	167.1	136.5	0.187	15.73	34.2	42.6	11.0	844	33.82	0.540	1.224	28055
28056	Rothley Brook at Rothley	458150 312200	91.75	114.1	118.1	0.165	27.04	31.0	39.4	11.0	687	41.81	0.754	0.792	28056
28058	Henmore Brook at Ashbourne	417500 346150	38.63	208.1	184.0	0.211	16.27	34.9	42.6	11.2	872	32.69	0.572	0.206	28058
28059	Maun at Mansfield	454800 362450	27.45	141.7	51.0	0.320	10.29	32.9	40.9	11.0	721	32.67	0.829	0.912	28059
28060	Dover Beck at Lowdham	465450 347850	62.78	87.6	119.5	0.253	16.27	33.0	42.6	10.2	687	41.96	0.637	0.964	28060
28061	Churnet at Basford Bridge	398250 351850	136.53	230.2	231.3	0.118	22.77	35.0	43.2	10.7	981	24.03	0.691	0.763	28061
28066	Cole at Coleshill	418300 287550	119.72	126.7	60.4	0.239	31.56	32.0	40.6	10.3	733	39.68	0.878	0.860	28066
28067	Derwent at Church Wilne	443900 331600	1176.06	240.8	134.4	0.138	105.42	35.8	47.3	10.3	984	28.08	0.718	0.503	28067
28069	Tame at Tamworth	420550 303800	1423.58	120.8	84.9	0.051	67.38	32.5	40.3	10.7	704	40.25	0.843	1.194	28069
28070	Burbage Brook at Burbage	425850 380250	8.36	385.8	212.3	0.343	5.91	38.8	52.3	10.1	990	31.11			28070
28082	Soar at Littlethorpe	454350 297300	180.84	102.6	65.0	0.095	23.24	31.3	38.5	10.8	668	41.81	0.726	0.843	28082
28804	Trent at Trent Bridge	458250 338550	7469.26	142.3	135.5	0.063	153.52	32.5	41.1	10.6	771	34.26	0.801	1.057	28804
29001	Waithe Beck at Brigsley	525150 401700	108.28	93.7	36.5	0.191	24.38	32.1	40.1	10.3	730	44.66			29001
29002	Great Eau at Claythorpe Mill	541600 379150	80.69	67.6	70.3	0.193	17.82	34.8	41.6	11.2	718	44.61	0.280	0.697	29002
29003	Lud at Louth	533550 387800	55.59	90.7	69.3	0.238	13.00	35.4	42.6	10.6	729	44.29	0.699	0.302	29003
29004	Ancholme at Bishopbridge	503150 390950	58.92	27.8	62.0	0.330	15.48	29.0	36.7	11.3	635	46.63			29004
29005	Rase at Bishopbridge	503200 391050	63.12	49.0	257.2	0.359	21.58	31.7	38.5	10.7	655	44.29	0.570	1.011	29005
29009	Ancholme at Toft Newton	503250 387550	29.55	31.6	71.7	0.486	10.72	28.5	36.4	11.5	640	47.43			29009
30001	Witham at Claypole Mill	484250 348150	296.04	86.1	26.4	0.139	52.79	31.7	41.1	10.9	632	45.90	0.625	0.880	30001
30002	Barlings Eau at Langworth Bridge	506750 376450	208.03	33.2	150.5	0.103	21.67	30.1	37.4	11.2	620	45.35	0.608	0.889	30002
30003	Bain at Fulsby Lock	524100 361250	200.26	79.5	208.5	0.201	41.27	32.6	39.8	11.1	704	44.29	0.531	0.730	30003
30004	Partney Lymn at Partney Mill	540350 367500	59.94	64.9	90.5	0.271	17.24	33.9	41.3	11.3	696	44.30	0.395	0.868	30004
30005	Witham at Saltersford Total	492600 333650	124.06	120.6	82.3	0.239	25.81	32.7	42.2	11.6	652	45.38			30005
30006	Slea at Leasingham Mill	508500 347050	52.26	57.6	82.2	0.311	23.30	31.7	41.7	11.4	629	49.34	0.679	0.485	30006
30011	Bain at Goulceby Bridge	524450 379600	64.02	108.5	148.2	0.112	17.94	33.3	41.1	10.7	745	44.29			30011
30012	Stainfield Beck at Stainfield	512850 374050	37.72	59.2	225.3	0.358	16.94	31.7	38.3	10.9	661	44.29	0.487	0.878	30012
30013	Heighington Beck at Heighington														30013
30014	Pointon Lode at Pointon	512950 331250	11.09	43.2	83.1	0.374	10.76	31.5	40.5	11.8	624	52.29	0.449	0.593	30014
30015	Cringle Brook at Stoke Rochford														30015
30017	Witham at Colsterworth	492850 324750	50.23	123.2	80.0	0.283	14.17	32.4	42.5	12.1	649	44.07	0.399	0.798	30017
31002	Glen at Kates Bridge	510750 315050	338.45	70.3	101.6	0.282	52.71	31.1	41.0	11.6	616	49.39	0.435	0.872	31002
31004	Welland at Tallington	509650 307650	715.25	103.8	97.1	0.167	79.19	31.1	40.0	12.0	637	42.36	0.627	0.760	31004
31005	Welland at Tixover	496850 299650	419.59	110.8	98.0	0.107	56.84	31.7	40.4	12.1	644	41.60	0.592	1.061	31005
31006	Gwash at Belmesthorpe	503800 309550	149.49	103.0	100.3	0.339	37.94	30.2	39.5	11.8	638	42.65	0.526	0.861	31006
31010	Chater at Fosters Bridge	496100 303100	68.86	112.8	108.6	0.168	23.41	30.6	39.6	12.2	640	41.60			31010
31021	Welland at Ashley	482050 291500	247.19	115.3	105.2	0.098	32.24	32.0	40.7	12.1	654	41.60	0.649	1.057	31021
31023	West Glen at Easton Wood	496650 325850	4.41	107.7	84.9	0.369	3.86	33.1	42.7	11.7	647	46.27			31023
31025	Gwash South Arm at Manton	487650 305250	24.11	146.4	125.3	0.177	12.06	30.3	40.7	12.4	675	41.60			31025
31026	Egleton Brook at Egleton														31026

99

Number	Name	IHDTM NGR	AREA km²	ALTBAR m	ASPBAR degrees	ASPVAR	LDP km	RMED-1D mm	RMED-2D mm	RMED-1H mm	SAAR₄₁₇₀ mm	SMDBAR mm	URBCONC	URBLOC	Number
32002	Willow Brook at Fotheringhay	506550	94.36	87.4	110.9	0.228	37.40	30.8	38.8	12.2	607	44.56	0.743	1.395	32002
32003	Harpers Brook at Old Mill Bridge	498450	70.62	89.3	112.1	0.199	27.06	31.5	39.9	12.6	618	41.56	0.528	1.113	32003
32004	Ise Brook at Harrowden Old Mill	489950	194.93	108.3	97.0	0.161	45.20	30.8	39.2	12.6	631	40.78	0.752	0.585	32004
32006	Nene/Kislingbury at Upton	472250	221.91	124.4	97.0	0.125	31.30	33.0	41.6	12.0	675	40.47	0.593	1.254	32006
32007	Nene Brampton at St Andrews	474850	232.32	117.7	156.5	0.135	24.45	31.5	40.8	12.4	642	40.19	0.667	0.372	32007
32008	Nene/Kislingbury at Dodford	462850	104.82	130.7	123.2	0.130	18.02	33.2	41.6	12.3	687	40.52	0.671	1.364	32008
32010	Nene at Wansford	260550	1516.83	93.0	91.3	0.097	115.60	30.7	39.3	12.2	626	42.25	0.703	0.986	32010
32029	Flore at Experimental Catchment	465950	7.55	106.1	174.3	0.313	3.55	32.0	41.6	12.1	646	40.19			32029
33002	Bedford Ouse at Bedford	505350	1470.12	101.3	94.9	0.056	134.85	29.9	38.0	10.7	648	40.22	0.619	0.851	33002
33005	Bedford Ouse at Thornborough Mill	473550	387.87	113.8	147.4	0.060	39.72	30.4	38.4	10.3	667	39.40	0.585	0.881	33005
33006	Wissey at Northwold	576950	259.81	46.0	204.3	0.132	39.21	28.1	36.1	11.2	665	42.29	0.593	1.209	33006
33007	Nar at Marham	572150	147.29	57.7	269.3	0.094	42.02	29.2	37.8	11.1	688	44.64	0.524	0.940	33007
33009	Bedford Ouse at Harrold Mill	494950	1323.64	105.6	81.8	0.047	94.14	30.1	38.1	10.7	655	39.80	0.610	0.856	33009
33011	Little Ouse at County Bridge Euston	589050	130.18	39.0	351.7	0.127	30.32	27.5	34.9	10.7	602	44.97	0.415	0.984	33011
33012	Kym at Meagre Farm	515450	137.86	61.2	87.1	0.188	31.28	29.0	36.3	11.8	610	49.16	0.380	0.883	33012
33013	Sapiston at Rectory Bridge	589600	195.93	52.4	1.6	0.172	36.95	28.2	35.1	10.7	606	46.40	0.424	1.042	33013
33014	Lark at Temple	575650	278.43	59.2	18.1	0.149	32.99	28.0	36.8	10.6	608	46.84	0.604	1.025	33014
33015	Ouzel at Willen	488250	279.06	109.0	356.9	0.077	42.66	30.7	38.4	10.2	658	39.71	0.653	0.750	33015
33017	Bedford Ouse at St Ives Staunch	531850	2869.58	79.3	65.9	0.085	186.20	29.6	37.3	10.9	616	43.88	0.648	0.843	33017
33018	Tove at Cappenham Bridge	471550	133.20	132.5	85.3	0.133	22.74	31.5	40.2	11.4	696	40.39	0.522	0.599	33018
33019	Thet at Melford Bridge	587850	311.82	38.5	219.4	0.084	46.14	28.2	35.4	11.0	636	42.07	0.615	0.925	33019
33020	Alconbury Brook at Brampton	520650	212.60	46.9	95.0	0.205	29.97	29.3	37.5	11.8	605	50.82	0.489	0.698	33020
33021	Rhee at Burnt Mill	541650	308.09	49.5	9.8	0.241	35.20	28.3	35.0	10.6	573	48.18	0.521	0.852	33021
33022	Ivel at Blunham	515350	539.94	73.2	22.3	0.155	42.75	29.9	36.9	10.6	587	44.66	0.667	0.942	33022
33023	Lea Brook at Beck Bridge														33023
33024	Cam at Dernford	546750	198.05	82.9	353.8	0.098	35.04	28.9	36.2	10.7	603	43.62	0.581	0.838	33024
33027	Rhee at Wimpole	533150	125.50	49.3	18.6	0.212	21.19	28.9	35.9	10.6	567	48.64	0.390	0.908	33027
33028	Flit at Shefford	514300	119.61	88.9	79.5	0.185	25.27	30.1	38.1	10.5	598	43.06	0.654	0.946	33028
33029	Stringside at White Bridge	571700	97.08	25.2	203.3	0.180	19.39	28.4	36.3	11.1	633	50.14	0.640	1.245	33029
33030	Clipstone Brook at Clipstone	493300	40.28	122.7	187.1	0.159	11.63	30.6	38.1	10.5	654	39.74	0.588	0.928	33030
33031	Broughton Brook at Broughton	488900	69.46	97.4	304.9	0.168	21.31	29.1	37.4	10.4	621	39.70	0.427	0.982	33031
33032	Heacham at Heacham	568350	56.19	56.6	333.7	0.134	21.74	30.6	38.3	11.1	694	49.19	0.512	1.024	33032
33033	Hiz at Arlesey	518850	108.97	87.8	33.7	0.186	25.26	29.6	36.1	10.4	620	42.70	0.687	0.907	33033
33034	Little Ouse at Abbey Heath	585200	708.28	42.2	352.1	0.055	50.82	28.2	35.3	10.4	618	44.01	0.566	0.886	33034
33037	Bedford Ouse at Newport Pagnell	487550	801.81	111.0	110.0	0.087	66.03	30.2	38.4	10.7	667	39.76	0.597	0.682	33037
33039	Bedford Ouse at Roxton	515850	1662.59	95.0	78.0	0.064	150.74	29.9	37.8	10.8	638	41.16	0.645	0.761	33039
33044	Thet at Bridgham	595550	275.60	39.7	228.0	0.091	34.15	28.1	35.2	11.0	640	42.07	0.579	0.994	33044
33045	Wittle at Quidenham	602550	27.65	42.4	293.3	0.223	9.94	27.6	34.0	11.0	627	42.07	0.539	0.870	33045
33046	Thet at Red Bridge	599550	144.95	43.9	217.3	0.169	21.71	28.2	35.5	11.1	658	42.07	0.608	0.911	33046
33048	Larling Brook at Stonebridge														33048
33049	Stanford Water at Buckenham Tofts	583550	46.24	39.1	205.1	0.164	17.92	28.2	35.7	11.1	635	42.07	0.603	0.885	33049
33050	Snail at Fordham	563000	57.91	64.7	323.2	0.379	20.51	30.9	37.7	10.9	589	47.93	0.603	0.829	33050
33051	Cam at Chesterford	550350	140.25	93.3	26.3	0.040	22.89	29.1	36.7	10.8	611	42.00			33051
33052	Swaffham Lode at Swaffham Bulbeck														33052
33054	Babingley at Castle Rising	568150	48.49	51.5	288.3	0.155	17.61	29.9	37.6	11.0	694	48.78	0.470	0.947	33054
33055	Granta at Babraham	551100	101.29	80.0	297.5	0.153	20.93	28.3	36.1	10.7	614	47.73	0.541	0.841	33055
33057	Ouzel at Leighton Buzzard	491700	122.76	113.8	334.4	0.108	17.51	31.1	38.6	10.0	665	39.83	0.567	1.138	33057
33058	Ouzel at Bletchley	488450	221.21	113.5	334.9	0.054	31.03	30.9	38.6	10.2	661	39.75	0.643	0.933	33058
33063	Little Ouse at Knettishall	595300	103.56	41.1	350.5	0.153	22.09	27.3	34.6	10.7	602	45.34	0.418	0.823	33063
33805	Beechamwell Brook at Beechamwell	573950	34.50	39.5	234.6	0.478	14.62	27.6	36.5	11.1	651	48.92	0.757	1.362	33805

Number	Name	IHDTM NGR	AREA km²	ALTBAR m	ASPBAR degrees	ASPVAR	LDP km	RMED-1D mm	RMED-2D mm	RMED-1H mm	$SAAR_{4170}$ mm	SMDBAR mm	URBCONC	URBLOC	Number
33809	Bury Brook at Bury Weir	528600 283850	61.97	31.0	45.2	0.232	22.05	28.5	36.4	11.4	558	50.75	0.495	0.723	33809
33813	Mel at Meldreth														33813
34001	Yare at Colney	618250 308350	227.90	45.9	67.2	0.101	40.14	28.8	36.1	11.2	666	42.07	0.618	0.888	34001
34002	Tas at Shotesham	622450 299300	150.95	44.0	58.6	0.107	26.23	28.0	34.3	11.1	616	43.86	0.540	0.861	34002
34003	Bure at Ingworth	619050 329750	168.00	50.1	127.7	0.242	24.80	29.6	37.1	11.3	686	40.97	0.417	1.052	34003
34004	Wensum at Costessey Mill	617550 312950	560.95	50.0	80.2	0.107	76.38	29.8	37.9	11.2	670	41.60	0.589	0.966	34004
34005	Tud at Costessey Park	617150 311150	72.02	46.3	64.0	0.151	25.43	28.6	36.1	11.3	643	42.07	0.670	1.238	34005
34006	Waveney at Needham Mill	622750 280950	379.26	46.3	44.4	0.059	34.58	27.3	35.4	10.8	604	45.58	0.529	0.932	34006
34007	Dove at Oakley Park	617400 277050	140.10	50.8	37.5	0.143	25.28	26.5	34.8	10.6	601	46.40	0.412	1.045	34007
34008	Ant at Honing Lock														34008
34010	Waveney at Billingford Bridge	616650 278250	152.63	41.3	148.4	0.089	20.72	27.6	35.1	10.9	607	43.54	0.611	0.766	34010
34011	Wensum at Fakenham	591450 329300	162.10	62.0	49.3	0.122	25.99	30.4	38.6	11.1	701	41.82	0.493	0.944	34011
34012	Burn at Burnham Overy	584250 342650	81.33	48.7	29.2	0.133	16.80	30.9	38.9	11.1	677	41.58	0.502	0.726	34012
34018	Stiffkey at Warham All Saints	594550 341450	86.39	50.2	347.4	0.071	29.05	30.4	39.2	11.1	658	41.02	0.466	1.130	34018
35001	Gipping at Constantine Weir	615250 244250	315.02	53.1	97.2	0.093	42.26	27.8	35.0	10.6	595	46.40	0.653	0.581	35001
35003	Alde at Farnham	636000 259950	62.95	40.6	128.7	0.203	21.50	29.3	36.9	10.9	608	49.03			35003
35004	Ore at Beversham Bridge	635750 258150	56.12	36.3	139.7	0.186	20.59	29.5	37.7	10.9	609	49.03	0.407	1.115	35004
35008	Gipping at Stowmarket	605950 257850	127.43	62.3	69.5	0.149	17.65	26.7	34.0	10.5	606	46.40	0.619	0.470	35008
35010	Gipping at Bramford	612700 246400	297.50	54.8	93.3	0.093	36.13	27.6	34.9	10.5	598	46.40	0.562	0.860	35010
35011	Belstead Brook at Belstead	614150 242100	43.69	50.7	103.7	0.265	18.11	29.1	35.4	10.7	560	46.40	0.634	0.421	35011
35014	Bucklesham Mill at Newbourn														35014
36001	Stour at Stratford St Mary	603900 233850	837.33	70.3	132.8	0.120	81.76	27.3	34.5	10.5	599	48.17	0.541	1.019	36001
36002	Glem at Glemsford	584450 247050	86.09	88.7	139.5	0.168	21.24	27.8	35.4	10.5	618	47.32	0.480	0.838	36002
36003	Box at Polstead	598350 237850	56.63	59.7	145.3	0.136	15.40	25.5	32.2	10.4	602	47.71	0.432	1.214	36003
36004	Chad Brook at Long Melford	586950 245900	50.07	80.0	182.6	0.190	20.17	25.6	35.1	10.3	609	46.44	0.441	1.026	36004
36005	Brett at Hadleigh	602400 242900	155.98	69.0	159.3	0.125	34.10	26.2	33.7	10.3	603	46.40	0.450	0.752	36005
36006	Stour at Langham	602150 234550	571.79	74.5	122.9	0.120	77.87	27.7	35.0	10.6	599	48.46	0.563	0.987	36006
36007	Belchamp Brook at Bardfield Bridge	584850 242200	58.56	64.4	73.2	0.102	13.75	27.3	34.1	10.5	562	47.90	0.439	1.144	36007
36008	Stour at Westmill	582850 246450	223.63	89.2	123.0	0.123	40.91	28.7	36.3	10.7	606	47.66	0.579	0.970	36008
36009	Brett at Cockfield	591400 252550	25.70	87.3	152.9	0.102	10.54	25.2	32.6	10.2	609	46.40			36009
36010	Bumpstead Brook at Broad Green	569050 241800	28.03	96.2	94.2	0.243	9.29	29.1	36.9	11.2	616	46.27	0.352	0.520	36010
36011	Stour Brook at Sturmer	569700 244000	34.56	97.4	100.6	0.152	13.74	28.6	36.8	10.9	625	47.93	0.703	0.595	36011
36012	Stour at Kedington	570850 245150	76.79	97.2	147.0	0.065	21.38	29.8	38.3	10.7	613	47.93	0.493	0.555	36012
36015	Stour at Lamarsh	589650 235750	481.44	79.9	135.6	0.120	59.26	27.7	35.1	10.6	600	47.66	0.580	0.880	36015
37001	Roding at Redbridge	541500 188250	301.20	67.6	124.3	0.096	64.28	31.2	39.4	11.2	610	43.54	0.733	0.427	37001
37003	Ter at Crabbs Bridge	578500 210750	77.81	59.4	150.1	0.216	28.72	28.8	36.9	11.5	591	40.80	0.419	0.826	37003
37005	Colne at Lexden	596350 226000	236.04	66.1	121.3	0.150	46.29	27.8	34.5	11.0	595	47.36	0.537	0.836	37005
37006	Can at Beach's Mill	569150 207200	228.28	65.9	82.5	0.156	29.95	30.9	38.4	11.6	604	43.98	0.662	1.114	37006
37007	Wid at Writtle	568450 206050	135.73	69.0	63.2	0.179	27.86	31.8	38.7	11.7	606	46.15	0.677	1.077	37007
37008	Chelmer at Springfield	571150 206950	190.13	77.4	131.8	0.176	45.09	28.7	35.7	11.3	600	40.80	0.637	0.528	37008
37009	Brain at Guithavon Valley	581750 214700	60.22	63.9	105.7	0.234	27.87	28.7	36.0	11.6	596	42.00	0.719	0.790	37009
37010	Blackwater at Appleford Bridge	584550 215900	246.98	67.6	142.0	0.166	58.21	28.4	35.3	11.4	594	45.63	0.571	0.856	37010
37011	Chelmer at Churchend	562750 223400	72.94	94.2	133.3	0.188	18.05	28.1	34.9	11.2	601	40.80	0.432	1.017	37011
37012	Colne at Poolstreet	577250 236350	64.68	81.8	89.4	0.197	15.55	28.3	35.0	11.1	604	42.06	0.409	0.837	37012
37013	Sandon Brook at Sandon Bridge	575550 205500	75.05	52.7	32.8	0.173	16.14	31.8	38.9	12.1	586	44.82	0.553	0.942	37013
37014	Roding at High Ongar	556050 203850	93.08	75.7	130.5	0.166	30.90	29.9	38.0	11.2	610	40.80	0.415	0.903	37014
37016	Pant at Copford Hall	566800 231450	63.64	97.0	116.4	0.151	17.96	28.2	35.2	11.3	612	41.01	0.466	1.024	37016
37017	Blackwater at Stisted	579150 224350	140.34	84.1	135.1	0.160	38.81	28.4	35.3	11.4	604	40.93	0.577	0.642	37017
37018	Ingrebourne at Gaynes Park	555150 186100	44.78	61.6	202.6	0.094	16.84	31.1	37.9	11.1	609	49.30	0.779	0.826	37018
37019	Beam at Bretons Farm	551650 185450	50.21	41.4	185.8	0.219	17.88	31.5	38.9	11.1	598	49.30	0.883	0.669	37019

Number	Name	IHDTM NGR	AREA km²	ALTBAR m	ASPBAR degrees	ASPVAR	LDP km	RMED-1D mm	RMED-2D mm	RMED-1H mm	SAAR$_{4170}$ mm	SMDBAR mm	URBCONC	URBLOC	Number
37020	Chelmer at Felsted	567100	133.70	86.6	138.0	0.169	26.31	28.5	35.1	11.2	602	40.80	0.495	0.825	37020
37021	Roman at Bounstead Bridge	598600	52.56	38.9	121.6	0.165	18.02	27.8	35.0	10.9	569	52.79	0.622	0.819	37021
37031	Crouch at Wickford	574850	70.37	36.6	86.9	0.243	16.02	31.5	38.0	11.9	594	49.30	0.769	1.016	37031
37033	Eastwood Brook at Eastwood	586050	9.93	44.8	62.7	0.460	7.97	31.4	37.9	12.5	570	53.78	0.848	0.939	37033
38001	Lea at Feildes Weir	539050	1040.78	99.1	150.4	0.116	63.80	30.8	38.3	10.9	636	42.00	0.715	1.152	38001
38002	Ash at Mardock	539300	78.23	93.4	165.5	0.207	24.85	31.5	38.7	11.2	629	40.90	0.481	0.777	38002
38003	Mimram at Panshanger Park	528350	130.53	120.7	133.5	0.184	32.01	31.0	38.1	10.6	641	42.70	0.658	0.860	38003
38004	Rib at Wadesmill	536150	136.55	112.3	163.7	0.152	29.43	31.8	38.9	11.2	646	42.30	0.507	0.834	38004
38007	Canons Brook at Elizabeth Way	543200	20.80	74.6	334.9	0.378	7.77	31.8	38.9	11.1	611	40.80	0.760	0.880	38007
38011	Mimram at Fulling Mill	522550	98.90	129.6	133.7	0.199	23.60	29.9	38.1	10.6	644	42.70	0.685	1.143	38011
38013	Upper Lee at Luton Hoo	511750	70.67	137.7	72.1	0.090	19.97	29.6	37.4	10.2	656	42.70	0.823	0.952	38013
38018	Upper Lee at Water Hall	529800	157.21	114.1	93.6	0.106	45.62	30.0	37.8	10.4	653	42.70	0.793	1.330	38018
38020	Cobbins Brook at Sewardstone Road	538700	38.81	70.9	256.6	0.148	12.69	32.8	40.5	11.1	609	41.79	0.803	0.745	38020
38021	Turkey Brook at Albany Park	536050	41.55	77.9	119.4	0.257	14.42	32.8	39.7	10.9	663	43.12	0.686	0.833	38021
38022	Pymmes Brook at Edmonton Silver Street	534150	40.71	64.7	94.7	0.321	16.07	33.9	43.7	10.9	674	44.55	0.890	0.877	38022
38026	Pincey Brook at Sheering Hall	549450	52.71	81.7	214.4	0.102	20.67	31.0	38.8	11.3	617	40.80	0.420	1.273	38026
39001	Thames at Kingston	517750	9950.95	108.7	110.9	0.083	273.09	32.7	41.5	10.8	724	39.07	0.681	0.735	39001
39002	Thames at Days Weir	456850	3483.91	121.9	132.2	0.155	139.05	32.3	40.5	10.1	716	37.47	0.674	0.895	39002
39003	Wandle at Connollys Mill														39003
39004	Wandle at Beddington Park	529450	118.34	144.7	345.5	0.283	23.87	33.3	43.8	11.0	768	37.50	0.698	0.618	39004
39005	Beverley Brook at Wimbledon Common	521700	39.71	41.2	346.3	0.325	17.37	33.3	39.9	10.4	634	44.39	0.870	1.016	39005
39006	Windrush at Newbridge	440200	362.05	177.8	140.4	0.206	68.50	33.7	42.1	10.4	770	36.62	0.595	0.674	39006
39007	Blackwater at Swallowfield	473200	360.37	88.2	351.6	0.185	37.25	32.0	41.3	11.8	711	38.48	0.680	1.137	39007
39008	Thames at Eynsham	444350	1623.06	134.8	134.7	0.181	97.27	32.3	40.7	10.0	755	35.92	0.663	0.965	39008
39010	Colne at Denham	505300	733.19	119.8	126.8	0.161	68.50	32.0	39.8	10.8	710	42.64	0.689	0.931	39010
39011	Wey at Tilford	487550	391.08	131.0	12.0	0.039	49.63	35.9	48.0	11.0	868	37.23	0.560	0.747	39011
39012	Hogsmill at Kingston Upon Thames	518350	72.89	71.7	342.5	0.380	21.18	33.0	42.4	10.7	684	41.75	0.780	0.760	39012
39014	Ver at Hansteads	514950	135.10	136.0	122.5	0.264	21.92	33.2	38.2	10.5	705	42.70	0.699	0.721	39014
39015	Whitewater at Lodge Farm	473000	45.35	132.3	9.9	0.294	12.01	34.3	44.8	11.2	804	37.23	0.427	0.733	39015
39016	Kennet at Theale	464750	1032.62	150.7	100.0	0.132	88.22	32.9	42.3	10.5	769	37.91	0.609	0.815	39016
39017	Ray at Grendon Underwood														39017
39018	Ock at Abingdon	448450	248.23	87.4	67.8	0.196	34.36	32.1	39.5	9.7	646	39.14	0.625	0.915	39018
39019	Lambourn at Shaw	446850	235.09	163.6	134.6	0.224	34.20	34.3	43.5	10.3	737	39.21			39019
39020	Coln at Bibury	412250	107.29	197.4	147.7	0.180	35.12	35.3	45.0	10.6	818	35.88	0.390	1.013	39020
39021	Cherwell at Enslow Mill	448350	557.53	133.3	138.6	0.124	63.71	33.0	41.0	10.9	700	39.58	0.672	0.916	39021
39022	Loddon at Sheepbridge	471850	176.49	94.1	31.0	0.281	31.00	32.4	41.1	11.1	759	37.90	0.610	1.184	39022
39023	Wye at Hedsor	489550	134.24	149.4	129.0	0.185	26.88	34.6	44.1	11.8	780	42.87	0.657	0.750	39023
39024	Gatwick Stream at Gatwick	528700	30.50	104.1	340.4	0.280	13.50	36.7	49.0	11.9	849	35.11	0.755	0.670	39024
39025	Enborne at Brimpton	456800	142.13	120.1	38.8	0.279	26.89	33.2	43.5	11.2	795	38.24	0.454	0.910	39025
39026	Cherwell at Banbury	445650	204.60	139.8	154.0	0.117	30.04	33.8	41.9	11.4	700	40.98	0.601	0.755	39026
39027	Pang at Pangbourne	463500	175.49	120.7	116.9	0.207	41.21	31.9	40.6	10.9	703	39.66			39027
39028	Dun at Hungerford	432250	100.36	157.3	60.5	0.168	18.61	32.7	42.0	10.4	789	38.60	0.518	1.108	39028
39029	Tillingbourne at Shalford	499950	58.87	132.4	310.8	0.190	21.00	35.1	46.7	11.7	822	35.11	0.325	0.692	39029
39031	Lambourn at Welford														39031
39032	Lambourn at East Shefford	439150	144.99	178.4	129.1	0.208	21.51	34.5	43.4	10.3	750	39.21			39032
39033	Winterbourne at St Bagnor	445250	45.46	147.9	164.0	0.306	18.12	34.0	43.2	10.4	714	39.21			39033
39034	Evenlode at Cassington Mill	444950	427.35	141.7	131.4	0.176	60.61	33.1	41.7	10.2	730	37.91	0.582	0.997	39034
39035	Churn at Cerney Wick														39035
39036	Law Brook at Albury	504600	16.00	139.1	335.7	0.342	8.86	35.3	47.5	11.9	836	35.11	0.464	0.815	39036
39037	Kennet at Marlborough	418800	136.49	186.4	95.2	0.069	27.71	31.7	41.1	10.2	817	32.99			39037

Number	Name	IHDTM NGR	AREA km²	ALTBAR m	ASPBAR degrees	ASPVAR	LDP km	RMED-1D mm	RMED-2D mm	RMED-1H mm	SAAR$_{4170}$ mm	SMDBAR mm	URBCONC	URBLOC	Number
39038	Thame at Shabbington	466650 205600	443.86	101.4	315.8	0.150	50.23	31.6	38.9	10.1	663	39.68	0.637	1.074	39038
39040	Thames at West Mill Cricklade	422850 199550	77.44	143.6	158.2	0.324	34.55	31.8	40.3	10.0	776	36.24	0.490	0.989	39040
39042	Leach at Priory Mill Lechlade	475350 159350	83.72	87.6	352.7	0.239	19.93	31.7	41.2	11.8	702	37.23	0.614	1.024	39042
39044	Hart at Bramshill House	521550 189650	28.24	81.2	162.6	0.381	9.88	32.4	42.2	10.7	699	44.55	0.864	0.799	39044
39049	Silk Stream at Colindeep Lane	485300 171400	50.20	74.8	341.3	0.182	13.88	35.8	40.8	12.6	688	43.20	0.696	0.861	39049
39052	The Cut at Binfield	527050 143250	91.59	87.6	9.9	0.301	17.60	35.8	47.6	11.7	825	35.11	0.732	0.928	39052
39053	Mole at Horley	508400 184600	17.71	50.2	189.5	0.347	12.13	31.5	40.3	10.9	675	44.55	0.898	1.103	39053
39055	Yeading Bk West at Yeading West	537250 173050	127.88	104.2	357.9	0.342	22.83	33.6	44.7	11.1	711	43.86	0.849	0.669	39055
39056	Ravensbourne at Catford Hill														39056
39057	Crane at Cranford Park														39057
39058	Pool at Winsford Road	537200 172600	38.33	57.9	10.6	0.316	11.66	33.7	43.3	11.1	658	44.55	0.882	0.953	39058
39069	Mole at Kinnersley Manor	526200 146050	146.03	81.4	354.3	0.251	22.56	35.1	46.9	11.6	808	35.11	0.719	0.984	39069
39081	Ock at Abingdon	448100 196450	245.85	87.7	66.2	0.197	33.71	32.1	39.5	9.7	646	39.14	0.625	0.945	39081
39086	Gatwick Stream at Gatwick Link	528400 141850	32.42	101.4	340.7	0.290	15.15	36.6	48.8	11.9	844	35.11	0.747	0.731	39086
39088	Chess at Rickmansworth	506550 194550	97.23	152.8	127.8	0.293	27.97	35.0	44.0	11.3	763	40.76	0.583	0.922	39088
39089	Gade at Bury Mill	505400 207550	46.26	155.5	122.2	0.217	14.91	33.6	40.4	10.8	724	41.67	0.636	0.426	39089
39090	Cole at Inglesham	420850 196900	140.01	110.6	2.1	0.171	30.24	30.5	38.8	9.5	680	37.44	0.723	1.255	39090
39092	Dollis Bk at Hendon Lane Bridge	524050 189350	23.76	88.9	135.4	0.196	11.95	33.5	43.7	10.9	703	44.55	0.845	0.840	39092
39093	Brent at Monks Park	520150 184850	115.85	69.8	180.5	0.162	19.35	33.0	42.3	10.8	688	44.55	0.891	0.852	39093
39095	Quaggy at Manor House Gardens	539350 174700	33.93	60.7	296.5	0.255	18.12	32.9	41.5	11.2	652	49.12	0.867	0.873	39095
39096	Wealdstone Brook at Wembley	519100 186250	23.26	54.5	139.6	0.272	9.39	31.9	40.6	10.7	679	44.55	0.905	1.022	39096
39813	Mole at Ifield Weir	524500 136250	13.13	96.7	357.2	0.426	5.40	36.5	48.3	11.8	844	35.11	0.756	0.870	39813
39824	Ravensbourne East at Bromley South	540350 168550	10.18	75.1	290.4	0.341	8.06	33.8	44.1	11.2	698	49.30	0.867	0.750	39824
39827	Pool at Selworthy Road	536900 172050	37.77	58.4	10.3	0.313	10.99	33.7	43.3	11.1	658	44.55	0.882	0.949	39827
39830	Beck at Rectory Road														39830
39831	Chaffinch Brook at Beckenham														39831
39834	Brent at Hanwell														39834
40003	Medway at Teston	570650 152850	1258.80	73.4	81.9	0.049	65.78	33.3	44.3	11.7	755	35.85	0.611	0.968	40003
40004	Rother at Udiam	577450 124650	205.36	80.6	112.8	0.112	31.20	36.6	48.8	11.6	861	35.61	0.517	0.980	40004
40005	Beult at Stile Bridge	575950 147800	278.14	44.7	271.4	0.033	34.10	32.5	42.0	11.8	690	37.19	0.511	0.897	40005
40006	Bourne at Hadlow	563200 149550	50.21	97.7	155.8	0.208	16.32	33.6	44.7	11.9	733	35.58	0.564	1.044	40006
40007	Medway at Chafford Weir	551650 140650	252.41	108.3	28.0	0.062	29.24	34.8	47.2	11.7	852	35.47	0.605	1.229	40007
40008	Great Stour at Wye	605050 147150	226.07	76.9	205.4	0.162	35.37	33.7	44.0	11.9	750	37.69	0.664	0.721	40008
40009	Teise at Stone Bridge	571850 140050	134.43	93.1	50.5	0.114	22.50	35.0	47.9	11.8	809	35.52	0.549	1.220	40009
40010	Eden at Penshurst	552150 143850	224.88	82.6	137.0	0.107	33.56	32.9	44.1	11.4	764	35.33	0.630	1.006	40010
40011	Great Stour at Horton	611750 155550	341.29	83.9	188.8	0.044	50.83	34.4	45.4	12.0	761	37.69	0.662	0.822	40011
40012	Darent at Hawley	555250 171950	187.41	116.6	14.2	0.161	34.46	33.7	45.1	11.7	738	41.61	0.835	0.711	40012
40016	Cray at Crayford	551200 174450	125.52	96.7	10.0	0.274	24.55	34.0	43.6	11.4	686	47.59	0.203	1.042	40016
40017	Dudwell at Burwash	568050 124150	26.43	112.1	120.6	0.071	11.37	36.7	49.1	11.5	908	35.88			40017
40018	Darent at Lullingstone	552950 164200	117.11	129.9	37.7	0.091	23.38	34.3	46.5	11.7	773	37.06	0.596	0.874	40018
40020	Eridge Stream at Hendal Bridge	552050 136650	53.20	119.9	2.9	0.103	15.80	35.6	47.8	11.8	880	35.52	0.604	1.459	40020
40022	Great Stour at Chart Leacon	599350 142400	66.92	91.0	184.7	0.334	22.76	33.3	42.9	11.9	735	37.69	0.504	0.776	40022
40809	Pippingford Brook at Paygate	547800 134350	23.97	138.1	173.4	0.033	12.87	35.3	48.0	11.8	892	35.52			40809
41003	Cuckmere at Sherman Bridge	553250 105250	135.45	52.0	170.8	0.178	26.22	36.2	47.8	11.5	820	37.55	0.617	1.123	41003
41005	Ouse at Gold Bridge	542750 121500	182.26	76.9	176.6	0.160	29.18	35.9	47.5	11.7	836	35.20	0.690	0.976	41005
41006	Uck at Isfield	545900 118950	87.84	72.5	217.5	0.179	17.62	35.1	46.5	11.5	837	36.01	0.664	0.614	41006
41007	Arun at Park Mound	503700 121400	401.33	61.4	179.8	0.073	47.94	35.1	46.7	11.4	801	35.65	0.736	1.142	41007
41011	Rother at Iping Mill	485050 122850	157.02	91.0	125.8	0.125	26.98	39.7	51.0	10.2	935	37.25	0.501	1.076	41011
41012	Adur E Branch at Sakeham	521950 119150	93.97	48.7	244.3	0.098	23.14	37.6	48.2	11.6	823	36.05	0.785	1.127	41012
41014	Arun at Pallingham Quay	504550 122950	383.59	63.1	176.2	0.083	45.09	35.0	46.7	11.4	800	35.67	0.742	1.125	41014

Number	Name	IHDTM NGR		AREA km²	ALTBAR m	ASPBAR degrees	ASPVAR	LDP km	RMED-1D mm	RMED-2D mm	RMED-1H mm	SAAR₄₁₇₀ mm	SMDBAR mm	URBCONC	URBLOC	Number
41015	Ems at Westbourne	475450	107250	57.93	97.1	197.3	0.352	17.02	40.0	50.7	10.0	959	37.63	0.481	0.813	41015
41016	Cuckmere at Cowbeech	561150	115150	18.54	90.6	178.9	0.344	8.27	37.1	48.7	11.5	837	37.16	0.449	1.355	41016
41018	Kird at Tanyards	504350	125750	67.14	50.3	115.8	0.182	20.39	36.3	47.9	11.2	812	36.53			41018
41020	Bevern Stream at Clappers Bridge	542150	116450	35.23	51.4	52.0	0.258	14.52	37.1	49.0	11.5	881	37.34	0.448	1.122	41020
41021	Clayhill Stream at Old Ship	544850	115300	7.09	20.7	252.5	0.244	6.47	35.3	45.8	11.4	803	37.76			41021
41022	Lod at Halfway Bridge	493250	122350	52.22	82.1	147.4	0.152	18.27	38.5	49.3	10.9	886	37.23	0.407	0.474	41022
41023	Lavant at Graylingwell	487550	106350	86.63	121.8	191.1	0.203	21.14	40.6	50.9	10.3	964	37.63	0.353	0.828	41023
41025	Loxwood Stream at Drungewick	505850	130750	93.81	69.2	113.8	0.153	27.60	36.1	48.7	11.6	806	36.39	0.438	0.809	41025
41026	Cockhaise Brook at Holywell	537650	126250	36.10	100.4	206.1	0.274	10.35	35.4	47.2	11.7	849	35.17	0.431	0.553	41026
41027	Rother at Princes Marsh	477150	127050	37.57	109.3	127.1	0.038	10.68	39.1	50.3	10.4	932	37.23			41027
41028	Chess Stream at Chess Bridge	521850	117400	24.96	43.1	334.0	0.332	11.39	36.5	46.9	11.4	847	37.26	0.565	0.972	41028
41801	Hollington Stream at Hollington	578800	110050	3.47	69.7	203.8	0.351	4.19	33.2	44.3	11.1	778	37.76	0.902	0.985	41801
41806	North End Stream at Allington	538400	113800	2.32	77.6	37.8	0.568	2.41	37.4	49.7	11.5	951	37.26			41806
41807	Bevern Stream at East Chiltington	536650	115200	5.95	82.3	31.9	0.521	4.32	38.1	50.9	11.6	963	37.26	1.014		41807
42001	Wallington at North Fareham	458700	107650	112.18	69.6	199.2	0.268	23.83	35.2	45.8	9.2	865	37.75	0.638	1.043	42001
42005	Wallop Brook at Broughton	431100	132900	53.61	87.1	131.7	0.221	12.11	32.8	43.9	10.6	801	36.46	0.454	0.922	42005
42006	Meon at Mislingford	459050	114150	72.75	114.3	244.1	0.149	24.74	36.7	49.5	9.6	927	37.42			42006
42007	Alre at Drove Lane	457550	132600	57.40	125.7	251.5	0.279	12.80	35.5	46.8	10.3	878	37.08	0.452	0.513	42007
42008	Cheriton Stream at Sewards Bridge	457250	132350	74.28	120.8	292.1	0.144	21.61	37.0	48.9	9.9	922	36.90			42008
42009	Candover Stream at Borough Bridge	456950	132450	71.99	139.4	234.8	0.116	25.42	34.3	43.3	10.6	875	36.94			42009
42010	Itchen at Highbridge	446800	121150	342.26	108.3	239.6	0.116	50.00	34.7	45.2	10.1	872	36.76	0.549	0.567	42010
42011	Hamble at Frog Mill	452150	114900	56.33	77.0	221.4	0.349	14.90	33.7	46.1	9.5	875	38.23	0.455	0.731	42011
42012	Anton at Fullerton	437900	139450	186.13	113.4	159.9	0.274	28.99	32.8	41.7	10.7	802	36.46	0.622	0.740	42012
42014	Blackwater at Ower	432850	117250	102.51	59.7	124.0	0.179	18.69	35.7	46.3	10.7	868	37.61	0.323	0.878	42014
42017	Hermitage at Havant	471100	106900	16.93	38.1	165.8	0.359	7.85	35.8	45.1	9.1	832	37.63	0.736	0.890	42017
43001	Avon at Ringwood	414050	105250	1616.64	124.3	144.3	0.142	103.35	33.6	44.2	10.7	842	35.88	0.549	0.920	43001
43002	Stour at Ensbury	408950	96250	1052.35	92.2	132.6	0.126	99.14	35.5	45.9	10.8	901	34.99	0.586	0.660	43002
43003	Avon at East Mills Flume	416250	115250	1455.28	130.2	143.9	0.136	88.79	33.4	43.8	10.7	838	35.81	0.557	0.870	43003
43004	Bourne at Laverstock Mill	415750	130550	165.03	130.7	177.1	0.143	46.57	32.4	40.9	10.7	788	36.36	0.525	0.739	43004
43005	Avon at Amesbury	415050	141450	326.46	134.5	176.5	0.163	47.63	31.0	40.5	10.4	768	35.28	0.538	0.938	43005
43006	Nadder at Wilton Park	409950	130850	215.69	138.3	125.0	0.147	33.10	35.6	46.2	10.9	943	35.91	0.348	0.790	43006
43007	Stour at Throop Mill	411750	95850	1063.99	91.4	131.3	0.127	103.77	35.5	45.9	10.8	900	35.00	0.618	0.608	43007
43008	Wylye at South Newton	408450	134450	447.95	144.0	119.5	0.159	49.71	33.7	45.8	10.9	845	35.83	0.570	0.907	43008
43009	Stour at Hammoon	382050	114550	519.04	100.1	108.3	0.073	44.83	34.6	44.3	10.8	894	33.62	0.512	0.970	43009
43010	Allen at Loverley Mill	400750	108550	94.86	111.9	166.8	0.301	20.04	34.9	46.7	10.6	942	36.29			43010
43012	Wylye at Norton Bavant	390750	142950	114.07	167.6	101.2	0.203	24.39	34.9	47.8	11.0	949	35.59	0.679	0.504	43012
43014	East Avon at Upavon	413350	156000	85.82	144.6	206.9	0.220	18.10	31.1	41.7	10.2	788	35.08	0.481	0.908	43014
43017	West Avon at Upavon															43017
43018	Allen at Walford Mill	400950	100650	171.64	88.5	157.0	0.271	31.82	35.2	46.6	10.5	921	36.32			43018
44002	Piddle at Baggs Mill	391200	87750	183.76	105.4	143.9	0.213	37.59	37.0	48.9	11.0	1004	33.85			44002
44003	Asker at Bridport	346850	92650	48.69	99.7	250.7	0.160	12.31	38.4	47.6	11.1	980	32.55	0.554	0.304	44003
44004	Frome at Dorchester Total	370950	90300	197.61	154.3	124.2	0.124	31.19	39.9	51.4	11.3	1077	32.55	0.513	0.382	44004
44006	Sydling Water at Sydling St Nicholas	363300	99550	12.16	187.9	170.6	0.172	6.34	40.8	51.5	11.5	1098	32.55			44006
44008	Sth Winterbourne at W'bourne Steepleton	362850	89850	19.89	161.0	118.5	0.216	9.90	39.3	50.1	11.3	1045	32.55			44008
44009	Wey at Broadwey															44009
45001	Exe at Thorverton	293600	101750	600.03	246.3	163.3	0.141	76.10	42.3	57.6	11.8	1307	19.64			45001
45002	Exe at Stoodleigh	294250	117650	420.87	283.8	167.6	0.150	55.44	45.8	62.3	12.1	1421	18.09			45002
45003	Culm at Wood Mill	302100	105950	228.69	153.4	232.3	0.054	29.70	36.0	47.0	11.1	996	28.71			45003
45004	Axe at Whitford	326250	95400	288.58	137.6	124.9	0.035	36.06	40.1	51.9	11.4	1053	29.75			45004
45005	Otter at Dotton	308700	88550	202.52	143.8	195.8	0.108	39.89	38.4	49.5	11.4	1016	29.18	0.778	0.822	45005

Number	URBLOC	URBCONC	SMDBAR mm	SAAR₄₁₇₀ mm	RMED-1H mm	RMED-2D mm	RMED-1D mm	LDP km	ASPVAR	ASPBAR degrees	ALTBAR m	AREA km²	IHDTM NGR	Name	Number
45006			16.34	1525	12.2	67.3	50.2	11.18	0.265	176.3	328.6	20.25	292000	Quarme at Enterwell	45006
45008	0.577	0.819	29.18	1070	11.5	52.2	40.4	26.31	0.098	181.0	179.5	110.20	311500	Otter at Fenny Bridges	45008
45009			17.20	1446	12.2	65.5	47.7	35.76	0.204	185.1	309.2	147.81	293450	Exe at Pixton	45009
45011			16.34	1671	12.9	69.4	52.4	40.13	0.171	152.7	346.6	128.01	292700	Barle at Brushford	45011
45012			22.28	968	11.3	46.0	33.9	29.90	0.103	114.8	124.4	263.55	289950	Creedy at Cowley	45012
45801			29.18	908	11.2	46.4	35.0	2.22	0.364	126.3	127.6	2.45	305950	Back Brook at Hawkerland	45801
46002			22.20	1226	12.4	64.6	47.9	49.88	0.128	91.7	214.7	377.61	285450	Teign at Preston	46002
46003			21.83	1706	13.8	83.1	63.1	38.03	0.148	131.0	327.1	248.90	274950	Dart at Austins Bridge	46003
46005			22.11	2013	14.2	91.2	67.1	13.27	0.256	144.6	458.3	22.29	265750	East Dart at Bellever	46005
46006	0.401	0.555	21.86	1727	13.5	76.8	58.3	20.27	0.295	205.9	272.4	43.69	264250	Erme at Ermington	46006
46007			21.48	1894	14.2	87.9	66.2	14.25	0.237	142.4	424.1	47.47	264450	West Dart at Dunnabridge	46007
46008			21.86	1600	13.0	70.8	53.5	31.71	0.176	154.2	203.5	102.73	271900	Avon at Loddiswell	46008
46801			21.86	2045	15.1	96.7	73.5	7.65	0.247	186.1	424.3	14.64	264000	Erme at Erme Intake	46801
46806			21.86	2152	14.9	94.0	71.9	8.93	0.209	164.0	428.8	14.21	268100	Avon at Avon Intake	46806
47001			18.35	1239	12.2	52.7	40.1	71.05	0.031	220.0	155.1	920.01	242450	Tamar at Gunnislake	47001
47004	0.759	0.594	20.89	1502	12.4	61.0	45.5	34.83	0.075	128.5	175.2	135.37	236850	Lynher at Pillaton Mill	47004
47005			18.52	1207	12.2	53.9	39.0	27.35	0.136	75.3	147.7	121.51	233450	Ottery at Werrington Park	47005
47006	0.511	0.593	17.81	1300	12.3	53.8	41.6	24.28	0.193	269.1	187.8	220.33	238950	Lyd at Lifton Park	47006
47007			21.46	1481	12.5	63.2	48.1	18.56	0.290	196.6	168.5	56.42	257550	Yealm at Puslinch	47007
47008			17.78	1227	12.0	49.1	38.5	20.57	0.172	227.2	162.8	112.71	239850	Thrushel at Tinhay	47008
47009	1.578	0.557	20.92	1349	11.8	55.2	41.7	15.77	0.199	151.7	109.2	37.37	234400	Tiddy at Tideford	47009
47010	0.717	0.494	17.78	1204	12.4	49.1	37.8	24.12	0.164	192.8	145.0	77.47	228950	Tamar at Crowford Bridge	47010
47011	0.332	0.584	21.02	1587	13.3	68.0	54.1	20.00	0.296	249.1	277.6	79.56	252250	Plym at Carn Wood	47011
47014			20.72	1661	13.2	70.3	54.7	17.14	0.349	244.3	318.6	44.07	251400	Walkham at Horrabridge	47014
48001			21.84	1784	12.8	68.1	48.9	15.70	0.151	176.2	269.1	36.78	222550	Fowey at Trekeivesteps	48001
48002			23.20	1505	12.1	62.2	44.3	38.78	0.164	191.1	193.8	171.12	210850	Fowey at Restormel	48002
48003	1.019	0.541	23.86	1234	11.8	56.7	42.4	27.62	0.154	242.4	126.6	89.08	192200	Fal at Tregony	48003
48004			23.86	1518	12.2	63.4	44.2	12.40	0.209	206.1	218.6	25.21	215850	Warleggan at Trengoffe	48004
48005	0.449	0.853	27.09	1107	11.0	49.2	36.0	8.83	0.191	114.4	82.4	19.09	182150	Kenwyn at Truro	48005
48006	0.315	0.739	24.34	1206	11.5	53.6	41.7	13.52	0.203	189.2	137.6	40.27	165550	Cober at Helston	48006
48007	0.610	0.631	24.34	1297	11.6	57.1	43.7	10.97	0.237	79.4	161.6	26.65	176050	Kennall at Ponsanooth	48007
48009			23.86	1617	12.2	64.0	45.0	13.38	0.326	186.7	231.4	22.86	218400	St Neot at Craigshill Wood	48009
48010	1.395	0.580	20.92	1400	11.9	56.5	42.2	15.15	0.208	170.5	135.5	38.49	229950	Seaton at Trebrownbridge	48010
48011			23.18	1510	12.1	62.3	44.3	37.15	0.166	190.6	196.4	167.36	209950	Fowey at Restormel Ii	48011
49001			23.18	1357	12.1	59.2	42.9	33.63	0.156	257.8	174.1	209.76	201750	Camel at Denby	49001
49002	0.562	0.682	24.34	1044	11.2	47.4	38.1	16.16	0.192	267.9	80.2	48.57	154850	Hayle at St Erth	49002
49003	0.969	0.429	23.34	1725	12.9	66.3	47.7	7.70	0.165	245.3	283.1	21.70	213250	De Lank at De Lank	49003
49004			23.86	1061	11.1	46.5	34.6	11.20	0.157	295.3	78.3	40.96	182750	Gannel at Gwills	49004
50001	1.292	0.512	19.73	1191	11.9	51.6	38.3	61.23	0.071	219.9	181.8	832.32	260800	Taw at Umberleigh	50001
50002			18.46	1207	12.4	52.7	39.8	70.92	0.061	356.0	160.0	664.15	249950	Torridge at Torrington	50002
50005			18.12	2199	13.9	89.2	64.1	9.71	0.199	296.9	503.4	13.30	255800	West Okement at Vellake	50005
50006			16.53	1358	12.1	55.3	42.3	32.27	0.171	216.3	210.1	327.64	266050	Mole at Woodleigh	50006
50007			22.28	1225	12.2	57.1	41.2	27.71	0.215	15.8	233.8	72.13	267300	Taw at Taw Bridge	50007
50810			21.79	1119	11.5	48.3	35.2	28.92	0.144	210.1	186.3	125.96	267050	Little Dart at Dart Bridge	50810
51001	0.567	0.573	35.33	981	11.4	48.5	37.3	14.69	0.141	0.8	144.7	74.38	308850	Doniford Stream at Swill Bridge	51001
51002			16.34	1444	12.5	68.4	50.9	12.03	0.287	23.9	340.6	20.49	289850	Horner Water at West Luccombe	51002
51003			27.14	1234	11.8	59.8	44.0	11.94	0.202	35.7	253.1	36.43	303950	Washford at Beggearn Huish	51003
52003	0.587	0.659	35.33	887	11.2	47.0	35.7	19.06	0.296	158.8	108.8	93.55	320500	Halse Water at Bishops Hull	52003
52004	1.126	0.793	29.19	937	11.4	51.2	39.1	17.39	0.265	31.4	93.0	87.42	335950	Isle at Ashford Mill	52004
52005	0.648	0.828	34.09	991	11.1	48.8	36.2	39.93	0.178	68.2	143.8	203.63	320450	Tone at Bishops Hull	52005

Number	Name	IHDTM NGR	AREA km²	ALTBAR m	ASPBAR degrees	ASPVAR	LDP km	RMED-1D mm	RMED-2D mm	RMED-1H mm	SAAR$_{4170}$ mm	SMDBAR mm	URBCONC	URBLOC	Number
52006	Yeo at Pen Mill	357350	216.17	95.3	55.1	0.072	29.31	37.6	46.9	11.2	903	32.58	0.708	0.642	52006
52007	Parrett at Chiselborough	346000	74.43	72.9	11.5	0.214	13.77	41.8	51.3	11.6	888	32.55	0.790	0.886	52007
52009	Sheppey at Fenny Castle	349650	58.61	141.9	224.4	0.370	20.55	37.9	49.7	11.2	951	32.93	0.650	0.939	52009
52010	Brue at Lovington	359150	139.52	104.7	218.3	0.167	22.44	34.1	44.2	10.7	882	32.93	0.492	0.804	52010
52011	Cary at Somerton	349900	84.83	37.7	214.9	0.095	24.68	31.1	40.3	10.5	756	32.93	0.506	0.663	52011
52014	Tone at Greenham	307800	57.34	240.3	137.2	0.211	20.70	37.8	52.6	11.3	1157	35.11			52014
52015	Land Yeo at Wraxall Bridge														52015
52016	Currypool Stream at Currypool Farm	322000	15.72	181.1	63.1	0.457	8.93	36.6	48.2	11.5	969	35.33			52016
52017	Congresbury Yeo at Iwood	345050	60.64	111.7	325.7	0.233	16.26	37.5	48.9	11.1	964	32.95	0.528	0.793	52017
52020	Gallica Stream at Gallica Bridge	357050	16.44	119.1	0.0	0.261	7.05	41.0	50.2	11.5	1027	32.55			52020
52801	Tone at Wadhams Farm	305650	31.17	291.5	153.2	0.229	11.74	39.9	56.0	11.4	1234	35.33	0.658	0.753	52801
53001	Avon at Melksham	390400	668.05	103.1	120.2	0.114	66.55	33.0	42.1	10.3	795	32.99	0.626	1.139	53001
53002	Semington Brook at Semington	390550	153.62	89.4	316.7	0.103	23.81	30.3	40.1	10.2	756	35.09	0.662	0.820	53002
53003	Avon at Bath St Janes	375400	1611.04	109.2	84.9	0.100	97.35	34.3	44.6	10.6	840	33.46	0.483	0.871	53003
53004	Chew at Compton Dando	364900	129.10	119.6	28.8	0.240	29.19	38.6	51.0	11.2	957	32.95	0.626	1.070	53004
53005	Midford Brook at Midford	376350	147.40	125.3	52.4	0.151	23.25	37.9	50.9	11.2	971	32.93	0.759	0.796	53005
53006	Frome(bristol) at Frenchay	363850	150.61	73.5	288.2	0.098	26.77	34.4	46.9	10.6	795	32.97	0.646	0.772	53006
53007	Frome(somerset) at Tellisford	156250	261.85	143.2	55.2	0.176	39.51	37.5	48.9	11.2	967	33.38	0.562	0.870	53007
53008	Avon at Great Somerford	396450	305.11	118.6	113.2	0.280	33.57	33.0	42.0	10.3	835	32.99	0.623	0.964	53008
53009	Wellow Brook at Wellow	374000	73.47	135.3	46.2	0.221	17.79	38.2	52.1	11.3	1020	32.93			53009
53013	Marden at Stanley	172750	99.28	110.2	279.5	0.123	18.29	32.7	42.1	10.3	770	32.99	0.593	0.953	53013
53017	Boyd at Bitton	169650	47.88	110.7	270.1	0.238	15.45	35.8	46.6	10.8	806	32.97	0.631	0.860	53017
53018	Avon at Bathford	167000	1567.16	108.6	83.5	0.101	92.01	34.3	44.5	10.6	840	33.47	0.662	0.818	53018
53019	Woodbridge Brook at Crab Mill	186600	46.57	94.1	254.4	0.095	17.68	32.5	40.7	10.0	757	32.99			53019
53020	Gauze Brook at Rodbourne														53020
53023	Sherston Avon at Fosseway														53023
53025	Mells at Vallis	375850	118.04	178.5	70.2	0.261	27.39	39.5	51.8	11.4	1060	32.93	0.490	0.834	53025
54001	Severn at Bewdley	276300	4330.14	175.1	95.4	0.071	216.81	34.4	44.2	9.9	934	26.09	0.629	0.675	54001
54002	Avon at Evesham	404000	2200.66	99.2	291.1	0.035	130.05	32.9	40.9	11.0	672	41.63	0.737	1.039	54002
54003	Vyrnwy at Vyrnwy Reservoir														54003
54004	Sowe at Stoneleigh	433200	263.29	103.7	144.3	0.194	33.19	33.0	42.0	10.8	690	41.44	0.836	0.837	54004
54005	Severn at Montford	341050	2035.27	248.4	99.0	0.099	115.93	38.9	50.8	9.7	1161	18.00			54005
54006	Stour at Kidderminster	383050	311.45	113.4	250.4	0.078	41.56	31.2	38.8	10.7	700	38.61	0.824	1.158	54006
54007	Arrow at Broom	408700	312.20	102.3	154.0	0.154	34.92	32.4	41.6	10.7	694	44.40	0.661	0.981	54007
54008	Teme at Tenbury	359800	1123.29	231.1	141.6	0.118	80.48	33.4	44.3	10.2	878	29.35	0.515	0.728	54008
54010	Stour at Alscot Park	420650	316.96	122.0	1.1	0.114	42.72	34.2	41.9	10.9	678	39.27	0.567	0.985	54010
54011	Salwarpe at Harford Mill	386850	186.20	82.5	209.2	0.234	28.99	30.7	37.0	10.6	675	44.67	0.712	1.034	54011
54012	Tern at Walcot	359050	851.85	92.6	245.1	0.040	52.55	29.2	36.6	9.7	718	35.00	0.613	0.776	54012
54013	Clywedog at Cribynau	294350	57.00	374.3	100.8	0.193	20.62	59.9	78.6	11.9	1728	9.36			54013
54014	Severn at Abermule	316550	574.09	287.7	75.0	0.100	60.87	42.7	54.9	10.0	1232	15.01			54014
54016	Roden at Rodington	358900	261.90	89.6	119.3	0.105	46.37	29.0	36.5	9.4	712	35.19	0.520	0.865	54016
54017	Leadon at Wedderburn Bridge														54017
54018	Rea Brook at Hookagate	346750	170.09	180.7	47.9	0.190	30.07	32.0	41.0	9.7	778	24.82	0.756	0.823	54018
54019	Avon at Stareton	309350	346.32	118.8	272.6	0.125	30.30	31.6	39.6	11.5	692	41.13			54019
54020	Perry at Yeaton	343250	183.18	102.3	128.7	0.116	34.16	29.0	37.5	9.2	776	24.45	0.532	1.130	54020
54022	Severn at Plynlimon Flume	285300	8.68	500.2	115.1	0.433	5.65	72.9	97.8	13.2	2251	9.36			54022
54023	Badsey Brook at Offenham	406150	94.26	78.1	314.9	0.378	16.21	32.5	41.8	10.9	681	41.80	0.644	0.787	54023
54024	Worfe at Burcote	374750	258.46	97.0	169.1	0.090	33.93	29.6	36.4	10.5	714	35.30	0.652	1.237	54024
54025	Dulas at Rhos-y-pentref	295150	52.78	342.7	358.6	0.099	14.82	42.2	55.5	10.1	1291	10.87			54025
54026	Chelt at Slate Mill	282400													54026

Number	Name	IHDTM	NGR	AREA (km²)	ALTBAR (m)	ASPBAR (degrees)	ASPVAR	LDP (km)	RMED-1D (mm)	RMED-2D (mm)	RMED-1H (mm)	SAAR4170 (mm)	SMDBAR (mm)	URBCONC	URBLOC
54027	Frome at Ebley Mill	383000	204550	197.11	178.9	153.8	0.128	29.29	35.2	46.6	10.4	888	35.33	0.582	0.558
54028	Vyrnwy at Llanymynech	325050	319600	780.29	291.6	125.3	0.136	68.03	42.3	56.4	9.9	1367	17.47		
54029	Teme at Knightsford Bridge	373400	255850	1482.28	212.5	132.3	0.120	114.75	33.6	44.2	10.4	853	31.39	0.503	0.842
54032	Severn at Saxons Lode	386350	239150	6853.22	169.6	115.4	0.072	265.52	33.7	43.4	10.1	879	29.55	0.706	0.624
54034	Dowles Brook at Dowles	376650	276500	42.07	128.2	75.8	0.125	14.09	33.1	44.2	11.2	758	38.57		
54036	Isbourne at Hinton On The Green	402400	240650	92.82	126.7	328.4	0.276	21.17	32.4	42.1	10.5	738	35.97	0.564	0.826
54038	Tanat at Llanyblodwel	325050	322550	229.86	329.4	138.2	0.183	34.20	41.1	56.4	9.8	1294	18.73		
54040	Meese at Tibberton	367850	320550	160.42	98.3	226.2	0.142	32.21	29.1	35.1	10.1	737	34.91	0.346	0.985
54041	Tern at Eaton On Tern	364850	323150	195.63	106.3	223.2	0.122	36.81	28.9	37.4	9.6	755	35.28	0.544	0.994
54043	Severn at Upton On Severn	386350	240050	6850.07	169.7	115.4	0.072	264.58	33.7	43.4	10.1	879	29.55	0.706	0.621
54044	Tern at Ternhill	363050	331450	95.70	125.0	251.6	0.159	26.21	29.7	38.9	9.7	794	35.28	0.608	0.796
54052	Bailey Brook at Ternhill	362950	331750	37.41	91.0	182.5	0.253	15.01	28.2	36.0	9.3	738	35.28	0.535	0.959
54057	Severn at Haw Bridge	385250	227750	9884.28	144.9	121.7	0.036	280.96	33.3	42.5	10.3	815	33.14	0.711	0.755
54058	Stoke Park Brook at Stoke Park	364500	326150	14.46	86.6	268.0	0.363	7.54	28.2	34.9	9.5	715	35.28	0.374	1.302
54059	Allford Brook at Allford	365550	322400	10.23	76.7	234.1	0.376	6.25	28.5	34.3	9.7	696	35.28		
54060	Potford Brook at Potford														
54061	Hodnet Brook at Hodnet														
54062	Stoke Brook at Stoke														
54065	Roden at Stanton	356350	324100	212.50	93.7	112.9	0.083	31.21	28.9	36.2	9.4	723	35.28	0.510	0.888
54088	Little Avon at Berkeley Kennels	368150	198800	133.45	93.2	308.3	0.073	25.59	32.8	44.2	10.3	823	32.97	0.580	0.914
54090	Tanllwyth at Tanllwyth Flume														
54091	Severn at Hafren Flume	287650	284350	3.48	528.0	132.1	0.408	4.43	73.0	98.1	13.4	2225	9.36		
54092	Hore at Hore Flume	287250	284550	3.19	511.4	93.7	0.477	4.14	73.2	98.0	13.2	2322	9.36		
55001	Wye at Cadora	353450	209150	4046.38	226.2	127.3	0.098	246.13	38.7	50.3	10.1	1053	16.85	0.571	0.657
55002	Wye at Belmont	348350	238750	1918.89	295.4	130.0	0.083	157.38	42.3	55.9	10.2	1262	24.15		
55003	Lugg at Lugwardine	354950	239900	879.60	190.2	125.6	0.141	85.74	34.3	43.6	10.0	885	29.32	0.522	0.697
55004	Irfon at Abernant	289050	289150	73.08	412.6	152.1	0.190	22.67	52.8	70.0	11.4	1905	9.46		
55005	Wye at Rhayader	297050	267450	165.00	392.3	117.6	0.105	36.41	53.1	70.6	11.1	1625	10.99		
55007	Wye at Erwood	308450	244350	1283.61	343.6	132.2	0.086	82.78	44.7	60.0	10.3	1413	14.63		
55008	Wye at Cefn Brwyn	283700	282800	10.56	495.8	142.8	0.362	5.74	75.3	101.4	13.2	2394	9.36		
55009	Monnow at Kentchurch	341750	224950	355.11	228.1	103.8	0.143	39.26	39.8	51.3	10.1	997	21.49		
55010	Wye at Pant Mawr	284350	282550	27.22	483.3	137.8	0.242	9.55	72.4	96.8	13.0	2327	9.36		
55011	Ithon at Llandewi	310500	268250	110.47	379.2	121.6	0.123	27.79	37.5	48.8	9.8	1175	20.90		
55012	Irfon at Cilmery	299450	250550	246.41	333.4	135.5	0.112	38.83	50.0	66.4	10.8	1640	9.52		
55013	Arrow at Titley Mill	332950	258500	125.83	302.6	103.0	0.201	27.23	37.5	48.7	9.8	1088	20.50		
55014	Lugg at Byton	336550	264850	202.85	298.3	122.8	0.188	31.18	36.1	47.3	9.8	1065	20.50		
55015	Honddu at Tafolog	327700	229250	24.97	521.2	154.8	0.114	10.27	46.5	60.9	10.6	1402	16.66		
55016	Ithon at Disserth	302550	257750	358.64	324.5	157.9	0.068	60.70	36.2	48.5	9.6	1128	20.57		
55017	Chwefru at Carreg-y-wen	299800	252950	29.01	323.9	115.7	0.301	13.41	44.3	59.8	10.1	1420	9.48		
55018	Frome at Yarkhill	361350	242700	143.85	137.8	173.9	0.128	34.71	32.9	41.6	10.6	729	38.79	0.507	0.978
55021	Lugg at Butts Bridge	350350	258900	365.13	232.3	135.0	0.197	52.22	35.0	44.9	10.0	951	26.60	0.549	0.471
55022	Trothy at Mitchel Troy	350150	211250	142.41	114.7	139.2	0.127	32.66	37.9	47.8	10.1	944	27.87		
55023	Wye at Redbrook	352750	211150	4016.49	226.7	127.2	0.099	243.65	38.7	50.3	10.1	1054	24.05	0.569	0.664
55025	Llynfi at Three Cocks	316550	237450	131.48	238.8	354.5	0.038	20.06	39.2	49.7	9.9	1000	16.66		
55026	Wye at Ddol Farm	297650	267450	172.68	387.4	124.2	0.104	37.16	52.6	69.9	11.1	1611	10.99		
55029	Monnow at Grosmont	341650	224900	355.14	228.1	103.8	0.142	39.38	39.8	51.3	10.1	997	21.49		
55030	Clearwyn at Dol Y Mynach	291150	262150	94.32	465.6	103.0	0.085	19.76	55.0	75.5	11.3	1881	9.46		
55033	Wye at Gwy Flume	282450	285350	3.80	557.2	146.2	0.489	3.54	75.9	102.0	13.5	2418	9.36		
55034	Cyff at Cyff Flume	282250	284200	3.11	481.1	121.4	0.399	3.83	78.3	106.1	13.4	2414	9.36		
55035	Iago at Iago Flume	282500	285400	1.07	490.4	169.3	0.513	2.69	75.3	101.4	13.2	2374	9.36		

Number	Name	IHDTM NGR	AREA km²	ALTBAR m	ASPBAR degrees	ASPVAR	LDP km	RMED-1D mm	RMED-2D mm	RMED-1H mm	$SAAR_{170}$ mm	SMDBAR mm	URBCONC	URBLOC	Number
56001	Usk at Chain Bridge	334650 205600	925.30	312.5	111.0	0.069	91.69	50.3	66.5	11.1	1385	14.57			56001
56002	Ebbw at Rhiwderyn	325900 188750	212.29	316.1	183.1	0.181	41.40	52.7	70.0	11.8	1527	18.98	0.629	1.004	56002
56003	Honddu at The Forge Brecon	305000 229850	62.53	311.5	175.0	0.216	20.75	43.1	56.6	10.4	1252	16.32			56003
56004	Usk at Llandetty	312700 220450	556.56	328.2	104.6	0.067	52.41	52.3	70.3	11.4	1491	13.18			56004
56005	Lwyd at Ponthir	332850 192400	98.33	283.9	136.5	0.264	27.88	53.6	68.1	11.7	1468	18.95	0.709	0.670	56005
56006	Usk at Trallong	294550 229650	193.99	344.3	47.1	0.051	24.16	59.5	81.9	12.2	1663	11.24			56006
56007	Senni at Pont Hen Hafod	292950 225600	19.51	387.9	345.4	0.127	9.58	67.9	94.0	13.0	1942	11.25			56007
56011	Sirhowy at Wattsville	320450 191150	76.26	320.2	164.8	0.182	33.71	53.5	71.8	11.9	1537	18.80	0.636	0.950	56011
56012	Grwyne at Millbrook	324050 217500	82.50	431.5	147.2	0.154	25.05	46.1	58.9	10.4	1278	16.66			56012
56013	Yscir at Pontaryscir	300300 230550	63.31	350.3	149.8	0.178	22.03	45.5	59.5	10.7	1429	11.25			56013
56015	Olway Brook at Olway Inn	338550 201150	111.27	91.9	240.1	0.075	17.86	41.1	51.7	10.6	1002	33.17	0.638	1.079	56015
56019	Ebbw at Aberbeeg	320950 201350	71.82	380.9	185.0	0.207	18.87	53.0	70.1	11.5	1556	16.66	0.635	0.811	56019
57003	Taff at Tongwynlais	313150 181900	486.89	306.9	160.1	0.143	56.97	62.6	83.1	12.7	1813	17.44	0.617	0.802	57003
57004	Cynon at Abercynon	308050 195600	103.54	270.4	169.9	0.109	28.69	66.8	90.0	13.1	1766	14.77	0.639	0.742	57004
57005	Taff at Pontypridd	308050 189650	451.99	320.1	156.1	0.140	45.54	63.6	84.7	12.7	1842	17.05	0.638	0.705	57005
57006	Rhondda at Trehafod	305250 191000	102.57	328.6	117.2	0.163	24.93	71.8	94.9	13.7	2201	17.25	0.653	0.720	57006
57007	Taff at Fiddlers Elbow	308750 195150	194.06	367.4	179.5	0.200	37.80	58.4	78.7	12.0	1730	16.72	0.681	1.009	57007
57008	Rhymney at Llanedeyrn	322500 182250	184.64	225.5	154.2	0.173	51.49	50.6	66.6	11.9	1444	20.57			57008
57009	Ely at St Fagans	311950 177000	145.67	103.6	146.2	0.100	30.63	47.1	61.0	12.1	1403	22.17	0.677	1.168	57009
57010	Ely at Lanelay	303400 182550	38.99	171.9	148.6	0.223	12.79	55.5	70.1	12.8	1603	21.43	0.627	1.178	57010
57015	Taff at Merthyr Tydfil	304150 206800	111.28	430.5	175.3	0.226	20.91	60.5	82.4	12.1	1885	15.49	0.628	0.200	57015
57803	Clun at Cross Inn	305450 182500	26.40	116.7	210.9	0.159	9.18	48.9	61.9	12.2	1445	22.43	0.729	1.135	57803
58001	Ogmore at Bridgend	290300 179350	157.97	211.0	185.9	0.185	25.01	54.3	72.3	12.5	1844	16.92	0.649	0.784	58001
58002	Neath at Resolven	281450 201650	190.93	318.1	198.0	0.169	31.62	63.8	88.1	12.5	1975	11.29	0.642	0.650	58002
58003	Ewenny at Ewenny Priory	291550 178100	63.85	84.5	211.2	0.237	14.73	43.2	58.2	11.6	1374	17.22	0.652	0.739	58003
58004	Afan at Cwmavon	278200 192000	85.69	313.8	265.4	0.182	21.73	60.7	81.5	12.7	2093	16.21	0.513	0.733	58004
58005	Ogmore at Brynmenyn	290350 184350	74.32	268.1	191.8	0.219	16.19	59.5	78.8	12.9	2014	16.92	0.561	0.958	58005
58006	Mellte at Pontneddfechan	291350 208100	65.18	400.9	194.6	0.280	17.48	63.5	86.4	12.5	2111	11.25			58006
58007	Llynfi at Coytrahen	289250 185650	50.82	211.4	166.8	0.131	16.91	48.9	65.0	12.5	1866	16.92	0.655	1.152	58007
58008	Dulais at Cilfrew	277900 200950	43.36	229.1	257.5	0.196	15.55	51.8	73.6	11.5	1757	11.25	0.603	1.276	58008
58009	Ewenny at Keepers Lodge	292150 178250	63.25	85.1	211.2	0.237	14.07	43.3	58.2	11.6	1381	17.22	0.656	0.727	58009
58010	Hepste at Esgair Carnau	296900 213250	10.86	461.5	166.2	0.655	7.23	64.1	86.5	12.5	2162	11.25			58010
58011	Thaw at Gigman Bridge	301750 171600	49.20	67.5	221.4	0.113	17.70	39.9	53.3	11.6	1217	19.40	0.600	0.820	58011
59001	Tawe at Yynstanglws	268500 199900	227.71	286.9	195.7	0.263	38.73	58.0	81.0	12.1	1948	11.25	0.564	0.553	59001
59002	Loughor at Tir-y-dail	262300 212650	46.52	156.9	159.8	0.081	13.90	47.3	62.7	11.6	1602	13.18	0.569	0.594	59002
60002	Cothi at Felin Mynachdy	250850 222500	298.54	231.4	183.9	0.113	51.31	51.0	68.1	11.5	1637	13.66			60002
60003	Taf at Clog-y-fran	223950 215850	216.73	124.8	177.5	0.089	36.60	43.3	60.4	12.2	1410	21.72			60003
60004	Dewi Fawr at Glasfryn Ford	228950 217350	36.77	143.0	188.5	0.247	19.58	47.4	64.0	12.2	1507	17.23			60004
60005	Bran at Llandovery	277100 234300	63.78	252.5	207.7	0.227	19.58	48.9	64.0	10.8	1507	10.19			60005
60006	Gwili at Glangwili	242950 222050	130.98	188.1	194.1	0.136	26.09	51.9	70.2	12.3	1614	17.23			60006
60007	Tywi at Dolau Hirion	276200 236050	220.53	350.5	165.7	0.110	39.08	51.1	68.0	11.2	1744	9.63			60007
60009	Sawdde at Felin-y-cwm	271100 226750	79.10	307.8	321.6	0.316	16.61	56.6	78.5	12.3	1778	11.25			60009
60010	Tywi at Nantgaredig	248950 220400	1079.79	232.7	213.9	0.087	87.47	49.7	66.4	11.3	1587	12.02			60010
60012	Twrch at Ddol Las	265100 243900	19.78	304.9	191.9	0.204	12.17	49.4	66.2	11.2	1684	9.46			60012
60013	Cothi at Pont Ynys Brechfa	253550 230000	242.98	241.6	197.1	0.106	40.69	50.7	67.5	11.5	1636	12.84			60013
61001	Western Cleddau at Prendergast Mill	195250 217850	197.76	108.4	206.4	0.108	29.45	42.5	57.8	11.6	1282	24.96			61001
61002	Eastern Cleddau at Canaston Bridge	207050 215250	181.98	152.1	184.5	0.235	27.28	43.8	59.9	11.5	1447	24.96			61002
61003	Gwaun at Cilrhedyn Bridge	200400 235000	31.29	231.1	294.5	0.175	11.05	50.8	66.7	12.0	1468	24.96			61003
62001	Teifi at Glan Teifi	224550 241550	897.27	209.2	285.7	0.103	102.55	44.8	59.8	11.0	1361	15.79			62001
62002	Teifi at Llanfair	243450 240450	517.05	242.7	272.4	0.091	73.28	43.3	59.3	10.7	1414	14.06			62002

Number	Name	IHDTM NGR	AREA km²	ALTBAR m	ASPBAR degrees	ASPVAR	LDP km	RMED-1D mm	RMED-2D mm	RMED-1H mm	SAAR$_{4170}$ mm	SMDBAR mm	URBCONC	URBLOC
63001	Ystwyth at Pont Llolwyn	259250 277250	170.26	265.6	278.7	0.122	41.00	45.6	60.6	10.5	1501	9.87		
63002	Rheidol at Llanbadarn Fawr	260250 280450	182.90	340.2	259.5	0.142	44.21	52.2	69.1	11.0	1758	9.39		
63003	Wyre at Llanrhystyd	254350 269750	40.70	197.5	304.8	0.289	17.73	37.5	49.3	10.0	1256	14.66		
64001	Dyfi at Dyfi Bridge	274350 301900	464.56	281.2	222.2	0.071	39.92	58.4	75.6	11.1	1838	9.28		
64002	Dysynni at Pont-y-garth	263100 306550	75.20	313.1	206.6	0.203	18.54	67.0	90.7	11.8	2037	9.36		
64005	Wnion at Dolgellau	272850 317950	109.22	332.6	293.5	0.218	19.10	63.7	80.4	11.6	2066	8.31		
64006	Leri at Dolybont	263500 288050	47.24	261.2	263.7	0.234	17.26	42.8	57.2	10.0	1512	9.36		
65001	Glaslyn at Beddgelert	259200 347650	67.23	339.0	208.8	0.072	17.22	80.0	105.9	13.0	3030	10.37		
65002	Dwyryd at Maentwrog	267050 341400	78.15	336.2	236.0	0.156	11.99	69.5	95.7	12.3	2304	7.41	0.402	0.906
65004	Gwyrfai at Bontnewydd	248250 359900	46.17	294.0	267.8	0.286	18.77	62.9	81.0	11.7	2385	16.57		
65005	Erch at Pencaenewydd	240000 340550	19.47	177.0	179.0	0.500	11.94	47.5	61.2	9.9	1537	15.91		
65006	Seiont at Peblig Mill	249450 362300	80.15	320.9	301.8	0.244	22.14	65.1	87.5	12.0	2300	18.77	0.368	0.696
65007	Dwyfawr at Garndolbenmaen	249750 342800	52.01	267.5	217.2	0.246	13.18	64.3	85.2	12.0	2154	15.91		
66001	Clwyd at Pont-y-cambwll	307050 370950	404.60	206.5	14.6	0.091	42.96	34.8	45.9	9.6	911	25.63		
66002	Elwy at Pant Yr Onen	302150 370300	218.63	269.5	33.9	0.161	40.26	42.8	59.1	10.1	1084	12.89		
66003	Aled at Bryn Aled	295850 370150	69.99	309.9	13.7	0.192	19.60	41.3	58.4	10.0	1145	12.14		
66004	Wheeler at Bodfari	310600 371550	62.94	206.9	239.9	0.081	13.83	33.3	44.1	10.1	854	33.31		
66005	Clwyd at Ruthin Weir	312100 359050	96.12	234.3	47.3	0.178	26.43	35.0	46.3	9.3	957	18.95		
66006	Elwy at Pont-y-gwyddel	295350 371950	191.40	284.3	27.5	0.160	29.70	43.9	60.8	10.1	1128	12.31		
66011	Conwy at Cwm Llanerch	280300 358250	339.86	341.6	19.9	0.010	31.83	64.0	85.8	11.7	2165	7.61		
66801	Uppercorway at Blaen Y Coed													
67002	Dee at Erbistock Rectory	335850 341250	1028.67	334.7	82.4	0.090	93.25	43.9	59.0	10.2	1386	13.34		
67003	Brenig at Llyn Brenig Outflow	297500 354050	22.17	418.9	172.2	0.247	7.57	42.0	58.1	10.2	1301	7.55		
67005	Ceiriog at Brynkinalt Weir	329650 337250	111.94	384.7	98.7	0.186	30.21	41.7	55.3	12.0	1251	18.95		
67006	Alwen at Druid	304050 343600	185.40	356.6	128.5	0.098	30.17	46.7	56.2	10.0	1301	9.57		
67007	Dee at Glyndyfrdwy	315350 342850	729.08	357.1	56.3	0.046	56.65	35.0	63.2	10.3	1510	11.03		
67008	Alyn at Pont-y-capel	333450 353950	227.16	232.1	62.4	0.179	50.03	36.3	45.5	10.1	902	25.16	0.683	0.557
67009	Alyn at Rhydymwyn	320450 366550	82.50	303.0	38.6	0.123	26.57	61.9	47.5	10.0	960	24.46		
67010	Gelyn at Cynefail	284350 341950	12.89	423.1	234.6	0.020	7.42	32.1	84.4	12.2	2046	7.41		
67013	Hirnant at Plas Rhiwedog	294750 335050	32.58	434.0	334.9	0.247	10.61	47.8	66.0	10.5	1755	7.41		
67014	Dee at Corwen	306750 343150	656.90	362.5	77.7	0.046	45.49	47.8	64.9	10.4	1554	10.17		
67015	Dee at Manley Hall	334950 341350	1008.78	339.4	85.3	0.087	92.16	44.2	59.4	10.2	1397	13.23		
67018	Dee at New Inn	287450 330850	54.30	384.5	89.3	0.169	14.49	59.4	78.7	11.2	1930	7.41		
67019	Tryweryn at Weir X	293200 335900	111.33	392.9	123.4	0.109	22.16	58.6	80.3	11.6	1855	7.41		
67020	Dee at Chester Weir	341650 366400	1801.07	242.5	61.1	0.104	148.30	38.8	51.3	11.0	1133	19.51	0.663	0.541
67025	Clywedog at Bowling Bank	339450 348350	103.02	164.4	94.7	0.457	25.45	33.8	42.3	9.9	861	18.95	0.743	0.869
68001	Weaver at Ashbrook	366950 363150	622.68	79.4	11.7	0.069	58.76	29.8	39.4	9.5	765	34.90	0.721	0.760
68002	Gowy at Picton	344150 371550	152.04	51.2	293.5	0.173	33.36	28.7	39.1	9.9	723	34.76	0.499	0.917
68003	Dane at Rudheath	366950 371700	414.20	143.7	280.6	0.252	66.26	32.1	41.5	9.9	881	26.53	0.719	0.851
68004	Wistaston Brook at Marshfield Bridge	367550 355250	94.85	85.5	297.2	0.284	21.62	29.7	39.4	9.4	765	33.97	0.790	0.630
68005	Weaver at Audlem	365300 343250	202.54	88.5	63.0	0.078	27.89	29.6	38.6	9.4	756	35.28	0.553	0.849
68006	Dane at Hulme Walfield	384600 364250	151.10	262.0	260.4	0.207	33.91	36.6	45.8	10.4	1059	20.25	0.731	0.381
68007	Wincham Brook at Lostock Gralam	369550 375650	147.62	73.2	234.5	0.189	29.46	30.5	39.7	10.2	813	29.67	0.520	0.948
68010	Fender at Ford	327950 388150	17.59	44.6	7.9	0.212	8.91	30.0	38.9	10.4	784	33.31	0.849	0.827
68011	Arley Brook at Gore Farm	369750 379900	34.79	61.4	116.7	0.191	13.10	31.5	39.2	10.8	801	34.59	0.506	1.364
68014	Sandersons Brook at Sandbach													
68015	Gowy at Huxley	349850 362250	49.47	64.4	355.4	0.234	20.37	29.7	41.0	9.7	737	35.10	0.298	1.200
68018	Dane at Congleton Park	385950 363300	144.15	270.0	257.1	0.209	31.20	36.8	46.0	10.4	1070	20.27	0.705	0.355
68020	Gowy at Bridge Trafford	344650 371200	150.57	51.6	294.7	0.169	32.73	28.8	39.1	9.9	723	34.76	0.502	0.924
69001	Mersey at Irlam Weir	376800 393850	673.90	239.5	275.8	0.243	67.76	38.4	51.4	10.8	1103	19.13	0.751	0.584

Number	Name	IHDTM NGR	AREA km²	ALTBAR m	ASPBAR degrees	ASPVAR	LDP km	RMED-1D mm	RMED-2D mm	RMED-1H mm	SAAR4170 mm	SMDBAR mm	URBCONC	URBLOC	Number
69002	Irwell at Adelphi Weir	382450 398850	553.61	212.7	184.7	0.153	61.17	41.2	56.7	11.6	1254	17.33	0.762	0.821	69002
69003	Irk at Scotland Weir	384250 399200	73.18	115.3	229.2	0.353	20.56	36.2	49.5	11.0	1049	15.44	0.816	0.957	69003
69006	Bollin at Dunham Massey	372850 387450	257.22	123.9	302.2	0.253	44.02	31.7	42.4	10.3	862	23.90	0.656	1.071	69006
69007	Mersey at Ashton Weir	377350 393450	673.48	239.6	275.8	0.243	66.98	38.4	51.4	10.8	1103	19.12	0.751	0.576	69007
69008	Dean at Stanneylands														69008
69011	Micker Brook at Cheadle														69011
69012	Bollin at Wilmslow	384850 381550	67.89	183.6	319.1	0.238	22.67	33.5	43.6	10.3	923	19.73	0.735	1.010	69012
69013	Sinderland Brook at Partington	372700 390550	45.08	37.2	327.5	0.472	16.93	31.3	41.3	10.8	823	30.06	0.749	1.113	69013
69015	Etherow at Compstall	396050 390800	149.55	341.6	259.3	0.148	29.72	43.9	58.8	11.0	1312	18.73	0.650	0.656	69015
69017	Goyt at Marple Bridge	396400 389650	183.83	308.9	286.1	0.149	28.42	37.6	50.8	10.4	1142	19.73	0.521	0.780	69017
69018	Newton Brook at Newton Le Willows	358400 393300	32.25	49.4	143.5	0.315	16.86	34.4	46.5	11.6	908	32.19	0.774	1.016	69018
69019	Worsley Brook at Eccles	375350 397850	23.74	60.4	188.7	0.555	12.30	34.3	46.3	11.2	962	23.12	0.771	0.997	69019
69020	Medlock at London Road	384750 397550	52.72	153.6	233.2	0.426	21.42	38.0	51.7	11.2	1053	16.50	0.821	0.866	69020
69023	Roch at Blackford Bridge	380800 407850	187.63	223.1	216.2	0.194	33.00	42.1	57.9	11.4	1228	15.36	0.756	0.882	69023
69024	Croal at Farnworth Weir	374450 406950	142.80	200.7	157.6	0.215	23.54	41.5	56.4	12.0	1280	19.69	0.793	0.582	69024
69025	Irwell at Manchester Racecourse	382150 400250	551.78	213.3	185.4	0.154	58.90	41.2	56.7	11.6	1255	17.32	0.761	0.819	69025
69027	Tame at Portwood	390450 391900	146.60	258.0	254.8	0.278	44.58	42.4	56.3	12.1	1181	17.09	0.770	0.598	69027
69034	Musbury Brook at Helmshore	377400 421300	3.14	318.5	71.8	0.477	3.18	43.9	62.4	12.1	1474	19.69	0.665	0.731	69034
69035	Irwell at Bury Bridge	379800 411050	156.03	268.8	199.6	0.112	30.66	41.9	59.2	11.5	1342	17.16	0.593	0.823	69035
69040	Irwell at Stubbins	379150 418650	104.78	297.5	228.8	0.073	19.03	42.3	60.3	11.5	1383	16.74			69040
69041	Tame at Broomstair Bridge	393750 395450	115.71	294.9	250.5	0.257	32.28	44.5	58.9	11.6	1260	16.39	0.752	0.414	69041
69802	Etherow at Woodhead														69802
70002	Douglas at Wanes Blades Bridge														70002
70003	Douglas at Central Park Wigan														70003
70004	Yarrow at Croston Mill														70004
70005	Lostock at Littlewood Bridge	349550 419650	55.02	71.7	276.0	0.399	26.22	34.5	45.4	10.4	1014	19.69	0.763	0.757	70005
70006	Tawd at Newburgh	346900 410850	28.32	71.4	307.5	0.224	13.03	36.2	47.4	11.4	979	19.69	0.691	1.144	70006
71001	Ribble at Samlesbury	358950 430550	1146.10	219.6	222.7	0.078	97.11	43.9	59.5	10.9	1320	14.33	0.739	0.888	71001
71003	Croasdale at Croasdale Flume	370600 454750	10.66	345.4	148.2	0.348	5.99	55.3	75.4	12.0	1794	12.50			71003
71004	Calder at Whalley Weir	373050 436000	317.11	221.2	291.8	0.147	39.95	40.6	55.1	10.8	1211	16.43	0.769	0.842	71004
71005	Bottoms Beck at Bottoms Beck Flume	374500 456500	10.64	289.1	193.6	0.218	7.57	47.3	62.8	11.4	1458	12.50			71005
71006	Ribble at Henthorn	372100 439050	448.05	237.4	197.7	0.096	70.15	43.1	59.0	10.8	1340	12.36	0.665	0.584	71006
71007	Ribble at Hodderfoot	370950 437750	716.09	238.3	186.8	0.103	72.28	45.9	62.6	11.0	1407	12.59			71007
71008	Ribble at Hodder Place	370550 439950	258.39	245.2	165.9	0.131	41.10	50.9	69.0	11.4	1533	12.73			71008
71009	Ribble at Jumbles Rock	370750 437750	1049.08	230.8	226.9	0.073	74.28	44.2	60.2	11.0	1343	13.86	0.748	0.754	71009
71010	Pendle Water at Barden Lane	383600 435250	110.00	253.3	259.5	0.101	20.95	42.4	56.9	10.8	1236	14.03	0.746	0.563	71010
71011	Ribble at Arnford	384050 455600	203.87	318.9	202.7	0.101	39.84	45.0	61.8	11.1	1490	12.06			71011
71013	Darwen at Ewood Bridge	367650 426350	39.19	229.7	320.1	0.250	9.98	43.8	60.3	11.9	1335	19.69	0.674	0.759	71013
71014	Darwen at Blue Bridge	356650 427700	135.51	162.2	312.1	0.240	29.13	40.3	53.8	11.1	1155	19.69	0.744	1.158	71014
71802	Ribble at Halton West	385100 455200	206.68	316.6	200.1	0.098	41.11	44.9	61.7	11.1	1483	12.07			71802
71803	Hodder at Higher Hodder Bridge	369750 440950	254.97	247.1	167.2	0.129	39.14	51.0	69.2	11.5	1537	12.71			71803
72001	Lune at Halton	350250 464700	993.39	273.1	286.8	0.107	77.46	50.4	68.2	11.5	1522	9.69			72001
72002	Wyre at St Michaels	346450 441050	276.56	146.9	250.6	0.365	37.36	41.6	54.0	10.7	1253	14.37	0.633	0.688	72002
72004	Lune at Caton	352950 465450	984.20	275.1	286.7	0.108	73.49	50.5	68.4	11.5	1525	9.67			72004
72005	Lune at Killington New Bridge	362250 490850	219.03	317.0	107.3	0.030	34.80	55.1	78.2	12.0	1625	7.24			72005
72006	Lune at Kirkby Lonsdale	361500 477950	510.31	315.6	275.9	0.081	53.04	54.5	75.0	11.9	1622	7.34			72006
72009	Wenning at Wennington Road Bridge	361350 470200	140.12	226.5	351.7	0.069	26.53	42.7	57.9	10.8	1318	12.50			72009
72011	Rawthey at Brigg Flatts	363750 491150	195.88	365.1	290.0	0.139	27.27	57.5	78.0	12.1	1698	7.24			72011
72013	Borrowbeck at Borrow Bridge Weir	360750 501450	26.10	389.2	106.2	0.211	16.43	59.2	84.2	12.4	2014	7.24			72013
72014	Conder at Galgate	348250 455350	28.56	133.6	273.1	0.321	13.54	40.2	51.3	10.6	1280	12.50			72014

Number	Name	IHDTM NGR	AREA km²	ALTBAR m	ASPBAR degrees	ASPVAR	LDP km	RMED-1D mm	RMED-2D mm	RMED-1H mm	SAAR₄₁₇₀ mm	SMDBAR mm	URBCONC	URBLOC	Number
72015	Lune at Lunes Bridge	361300	502750	141.01	317.7	42.7	0.067	19.81	55.4	80.0	12.1	1586	7.24			72015
72016	Wyre at Scorton Weir	349950	450100	88.44	242.1	239.0	0.320	22.10	48.6	62.3	11.3	1500	12.50			72016
72803	Lune at Halton Upper Weir	351450	464900	991.03	273.7	287.1	0.107	76.10	50.5	68.3	11.5	1523	9.69			72803
72804	Lune at Broadraine	362150	489950	219.91	316.1	108.2	0.032	35.82	55.1	78.1	12.0	1624	7.24			72804
72807	Wenning at Hornby	358450	468400	230.27	234.8	338.5	0.180	30.75	45.4	61.3	11.1	1422	12.50			72807
73001	Leven at Newby Bridge	337200	486450	241.44	234.5	176.0	0.131	35.42	67.5	93.1	12.7	2234	6.95			73001
73002	Crake at Low Nibthwaite	329450	488300	73.13	212.3	145.2	0.213	18.64	61.4	85.0	12.2	2147	6.89			73002
73005	Kent at Sedgwick	350900	487550	212.38	235.0	181.6	0.155	32.98	54.1	74.7	11.5	1756	7.24	0.650	0.431	73005
73008	Bela at Beetham	349600	480450	132.15	131.6	248.0	0.200	27.73	43.6	56.5	10.5	1302	8.42			73008
73009	Sprint at Sprint Mill	351300	495950	34.46	328.6	158.6	0.187	18.27	60.9	86.1	12.2	2103	7.24			73009
73011	Mint at Mint Bridge	352350	494400	65.72	230.4	215.9	0.160	19.63	50.5	69.3	11.1	1671	7.24			73011
73013	Rothay at Miller Bridge House	337100	504050	59.92	334.9	194.1	0.180	15.65	71.0	98.5	13.1	2425	6.90			73013
73014	Brathay at Jeffy Knotts	336150	503400	56.69	288.9	91.9	0.160	15.53	84.2	122.0	14.4	2864	6.89			73014
73015	Keer at High Keer Weir															73015
73803	Winster at Lobby Bridge	342300	488550	22.20	100.6	143.4	0.112	11.79	49.5	65.0	11.1	1508	7.22			73803
73805	Kent at Kendal (nether Bridge)	351700	492050	193.31	249.6	181.6	0.159	26.74	55.1	76.3	11.6	1801	7.24	0.652	0.207	73805
74001	Duddon at Duddon Hall	319550	489550	85.69	315.0	157.0	0.087	21.41	62.3	83.9	12.7	2361	6.89			74001
74002	Irt at Galesyke	313450	503850	43.94	374.5	230.6	0.167	17.20	81.3	114.3	14.1	2731	6.89			74002
74005	Ehen at Braystones	300850	506250	128.52	220.3	243.7	0.171	36.01	51.7	69.3	11.7	1851	7.59	0.666	0.556	74005
74006	Calder at Calder Hall	303450	504350	43.10	282.6	241.5	0.356	15.44	48.1	63.0	11.5	1902	6.89			74006
75002	Derwent at Camerton	303650	530450	659.37	270.8	302.0	0.109	71.03	54.5	73.1	11.7	1912	10.79			75002
75004	Cocker at Southwaite Bridge	313250	527950	116.78	300.6	310.2	0.129	27.37	56.1	76.5	11.9	2161	10.12			75004
75005	Derwent at Portinscale	325250	523800	235.85	363.0	321.9	0.095	31.51	66.5	90.0	12.6	2380	9.63			75005
75006	Newlands Beck at Braithwaite	323950	524050	33.81	353.7	42.5	0.252	12.02	63.3	84.7	12.4	2377	9.43			75006
75007	Glenderamackin at Threlkeld	332150	524800	62.99	353.8	347.0	0.153	18.10	56.0	75.2	11.5	1837	12.44			75007
75009	Greta at Low Briery	328450	524100	145.56	376.3	321.5	0.085	27.18	60.7	81.3	12.0	2128	10.67			75009
75010	Marron at Ullock	307400	523900	26.85	206.1	307.8	0.335	9.84	44.3	59.3	10.9	1726	10.41			75010
75017	Ellen at Bullgill	309750	538550	102.25	164.5	321.1	0.311	29.84	39.9	51.5	10.7	1157	12.44			75017
76002	Eden at Warwick Bridge	347100	556550	1375.72	284.2	323.0	0.075	105.29	42.8	58.4	10.9	1327	9.37			76002
76003	Eamont at Udford	357650	530450	407.92	332.8	48.0	0.170	46.97	54.5	75.3	11.8	1792	8.80	0.596	0.445	76003
76004	Lowther at Eamont Bridge	352550	528600	155.74	360.2	49.2	0.240	30.43	57.5	80.0	12.3	1811	7.94			76004
76005	Eden at Temple Sowerby	360400	528100	618.58	283.1	322.5	0.105	60.86	41.0	56.5	10.7	1210	8.93			76005
76007	Eden at Sheepmount	338850	557100	2272.48	248.9	325.1	0.082	123.05	40.0	53.7	10.7	1226	10.19	0.643	0.462	76007
76008	Irthing at Greenholme	348500	558000	333.75	225.0	219.2	0.144	60.56	35.1	46.5	10.4	1073	11.52			76008
76009	Caldew at Holm Hill	337650	546750	147.80	324.2	15.0	0.194	35.32	48.2	62.7	11.7	1539	12.42			76009
76010	Petteril at Harraby Green	341200	554350	161.48	161.8	27.5	0.227	45.47	32.5	43.1	10.2	936	10.80			76010
76011	Coal Burn at Coalburn	369450	577850	1.55	306.0	163.9	0.491	1.79	39.3	52.4	10.6	1163	11.73			76011
76014	Eden at Kirkby Stephen	377250	509850	68.18	391.2	308.8	0.212	22.50	50.8	71.0	11.7	1383	8.10			76014
77001	Esk at Netherby	339150	571900	848.51	266.3	185.1	0.143	64.93	42.2	55.6	11.2	1449	11.66			77001
77002	Esk at Canonbie	339700	575250	495.86	279.3	182.1	0.143	59.90	44.6	58.6	11.6	1506	11.36			77002
77003	Liddel Water at Rowanburnfoot	341400	575850	318.90	266.1	182.0	0.143	45.58	39.3	52.0	10.7	1400	12.07			77003
77005	Lyne at Cliff Bridge	341350	566200	209.61	172.8	222.8	0.252	36.69	34.6	45.6	10.5	1131	11.73			77005
78003	Annan at Brydekirk	319150	570350	924.96	225.7	169.6	0.145	77.56	41.2	54.8	11.1	1446	10.85			78003
78004	Kinnel Water at Redhall	307700	586950	76.12	243.0	108.3	0.319	28.10	43.4	58.0	11.2	1552	10.85			78004
78005	Kinnel Water at Bridgemuir	309050	584650	229.21	241.3	128.7	0.264	35.55	41.9	55.8	11.2	1552	11.41			78005
79002	Nith at Friars Carse	292450	585100	797.72	293.9	83.7	0.041	79.69	45.2	61.9	10.8	1547	9.18			79002
79003	Nith at Hall Bridge	268450	612950	155.68	330.7	356.8	0.165	28.90	45.1	62.9	10.6	1568	10.36			79003
79004	Scar Water at Capenoch	284400	594100	142.47	318.1	106.5	0.167	27.15	47.2	64.8	11.6	1730	9.61			79004
79005	Cluden Water at Fiddlers Ford	292950	579600	237.44	215.2	109.5	0.132	43.61	45.1	59.1	11.4	1464	10.86			79005
79006	Nith at Drumlanrig	285750	599250	469.18	327.6	32.5	0.075	59.02	46.3	63.6	10.8	1581	8.72			79006

Number	Name	IHDTM NGR	AREA km²	ALTBAR m	ASPBAR degrees	ASPVAR	LDP km	RMED-1D mm	RMED-2D mm	RMED-1H mm	SAAR$_{4170}$ mm	SMDBAR mm	URBCONC	URBLOC	Number
80001	Urr at Dalbeattie	282150 560850	196.94	155.1	169.7	0.131	37.85	44.2	57.3	11.5	1352	10.88			80001
80003	White Laggan Burn at Loch Dee	246800 578000	5.71	440.5	2.9	0.367	4.22	71.8	99.9	14.3	2141	7.91			80003
80801	Pullaugh Burn at Diversion Works	254400 574100	18.22	306.1	45.3	0.198	9.07	66.9	90.5	14.0	2220	7.91			80801
81002	Cree at Newton Stewart	241300 565150	367.00	237.8	204.0	0.234	46.01	50.2	56.9	11.9	1712	7.91			81002
81003	Luce at Airyhemming	218150 559800	170.89	181.5	166.0	0.180	32.72	43.5	54.2	11.5	1418	14.48			81003
82001	Girvan at Robstone	221550 599550	243.98	192.9	312.1	0.116	57.73	39.1	57.1	10.0	1328	12.09			82001
82003	Stinchar at Balnowlart	210650 583200	324.48	200.4	289.8	0.070	50.81	42.3	63.2	10.9	1500	9.67			82003
83002	Garnock at Dalry	229300 648950	90.77	201.2	150.6	0.302	19.94	48.5	56.2	10.9	1693	12.52	0.679	0.537	83002
83003	Ayr at Catrine	252650 625800	166.90	280.9	247.2	0.170	38.52	39.1	56.2	9.6	1280	9.08			83003
83004	Lugar at Langholm														83004
83005	Irvine at Shewalton	234350 636950	368.45	151.1	241.6	0.242	53.70	37.3	52.7	9.4	1211	13.07	0.823	0.574	83005
83006	Ayr at Mainholm	236250 621550	579.01	219.4	288.2	0.159	69.38	36.2	51.7	9.4	1221	11.37			83006
83802	Irvine at Kilmarnock	243000 636750	212.38	166.5	249.6	0.219	40.54	37.0	52.9	9.3	1220	13.20	0.799	0.378	83802
84001	Kelvin at Killermont	255650 670600	321.31	140.5	165.1	0.125	38.19	37.6	51.5	9.2	1274	14.18	0.780	0.796	84001
84002	Calder at Muirshiel	230900 663650	12.27	358.4	50.6	0.383	8.60	57.6	80.4	12.5	2248	12.52			84002
84003	Clyde at Hazelbank	283600 645200	1093.20	317.3	22.2	0.051	95.20	37.5	51.8	9.5	1181	10.69			84003
84004	Clyde at Sills	292750 642550	741.89	343.0	359.0	0.043	78.29	39.5	54.1	9.8	1249	10.33			84004
84005	Clyde at Blairston	270250 657950	1700.10	278.6	7.6	0.066	120.60	36.2	54.1	9.2	1151	11.70	0.703	0.277	84005
84006	Kelvin at Bridgend	267350 675000	69.39	148.8	165.2	0.273	16.99	38.8	55.1	9.0	1373	15.01	0.618	0.855	84006
84007	South Calder Water at Forgewood	275000 658650	92.88	187.9	260.3	0.290	28.46	30.1	41.7	8.3	910	15.38	0.707	0.516	84007
84008	Rotten Calder Water at Redlees	267950 660250	54.84	192.2	21.1	0.293	22.03	37.3	52.1	9.2	1183	15.38	0.827	0.701	84008
84009	Nethan at Kirkmuirhill	281050 642750	66.88	291.6	39.4	0.223	21.75	35.5	50.8	9.1	1220	9.09			84009
84011	Gryfe at Craigend	250050 662900	229.68	148.3	7.8	0.248	37.19	40.7	56.6	9.7	1271	13.00	0.843	0.747	84011
84012	White Cart Water at Hawkhead	267050 661750	1901.66	265.3	356.7	0.063	128.76	35.8	49.6	9.2	1135	12.09	0.741	0.318	84012
84013	Clyde at Daldowie	275350 651900	263.25	245.6	37.7	0.154	43.25	37.8	53.0	9.2	1269	12.79	0.646	0.431	84013
84014	Avon Water at Fairholm	263650 673850	223.36	152.3	181.5	0.116	26.64	37.7	52.0	9.1	1289	14.66	0.727	0.760	84014
84015	Kelvin at Dryfield	273550 672550	35.30	138.9	305.8	0.260	13.30	35.1	46.2	8.8	1060	15.38	0.661	0.532	84015
84016	Luggie Water at Condorrat	241000 661900	103.20	174.8	87.9	0.095	24.74	50.9	69.9	10.9	1755	12.52	0.672	0.576	84016
84017	Black Cart Water at Milliken Park	289250 640400	938.79	330.0	7.9	0.071	85.24	38.5	53.3	9.6	1225	9.92			84017
84018	Clyde at Tulliford Mill														84018
84019	North Calder Water at Calderpark	268150 662350	129.15	150.8	247.5	0.225	38.44	31.7	42.7	8.6	932	15.38	0.776	0.712	84019
84020	Glazert Water at Milton Of Campsie	265600 676300	51.88	273.6	171.1	0.325	15.20	42.8	58.9	10.2	1569	12.76	0.589	0.381	84020
84023	Bothlin Burn at Auchengeich														84023
84025	Luggie Water at Oxgang														84025
84026	Allander Water at Milngavie	255800 673650	30.29	188.0	109.3	0.343	15.73	39.8	54.4	10.1	1391	12.19	0.880	0.252	84026
84806	Clyde at Cambusnethan	278750 652300	1262.66	303.9	10.5	0.056	107.60	36.7	50.7	9.3	1159	10.97			84806
85001	Leven at Linnbrane	239450 680400	783.04	239.0	188.7	0.136	65.00	50.3	69.7	10.7	2043	7.30			85001
85002	Endrick Water at Gaidrew	248350 686700	219.14	192.2	318.8	0.112	39.95	41.7	56.6	9.9	1432	9.07			85002
85003	Falloch at Glen Falloch	232100 719550	80.13	447.4	182.3	0.134	14.48	64.0	91.5	12.5	2767	4.98			85003
86001	Little Eachaig at Dalinlongart	214150 681950	31.77	274.4	66.7	0.103	9.83	55.4	75.5	11.9	2363	7.27			86001
86002	Eachaig at Eckford	214150 684200	139.47	297.7	238.0	0.087	30.71	54.2	77.5	11.6	2577	6.24			86002
87801	Allt Uaine at Intake	226200 711350	2.88	574.1	335.6	0.237	2.91	67.3	93.5	14.2	3448	6.88			87801
89804	Strae at Duiletter	214750 729550	37.34	343.7	231.6	0.078	13.59	65.1	95.0	12.7	2928	4.74			89804
90801	Nevis at Achreoch														90801
91002	Lochy at Camisky	214650 780650	1255.51	443.8	330.4	0.028	83.14	61.7	92.6	12.5	2148	3.50			91002
91802	Allt Leachdach at Intake	226200 778050	6.51	622.3	4.1	0.321	4.60	70.4	105.8	14.4	2412	3.29			91802
93001	Carron at New Kelso	194100 843050	138.96	356.4	185.6	0.020	27.90	63.6	89.5	10.7	2503	3.47			93001
94001	Ewe at Poolewe	186000 880850	441.14	311.3	6.1	0.107	47.39	63.7	89.5	10.6	2345	3.50			94001
95801	Little Gruinard at Little Gruinard	194550 889850	81.87	310.8	285.1	0.114	25.05	59.8	81.7	10.8	2061	4.06			95801
95803	Abhain Cuileg at Braemore	219350 879050	66.81	435.3	46.9	0.070	16.95	57.6	85.8	10.4	2526	3.49			95803

Number	Name	IHDTM NGR	AREA km²	ALTBAR m	ASPBAR degrees	ASPVAR	LDP km	RMED-1D mm	RMED-2D mm	RMED-1H mm	SAAR$_{4170}$ mm	SMDBAR mm	URBCONC	URBLOC
96001	Halladale at Halladale	289050 956250	194.04	174.5	1.5	0.137	28.36	33.2	46.3	8.2	1055	7.62		
96002	Naver at Apigill	271350 956950	474.79	223.5	79.0	0.063	57.05	40.4	55.2	8.7	1484	5.60		
97002	Thurso at Halkirk	312950 959500	414.26	148.6	39.6	0.212	58.29	33.8	46.9	8.4	1020	12.93		
201002	Fairy Water at Dudgeon Bridge	240750 375850	160.99	142.2	89.8	0.079	27.06	33.4	44.9	8.7	1246	11.24		
201005	Camowen at Camowen Terrace	246150 373100	276.27	158.6	231.3	0.103	38.82	31.3	41.4	8.5	1183	10.09		0.496
201006	Drumragh at Campsie Bridge	245850 372350	314.89	134.7	6.3	0.060	37.25	33.5	42.7	8.9	1153	11.35		0.507
201007	Burn Dennet at Burndennett Bridge	237350 404800	147.05	167.3	306.9	0.140	31.55	35.5	48.7	8.2	1156	11.90		
201008	Derg at Castlederg	226650 384250	335.74	177.2	118.5	0.119	38.34	42.1	56.8	9.5	1504	11.26		
201009	Owenkillen at Crosh	241700 386450	440.85	234.1	179.9	0.073	48.30	36.3	49.7	8.5	1332	10.09		
201010	Mourne at Drumnabuoy House	234800 396150	1838.57	168.2	167.1	0.034	78.34	35.0	47.0	8.7	1261	10.73		0.817
202001	Roe at Ardnargle	267250 424750	365.61	193.8	335.0	0.146	44.34	38.2	51.5	8.3	1242	12.81		0.362
202002	Faughan at Drumahoe	246250 414950	272.87	188.1	337.7	0.117	36.77	37.4	50.0	8.3	1173	12.54		0.382
203010	Blackwater at Maydown Bridge	281850 351950	971.30	110.0	86.6	0.083	75.86	31.1	41.6	9.1	1032	13.49		0.951
203011	Main at Dromona	305100 408750	242.95	168.6	225.9	0.137	32.67	36.6	50.2	8.8	1268	12.16		1.102
203012	Ballinderry at Ballinderry Bridge	292550 380050	426.42	118.5	119.0	0.149	46.44	32.8	44.0	8.8	1133	13.17		0.774
203017	Upper Bann at Dynes Bridge	304250 351050	316.13	135.4	297.4	0.070	56.04	40.9	55.2	10.5	1081	16.39		0.480
203018	Six Mile Water at Antrim	314750 386600	277.71	146.2	256.0	0.166	33.21	36.9	48.6	10.4	1106	17.34		0.749
203019	Claudy at Glenone Bridge	296350 403850	126.36	110.4	94.5	0.260	28.55	32.8	44.4	8.3	1128	12.55		0.879
203020	Moyola at Moyola New Bridge	295550 390350	304.32	147.9	88.2	0.202	47.09	36.3	48.5	8.5	1230	13.97		0.554
203021	Kells Water at Currys Bridge	310450 397100	126.29	212.1	252.5	0.248	32.99	41.5	54.9	10.6	1231	14.77		
203022	Blackwater at Derrymeen Bridge	262350 353100	183.45	139.8	84.4	0.107	29.04	32.0	42.4	9.0	1143	13.53		0.824
203024	Cusher at Gamble's Bridge	304750 347250	170.81	131.7	52.9	0.162	33.33	34.6	47.3	9.9	1021	15.96		0.501
203025	Callan at Callan New Bridge	289200 352300	166.79	128.3	330.2	0.189	35.45	33.1	44.8	9.7	983	15.96		0.645
203026	Glenavy at Glenavy	314750 372650	44.35	164.0	267.7	0.374	19.93	35.4	45.3	10.8	1025	17.42		0.103
203027	Braid at Ballee	309800 401550	182.85	168.9	233.6	0.209	31.70	36.9	51.4	9.5	1189	11.46		0.267
203028	Agivey at White Hill	288150 419300	100.19	179.8	50.7	0.333	27.06	35.4	49.1	8.2	1277	12.52		0.575
203033	Upper Bann at Bannfield	323400 334050	101.68	202.2	328.2	0.224	17.59	51.9	70.3	11.4	1341	16.61		
203039	Clogh at Tullynewey													
203042	Crumlin at Cidercourt Bridge	313650 376650	54.42	143.1	283.2	0.456	19.32	35.8	46.0	10.7	1013	17.42		0.404
203043	Oonawater at Shanmoy U/s	278050 355700	95.62	114.2	94.1	0.169	24.06	31.3	42.9	9.0	1052	12.36		0.342
203046	Rathmore at Rathmore Bridge	319950 383750	29.42	192.5	290.8	0.471	14.22	36.6	49.2	10.7	1066	17.29		
203049	Clady at Clady Bridge	305250 411200	219.82	172.5	234.8	0.154	29.38	37.1	50.8	9.0	1282	12.16		1.032
203092	Maine at Dumminning	308500 389750	705.35	157.8	224.2	0.113	60.89	36.4	49.6	9.5	1187	13.09		0.667
203093	Maine at Shanes Viaduct	294150 436350	299.79	118.7	245.4	0.169	46.96	36.3	48.6	8.2	1154	12.18		0.577
204001	Bush at Seneirl	329150 367900	448.27	103.8	296.5	0.040	70.02	35.8	46.7	10.4	945	16.72		0.413
205003	Lagan at Dunmurry	332750 369350	492.56	102.2	303.5	0.055	77.58	36.0	46.9	10.4	948	16.77		0.522
205004	Lagan at Newforge	326850 361300	73.54	100.1	230.4	0.090	18.83	37.9	48.7	10.5	937	16.93		
205005	Ravernet at Ravernet	323650 352550	84.78	167.7	337.9	0.187	19.36	40.8	52.9	10.7	1082	16.67		0.749
205008	Lagan at Drummiller	312300 354150	178.90	130.4	309.8	0.100	36.65	37.5	48.6	10.5	985	16.41		0.725
205010	Lagan at Banoge													
205011	Annacloy at Kilmore	344800 350750	186.41	94.7	84.6	0.153	29.68	38.7	51.0	10.4	971	16.72		0.940
205020	Enler at Comber	345750 369850	60.92	84.2	129.1	0.209	15.40	36.3	47.7	10.4	962	17.29		0.876
205101	Blackstaff at Easons													
206001	Clanrye at Mount Mill Bridge													
206002	Jerretspass at Jerretspass	306350 333350	105.20	82.5	206.4	0.084	20.74	32.4	44.6	9.7	941	15.96		1.001
206004	Bessbrook at Carnbane	307350 329350	24.98	120.8	86.4	0.230	10.11	37.8	49.5	10.0	1051	15.96		0.796
206006	Annalong at Recorder	334800 323350	13.74	391.7	146.5	0.284	6.50	61.7	77.3	11.7	1578	16.67		
206999	Woodburn at Control Area													
236005	Colebrooke at Ballindarragh Bridge	233250 336050	311.86	147.0	236.8	0.064	45.79	32.8	43.7	9.2	1137	13.06		0.637
236007	Sillees at Drumrainey Bridge	220500 340000	167.62	139.4	89.5	0.064	47.77	35.5	47.9	9.5	1363	12.42		

A.5 Catchment descriptors given in Table A.3

A brief description of each of the variables shown in Table A.3 is given below.

IHDTM NGR	The 12-figure National Grid Reference (Irish Grid Reference in Northern Ireland) of the IHDTM grid point, located nearest the gauging station and on the appropriate DTM drainage path.
AREA	Catchment drainage area using an IHDTM-derived boundary (km^2).
BFIHOST	Base Flow Index derived by using the HOST classification.
DPLBAR	Mean of distances between each node (on regular 50 m grid) and the catchment outlet (km). Characterises the catchment size and configuration.
DPSBAR	Mean of all the inter-nodal slopes for the catchment ($m\ km^{-1}$). Characterises the overall steepness.
FARL	Index of flood attenuation attributable to reservoirs and lakes.
PROPWET	Proportion of time when SMD was ≤ 6 mm during 1961-90.
SAAR	Standard period (1961-90) average annual rainfall (mm).
SPRHOST	Standard percentage runoff derived using the HOST classification.
URBEXT$_{1990}$	Extent of urban and suburban land cover (1990).

Table A.3 Catchment descriptors used in the flood estimation procedures – values for 252 UK Flood Event Archive catchments

Number	Name	IHDTM NGR	AREA km²	SAAR mm	BFIHOST	SPRHOST	FARL	PROPWET	DPLBAR km	DPSBAR m/km	URBEXT1990	Number
3003	Oykel at Easter Turnaig	240150 900150	331.92	1896	0.359	53.6	0.919	0.81	16.61	151.33	0.0000	3003
7001	Findhorn at Shenachie	282550 833550	415.87	1217	0.451	55.8	0.992	0.68	25.63	141.77	0.0002	7001
7003	Lossie at Sheriffmills	319250 862600	217.07	833	0.577	34.6	0.989	0.42	18.57	80.52	0.0002	7003
7006	Lossie at Torwinny	313350 848900	20.56	957	0.295	55.3	0.968	0.42	6.90	88.55	0.0000	7006
8009	Dulnain at Balnaan Bridge	297850 824750	272.27	1011	0.498	46.6	0.997	0.68	21.32	120.43	0.0002	8009
19001	Almond at Craigiehall	316500 675350	386.19	892	0.399	44.4	0.969	0.50	24.69	46.62	0.0338	19001
19002	Almond at Almond Weir	300250 665150	44.36	1016	0.364	47.0	0.998	0.57	10.74	37.76	0.0327	19002
19005	Almond at Almondell	308600 668450	239.27	963	0.362	46.0	0.957	0.52	16.86	47.69	0.0289	19005
20001	Tyne at East Linton	358950 676650	307.06	713	0.489	35.4	0.991	0.43	25.60	71.45	0.0035	20001
21018	Lyne Water at Lyne Station	320800 640150	180.58	945	0.538	36.6	0.977	0.49	15.91	131.65	0.0014	21018
21028	Mezion Burn at Mezion Farm											21028
21030	Megget Water at Henderland	323100 623050	56.31	1669	0.393	47.7	0.817	0.72	6.46	229.70	0.0000	21030
22009	Coquet at Rothbury	406600 601650	345.96	905	0.395	45.5	0.981	0.45	25.88	143.50	0.0015	22009
23002	Derwent at Eddys Bridge	404250 550800	117.97	943	0.316	48.1	0.835	0.59	11.31	98.39	0.0003	23002
23005	North Tyne at Tarset	377750 586050	283.49	1230	0.274	54.5	0.815	0.62	21.27	111.01	0.0000	23005
23006	South Tyne at Featherstone	367150 560950	323.09	1332	0.270	52.9	0.995	0.64	19.58	125.70	0.0008	23006
23008	Rede at Rede Bridge	386950 583350	345.10	941	0.322	49.4	0.978	0.47	25.12	96.26	0.0006	23008
23010	Tarset Burn at Greenhaugh	378800 587750	95.85	993	0.305	52.6	1.000	0.56	9.32	87.00	0.0001	23010
23011	Kielder Burn at Kielder	364400 594600	58.86	1199	0.362	55.0	1.000	0.59	7.42	139.66	0.0000	23011
23998	Redesdale RD3	382550 595850	1.95	916	0.263	56.4	1.000	0.45	1.19	67.78	0.0000	23998
23999	Redesdale RD2	383350 595950	4.13	915	0.262	56.0	1.000	0.45	1.84	62.81	0.0000	23999
24003	Wear at Stanhope	398250 539000	173.21	1279	0.300	50.8	0.979	0.59	13.05	133.62	0.0016	24003
24004	Bedburn Beck at Bedburn	411950 532150	74.32	894	0.362	43.8	0.999	0.59	9.62	109.67	0.0007	24004
24005	Browney at Burn Hall	425900 538800	178.35	743	0.331	39.3	1.000	0.41	19.60	77.88	0.0267	24005
24007	Browney at Lanchester	416350 546100	44.65	797	0.333	40.5	1.000	0.59	8.11	75.20	0.0018	24007
25003	Trout Beck at Moor House	375750 533500	11.69	1905	0.227	59.9	1.000	0.64	3.33	87.98	0.0000	25003
25004	Skerne at South Park	428350 513050	255.19	644	0.391	37.4	0.983	0.32	24.75	33.32	0.0604	25004
25005	Leven at Leven Bridge	444500 512100	193.57	726	0.381	40.5	0.998	0.34	25.49	75.96	0.0099	25005
25006	Greta at Rutherford Bridge	403250 512250	86.73	1125	0.242	55.1	0.999	0.62	12.40	67.67	0.0006	25006
25011	Langdon Beck at Langdon	385200 530900	12.73	1463	0.237	58.2	1.000	0.59	4.06	120.61	0.0006	25011
25012	Harwood Beck at Harwood	385050 530900	24.89	1574	0.261	53.5	1.000	0.59	5.41	115.15	0.0000	25012
25019	Leven at Easby	458550 508550	15.06	830	0.525	38.6	1.000	0.37	5.30	130.18	0.0009	25019
25809	Bog Weir at Moor House	377300 532700	0.05	1757	0.228	59.9	1.000	0.64	0.17	100.40	0.0000	25809
25810	Syke Weir at Moor House	377200 533200	0.04	1757	0.275	55.0	1.000	0.64	0.18	79.91	0.0000	25810
25811	Long Weir at Moor House	377050 531750	0.10	1799	0.226	60.0	1.000	0.64	0.30	95.06	0.0000	25811
27001	Nidd at Hunsingore Weir	442650 452900	490.05	965	0.406	39.6	0.954	0.37	36.90	77.27	0.0253	27001
27010	Hodge Beck at Bransdale Weir	462800 494350	18.87	987	0.342	50.5	1.000	0.40	5.10	151.64	0.0026	27010
27026	Rother at Whittington	439250 374250	167.04	811	0.491	27.9	0.975	0.38	10.10	74.68	0.1061	27026
27027	Wharfe at Ilkley	411050 448150	447.51	1371	0.366	46.6	0.975	0.62	32.71	139.79	0.0018	27027
27031	Colne at Colne Bridge	417350 419900	244.77	1145	0.607	24.2	0.957	0.52	15.35	124.65	0.0783	27031
27034	Ure at Kilgram Bridge	418850 486000	511.89	1336	0.386	46.9	0.990	0.63	32.91	132.03	0.0016	27034
27035	Aire at Kildwick Bridge	401400 445750	282.42	1151	0.385	42.5	0.980	0.62	21.08	101.84	0.0086	27035
27051	Crimple at Burn Bridge	428350 451900	8.13	855	0.309	40.8	1.000	0.34	2.52	63.32	0.0015	27051
28016	Ryton at Serlby Park	463950 389600	237.57	644	0.760	17.8	0.965	0.30	22.11	31.70	0.0652	28016
28023	Wye at Ashford	418250 369750	152.17	1165	0.679	14.3	0.984	0.52	16.28	120.15	0.0122	28023
28026	Anker at Polesworth	426250 303250	370.40	653	0.445	39.5	0.991	0.30	23.60	27.34	0.0681	28026
28033	Dove at Hollinsclough	406450 366850	7.96	1346	0.403	42.4	1.000	0.52	3.23	173.79	0.0000	28033
28041	Hamps at Waterhouses	408100 350350	36.91	1085	0.301	47.2	1.000	0.44	7.68	87.97	0.0033	28041
28070	Burbage Brook at Burbage	425850 380250	8.36	1006	0.427	40.2	1.000	0.38	2.74	87.07	0.0000	28070
28997	Upper Smisby	434350 318800	1.13	680	0.694	23.2	1.000	0.30	0.92	33.93	0.0364	28997

Number	Name	IHDTM NGR	AREA km²	SAAR mm	BFIHOST	SPRHOST	FARL	PROPWET	DPLBAR km	DPSBAR m/km	URBEXT 1990	Number
28998	Lower Smisby	435400 318200	2.49	680	0.666	24.2	1.000	0.30	1.61	36.36	0.0402	28998
28999	Cliftonthorpe	435700 318950	1.12	683	0.616	28.7	1.000	0.30	1.03	38.61	0.0033	28999
29001	Waithe Beck at Brigsley	525150 401700	108.28	691	0.883	11.3	0.971	0.29	13.66	53.21	0.0045	29001
29002	Great Eau at Claythorpe Mill	541600 379150	80.69	692	0.712	21.9	0.952	0.28	9.01	53.59	0.0057	29002
29004	Ancholme at Bishopbridge	503150 390950	58.92	615	0.558	29.4	1.000	0.26	8.39	11.61	0.0036	29004
30001	Witham at Claypole Mill	484250 348150	296.04	615	0.592	28.5	0.979	0.27	27.69	30.94	0.0188	30001
30004	Partney Lymn at Partney Mill	540350 367500	59.94	685	0.570	32.4	0.980	0.29	9.40	54.22	0.0110	30004
30017	Witham at Colsterworth	492850 324750	50.23	641	0.657	22.6	1.000	0.27	7.38	22.59	0.0066	30017
31005	Welland at Tixover	496850 299650	419.59	636	0.377	45.1	0.971	0.30	33.92	51.89	0.0081	31005
31006	Gwash at Belmesthorpe	503800 309950	149.49	630	0.668	23.9	0.758	0.28	22.10	37.30	0.0111	31006
31010	Chater at Fosters Bridge	496100 303100	68.86	640	0.529	33.1	0.998	0.30	10.90	62.65	0.0041	31010
31021	Welland at Ashley	482050 291500	247.19	640	0.326	47.9	0.993	0.30	17.23	48.05	0.0096	31021
31023	West Glen at Easton Wood	496650 325850	4.41	641	0.320	41.3	1.000	0.27	1.95	33.76	0.0000	31023
32801	Flore at Experimental Catchment											32801
32999	Easton Maudit	488400 259300	15.73	621	0.405	40.6	1.000	0.30	4.02	29.49	0.0062	32999
33014	Lark at Temple	575650 273100	278.43	593	0.785	18.2	0.955	0.27	17.89	23.65	0.0217	33014
33015	Ouzel at Willen	488250 240650	279.06	638	0.466	41.5	0.979	0.31	26.60	35.49	0.0364	33015
33029	Stringside at White Bridge	571700 300450	97.08	627	0.863	12.4	0.993	0.23	9.56	13.77	0.0073	33029
33045	Wittle at Quidenham	602550 287750	27.65	608	0.535	32.7	0.976	0.31	4.84	15.42	0.0122	33045
33809	Bury Brook at Bury Weir	528600 283850	61.97	547	0.414	47.4	0.970	0.22	11.45	16.52	0.0116	33809
33996	Toddington	502050 228400	0.88	632	0.652	32.3	1.000	0.30	1.01	49.78	0.1937	33996
33997	Letchworth	521000 233650	8.46	588	0.550	33.8	1.000	0.30	2.91	27.88	0.2399	33997
33998	Bedford	510050 249050	23.34	561	0.396	49.5	1.000	0.24	5.41	19.56	0.0208	33998
33999	Barton-Le-Clay											33999
34003	Bure at Ingworth	619050 329750	168.09	669	0.779	20.8	0.977	0.31	12.53	23.62	0.0121	34003
34005	Tud at Costessey Park	617150 311150	72.02	649	0.600	32.6	0.983	0.31	14.46	20.56	0.0303	34005
34007	Dove at Oakley Park	617400 277050	140.10	585	0.427	37.3	0.997	0.28	14.16	15.43	0.0101	34007
34011	Wensum at Fakenham	591850 329300	162.10	698	0.857	14.4	0.997	0.29	14.39	17.09	0.0146	34011
35008	Gipping at Stowmarket	605950 257850	127.43	577	0.401	43.4	0.998	0.28	8.80	25.05	0.0201	35008
36008	Stour at Westmill	582850 246450	223.63	589	0.414	42.9	0.986	0.26	21.94	33.94	0.0151	36008
37001	Roding at Redbridge	541500 188250	301.20	607	0.331	46.6	0.985	0.29	33.67	30.40	0.0495	37001
37003	Ter at Crabbs Bridge	578500 210750	77.81	570	0.461	41.8	0.977	0.31	13.33	18.89	0.0075	37003
37007	Wid at Writtle	568450 206050	135.73	592	0.244	47.6	0.996	0.28	15.72	27.90	0.0462	37007
37008	Chelmer at Springfield	571150 206950	190.13	584	0.492	39.3	0.976	0.31	25.63	28.28	0.0234	37008
37031	Crouch at Wickford	574850 193550	70.37	572	0.218	49.2	0.975	0.27	8.18	30.11	0.1426	37031
37999	North Weald	549450 203750	1.53	623	0.259	46.9	1.000	0.31	1.19	24.45	0.0057	37999
38003	Mimram at Panshanger Park	528350 213150	130.53	656	0.720	27.4	0.986	0.30	16.74	45.03	0.0424	38003
38007	Canons Brook at Elizabeth Way	543200 210550	20.80	601	0.355	45.8	0.990	0.31	4.39	29.84	0.1736	38007
39004	Wandle at Beddington Park	529450 165450	118.34	763	0.845	16.6	0.994	0.33	13.89	76.65	0.1432	39004
39005	Beverley Brook at Wimbledon Common	521700 171850	39.71	630	0.477	33.9	1.000	0.29	7.30	27.16	0.3766	39005
39007	Blackwater at Swallowfield	473200 164650	360.37	708	0.630	26.8	0.895	0.32	19.37	32.80	0.0664	39007
39012	Hogsmill at Kingston Upon Thames	518350 168700	72.89	671	0.599	27.2	0.993	0.30	10.99	32.76	0.2064	39012
39017	Ray at Grendon Underwood											39017
39018	Ock at Abingdon	448450 196900	248.23	637	0.635	29.1	0.984	0.31	16.57	23.97	0.0193	39018
39022	Loddon at Sheepbridge	471850 165050	176.49	735	0.594	26.4	0.931	0.33	19.24	33.54	0.0454	39022
39025	Enborne at Brimpton	456800 164950	142.13	789	0.500	32.8	0.985	0.32	14.15	54.61	0.0094	39025
39026	Cherwell at Banbury	445650 241250	204.60	664	0.416	42.4	0.971	0.30	15.48	43.52	0.0153	39026
39036	Law Brook at Albury	504600 146900	16.00	819	0.888	15.1	0.961	0.36	4.85	87.35	0.0010	39036
39052	The Cut at Binfield	485300 171400	50.20	676	0.354	41.6	0.942	0.29	7.62	25.36	0.1182	39052
39053	Mole at Horley	527050 143250	91.59	812	0.463	40.3	0.947	0.36	10.52	34.90	0.0913	39053

Number	Name	IHDTM NGR	AREA km²	SAAR mm	BFIHOST	SPRHOST	FARL	PROPWET	DPLBAR km	DPSBAR m/km	URBEXT1990	Number
39092	Dollis Bk at Hendon Lane Bridge	524050 189350	23.76	689	0.178	50.5	0.990	0.29	6.33	50.48	0.2525	39092
39813	Mole at Ifield Weir	524500 136250	13.13	827	0.684	29.1	0.889	0.36	2.89	43.95	0.1219	39813
39814	Crawters Brook at Hazlewick											39814
39830	Beck at Rectory Road											39830
39831	Chaffinch Brook at Beckenham											39831
39990	Wingrave											39990
39991	Tring											39991
39992	Stevenage	526800 222750	4.02	628	0.612	33.1	1.000	0.30	2.37	32.15	0.1922	39992
39993	South Hinksey	450650 203950	1.51	664	0.760	18.4	1.000	0.32	1.46	69.64	0.0000	39993
39994	Luton											39994
39995	Hook											39995
39996	Holme Green	482550 167000	10.21	664	0.513	34.7	1.000	0.29	2.96	25.20	0.0817	39996
39997	Bicester											39997
39998	Beenham	458450 169450	3.29	693	0.355	41.6	1.000	0.32	1.67	40.53	0.0072	39998
39999	Aylesbury											39999
40004	Rother at Udiam	577450 124650	205.36	857	0.388	44.4	0.975	0.35	17.22	94.28	0.0078	40004
40006	Bourne at Hadlow	563200 149550	50.21	719	0.628	29.5	0.969	0.36	8.34	65.44	0.0241	40006
40007	Medway at Chafford Weir	551600 140650	252.40	830	0.441	42.3	0.939	0.35	14.54	83.94	0.0200	40007
40008	Great Stour at Wye	605050 147150	226.07	741	0.658	28.0	0.984	0.34	18.97	39.87	0.0307	40008
40009	Teise at Stone Bridge	571850 140050	134.43	812	0.443	42.6	0.905	0.36	12.69	79.96	0.0050	40009
40010	Eden at Penshurst	552150 143850	224.88	742	0.425	41.2	0.925	0.35	20.01	48.03	0.0161	40010
41005	Ouse at Gold Bridge	542750 121500	182.26	835	0.493	40.9	0.924	0.35	15.30	74.92	0.0223	41005
41006	Uck at Isfield	545900 118950	87.84	822	0.431	43.2	0.983	0.35	10.62	73.27	0.0234	41006
41007	Arun at Park Mound	503700 121400	401.33	806	0.388	43.4	0.975	0.35	28.09	49.83	0.0186	41007
41015	Ems at Westbourne	475450 107250	57.93	899	0.904	9.3	0.981	0.34	9.46	82.87	0.0087	41015
41020	Bevern Stream at Clappers Bridge	542150 116450	35.23	886	0.355	43.2	0.987	0.34	7.85	47.69	0.0121	41020
41021	Clayhill Stream at Old Ship	544850 115300	7.09	805	0.252	48.3	1.000	0.34	2.84	27.65	0.0000	41021
41022	Lod at Halfway Bridge	493250 122350	52.22	857	0.478	38.8	0.951	0.35	9.31	80.67	0.0022	41022
41025	Loxwood Stream at Drungewick	505850 130750	93.81	812	0.320	46.5	0.982	0.35	14.96	57.52	0.0062	41025
41028	Chess Stream at Chess Bridge	521850 117400	24.96	850	0.499	35.9	0.984	0.34	6.42	48.40	0.0118	41028
41801	Hollington Stream at Hollington	578800 110050	3.47	781	0.366	46.2	1.000	0.34	2.17	85.21	0.4334	41801
45002	Exe at Stoodleigh	294250 117650	420.87	1360	0.495	38.0	0.980	0.48	26.49	145.44	0.0004	45002
45003	Culm at Wood Mill	302100 105950	228.69	971	0.585	31.8	0.996	0.40	15.23	72.19	0.0038	45003
45004	Axe at Whitford	326250 95400	288.58	994	0.498	38.8	0.992	0.39	18.70	92.15	0.0046	45004
45009	Exe at Pixton	293450 126150	147.81	1375	0.548	34.6	0.950	0.51	14.77	157.11	0.0001	45009
45011	Barle at Brushford	292700 125850	128.01	1585	0.449	42.8	0.999	0.54	21.81	139.27	0.0004	45011
46003	Dart at Austins Bridge	274950 66050	248.90	1771	0.523	32.8	0.996	0.47	19.82	124.02	0.0036	46003
46005	East Dart at Bellever	265750 77650	22.29	2096	0.362	47.5	1.000	0.46	6.22	96.98	0.0000	46005
46802	Swincombe at Swincombe Intake	263200 71850	14.18	1964	0.336	51.6	1.000	0.47	3.11	81.08	0.0000	46802
46805	Bala Brook at Bala Intake	267350 62800	5.59	2075	0.327	51.4	1.000	0.47	1.81	109.94	0.0000	46805
47007	Yealm at Puslinch	257550 51200	56.42	1427	0.549	33.2	0.992	0.47	9.97	106.67	0.0118	47007
47008	Thrushel at Tinhay	239850 85550	112.71	1144	0.422	39.1	1.000	0.50	10.78	91.19	0.0000	47008
47011	Plym at Carn Wood	252250 61400	79.56	1618	0.481	38.3	0.952	0.48	11.21	106.07	0.0076	47011
47013	Withey Brook at Bastreet	224550 76450	15.93	1684	0.367	49.1	1.000	0.48	3.56	83.22	0.0000	47013
48004	Warleggan at Trengoffe	215850 67250	25.21	1445	0.500	35.7	0.973	0.45	6.09	96.09	0.0013	48004
48005	Kenwyn at Truro	182150 44950	19.09	1100	0.601	32.6	0.988	0.42	4.98	92.38	0.0312	48005
48009	St Neot at Craigshill Wood	218400 66200	22.86	1512	0.463	40.0	0.635	0.45	7.12	79.52	0.0034	48009
49003	De Lank at De Lank	213350 76550	21.70	1627	0.379	47.8	0.995	0.45	4.73	78.05	0.0000	49003
51002	Horner Water at West Luccombe	289850 145950	20.49	1484	0.540	29.7	0.978	0.54	6.31	216.92	0.0000	51002
52004	Isle at Ashford Mill	335950 118850	87.42	891	0.499	39.8	0.980	0.40	10.28	65.80	0.0100	52004

Number	Name	IHDTM NGR	AREA km²	SAAR mm	BFIHOST	SPRHOST	FARL	PROPWET	DPLBAR km	DPSBAR m/km	URBEXT_1990	Number
52005	Tone at Bishops Hull	320450 125050	203.63	964	0.562	32.9	0.979	0.36	17.70	99.88	0.0068	52005
52006	Yeo at Pen Mill	357350 116050	216.17	865	0.569	34.3	0.965	0.38	14.01	64.79	0.0193	52006
52010	Brue at Lovington	359150 131800	139.52	867	0.524	36.4	0.998	0.37	13.46	72.51	0.0065	52010
52016	Currypool Stream at Currypool Farm	322000 138200	15.72	934	0.586	29.2	1.000	0.35	4.65	136.25	0.0000	52016
52020	Gallica Stream at Gallica Bridge	357050 109850	16.44	950	0.388	45.3	0.971	0.38	3.82	88.31	0.0000	52020
53005	Midford Brook at Midford	376350 161150	147.40	965	0.625	29.1	0.993	0.36	13.76	81.94	0.0301	53005
53007	Frome(somerset) at Tellisford	380650 156250	261.85	965	0.565	29.8	0.967	0.36	20.50	61.77	0.0163	53007
53008	Avon at Great Somerford	396450 183200	305.11	804	0.622	28.0	0.989	0.34	18.39	29.17	0.0077	53008
53009	Wellow Brook at Wellow	374000 157950	73.47	999	0.643	27.3	0.987	0.37	10.35	70.05	0.0383	53009
54004	Sowe at Stoneleigh	433200 273250	263.29	667	0.509	35.8	0.982	0.30	16.99	28.39	0.1348	54004
54006	Stour at Kidderminster	383050 276750	311.45	693	0.666	26.5	0.986	0.30	22.30	62.20	0.1527	54006
54010	Stour at Alscot Park	420650 250850	316.96	659	0.385	44.8	0.995	0.30	25.70	58.65	0.0150	54010
54011	Salwarpe at Harford Mill	386850 261950	186.20	666	0.523	35.2	0.992	0.28	13.43	42.82	0.0496	54011
54016	Roden at Rodington	358900 314250	261.90	693	0.616	27.5	0.984	0.34	28.81	22.76	0.0104	54016
54019	Avon at Stareton	433150 271500	346.32	654	0.424	42.5	0.954	0.29	37.53	30.75	0.0349	54019
54020	Perry at Yeaton	343250 319200	183.18	739	0.648	26.6	0.965	0.40	19.03	29.91	0.0082	54020
54022	Severn at Plynlimon Flume	285300 287200	8.68	2482	0.323	52.7	1.000	0.66	2.91	184.94	0.0000	54022
54027	Frome at Ebley Mill	383000 204550	197.11	827	0.738	20.5	0.951	0.32	12.50	126.79	0.0239	54027
54034	Dowles Brook at Dowles	376650 276500	42.07	715	0.632	19.2	0.999	0.32	7.49	93.30	0.0045	54034
54090	Tanllwyth at Tanllwyth Flume											54090
54999	Drayton DT2											54999
55008	Wye at Cefn Brwyn	282800 283700	10.56	2458	0.377	48.5	1.000	0.66	3.11	196.23	0.0000	55008
55012	Irfon at Cilmery	299450 250550	246.41	1627	0.431	42.8	0.998	0.65	19.91	161.90	0.0004	55012
55021	Lugg at Butts Bridge	350350 258900	365.13	877	0.610	30.3	0.994	0.37	26.86	128.15	0.0053	55021
55022	Trothy at Mitchel Troy	350150 211250	142.41	887	0.575	36.9	0.998	0.36	17.89	101.32	0.0014	55022
55025	Llynfi at Three Cocks	316550 237450	131.48	999	0.500	30.6	0.951	0.54	11.48	107.22	0.0017	55025
55026	Wye at Ddol Farm	297650 267450	172.68	1635	0.423	43.4	0.997	0.59	18.01	183.92	0.0015	55026
55034	Cyff at Cyff Flume	282250 284200	3.11	2417	0.395	47.1	1.000	0.66	1.90	186.13	0.0000	55034
56002	Ebbw at Rhiwderyn	325900 188750	212.29	1774	0.538	29.8	0.977	0.49	22.10	185.89	0.0507	56002
56003	Honddu at The Forge Brecon	305000 229850	62.53	1946	0.528	35.2	1.000	0.53	10.46	123.81	0.0002	56003
56004	Usk at Llandetty	312700 220450	556.56	1171	0.545	35.2	0.976	0.57	30.02	151.12	0.0019	56004
56005	Lwyd at Ponthir	332850 192400	98.33	1479	0.525	33.1	0.979	0.49	15.59	147.06	0.0783	56005
56006	Usk at Trallong	294550 229650	193.99	1394	0.475	40.7	0.966	0.62	12.78	138.64	0.0008	56006
56011	Sirhowy at Wattsville	320450 191150	76.26	1666	0.524	30.4	0.974	0.49	18.02	140.80	0.0456	56011
57004	Cynon at Abercynon	308050 195600	103.54	1482	0.422	40.1	0.980	0.53	15.18	145.76	0.0388	57004
57005	Taff at Pontypridd	308050 189650	451.99	1772	0.409	43.3	0.951	0.50	22.62	167.05	0.0406	57005
57006	Rhondda at Trehafod	305250 191000	102.57	2183	0.365	47.8	0.985	0.49	14.06	214.98	0.0593	57006
58001	Ogmore at Bridgend	290300 179350	157.97	1774	0.478	36.4	0.998	0.52	13.86	174.78	0.0396	58001
58002	Neath at Resolven	281450 201650	190.93	1946	0.347	47.7	0.987	0.62	17.58	149.90	0.0073	58002
58003	Ewenny at Ewenny Priory	291550 178100	63.85	1321	0.557	29.0	1.000	0.52	8.19	76.40	0.0377	58003
58006	Mellte at Pontneddfechan	291350 208100	65.18	1981	0.322	51.3	0.975	0.62	10.44	134.91	0.0000	58006
58008	Dulais at Cilfrew	277900 200950	43.36	1807	0.377	45.3	1.000	0.62	8.30	145.77	0.0095	58008
58009	Ewenny at Keepers Lodge	292150 178250	63.25	1323	0.556	29.1	1.000	0.52	7.60	76.94	0.0371	58009
60002	Cothi at Felin Mynachdy	250850 222500	298.54	1551	0.500	37.9	0.998	0.56	27.72	177.03	0.0002	60002
60003	Taf at Clog-y-fran	223950 215850	216.73	1420	0.553	34.0	0.999	0.46	17.13	154.81	0.0017	60003
60006	Gwili at Glangwili	242950 222050	130.98	1603	0.536	35.1	1.000	0.52	15.84	154.11	0.0008	60006
60007	Tywi at Dolau Hirion	276200 236050	220.53	1685	0.432	43.8	0.934	0.64	21.33	189.18	0.0001	60007
61001	Western Cleddau at Prendergast Mill	195250 217850	197.76	1276	0.560	32.6	0.997	0.44	15.65	69.42	0.0012	61001
61003	Gwaun at Cilrhedyn Bridge	200400 235000	31.29	1550	0.495	39.1	1.000	0.44	5.21	122.07	0.0000	61003
62002	Teifi at Llanfair	243450 240450	517.05	1392	0.484	39.0	0.993	0.54	36.83	108.39	0.0014	62002

Number	Name	IHDTM NGR	AREA km²	SAAR mm	BFIHOST	SPRHOST	FARL	PROPWET	DPLBAR km	DPSBAR m/km	URBEXT$_{1990}$	Number
63998	Trawsgoed	281050 278750	1.97	2170	0.289	55.3	1.000	0.66	1.73	72.00	0.0000	63998
63999	Pwllpeiran											63999
64001	Dyfi at Dyfi Bridge	274350 301900	464.56	1835	0.478	39.8	0.995	0.66	20.06	276.17	0.0004	64001
65001	Glaslyn at Beddgelert	259200 347650	67.23	2808	0.406	45.1	0.909	0.62	7.54	323.20	0.0003	65001
65801	Nant Peris at Tan-yr-allt	260750 358050	10.30	3463	0.548	28.4	0.996	0.71	3.24	503.96	0.0000	65801
66002	Elwy at Pant Yr Onen	302150 370300	218.63	1145	0.483	38.8	0.980	0.58	22.65	132.40	0.0000	66002
66004	Wheeler at Bodfari	310600 371550	62.94	863	0.696	25.2	0.995	0.38	7.52	110.18	0.0004	66004
66006	Elwy at Pont-y-gwyddel	295350 371950	191.40	1185	0.476	39.5	0.981	0.60	14.39	131.55	0.0021	66006
66011	Conwy at Cwm Llanerch	280300 358250	339.86	2041	0.363	48.9	0.980	0.70	16.42	173.11	0.0004	66011
67003	Brenig at Llyn Brenig Outflow	297500 354050	22.17	1317	0.319	53.0	0.595	0.70	3.75	73.08	0.0005	67003
67005	Ceiriog at Brynkinalt Weir	329650 337250	111.94	1197	0.462	40.8	1.000	0.51	17.58	189.84	0.0018	67005
67008	Alyn at Pont-y-capel	333450 353950	227.16	916	0.592	29.8	0.991	0.41	24.06	110.27	0.0209	67008
67010	Gelyn at Cynefail	284350 341950	12.89	2001	0.252	58.3	0.969	0.71	3.40	131.11	0.0000	67010
68006	Dane at Hulme Walfield	384600 364250	151.10	1020	0.417	39.1	0.983	0.50	18.90	117.90	0.0252	68006
68010	Fender at Ford	327950 388150	17.59	774	0.429	37.2	1.000	0.38	4.08	30.53	0.2038	68010
68014	Sandersons Brook at Sandbach											68014
69008	Dean at Stanneylands											69008
69011	Micker Brook at Cheadle											69011
69012	Bollin at Wilmslow	384850 381550	67.89	933	0.539	31.4	0.965	0.52	13.79	84.51	0.0755	69012
69013	Sinderland Brook at Partington	372700 390500	45.08	827	0.480	32.8	0.989	0.39	7.58	12.69	0.2034	69013
69018	Newton Brook at Newton Le Willows	358400 393300	32.25	916	0.480	34.7	0.942	0.38	7.98	24.15	0.1467	69018
69019	Worsley Brook at Eccles	375350 397850	23.74	955	0.349	37.6	0.969	0.43	5.25	22.55	0.2507	69019
69020	Medlock at London Road	384750 397550	52.72	1036	0.388	35.3	0.993	0.55	12.30	64.75	0.2518	69020
69027	Tame at Portwood	390450 391900	146.60	1212	0.365	42.6	0.926	0.54	26.46	124.05	0.1062	69027
69031	Ditton Brook at Greens Bridge	345550 386650	48.76	855	0.429	36.1	0.992	0.37	5.80	21.50	0.2331	69031
69034	Musbury Brook at Helmshore	377400 421300	3.14	1453	0.344	49.1	1.000	0.51	1.65	163.95	0.0000	69034
69802	Etherow at Woodhead											69802
70006	Tawd at Newburgh	346900 410850	28.32	946	0.514	23.2	1.000	0.51	6.42	34.08	0.1171	70006
71003	Croasdale at Croasdale Flume	370600 454750	10.66	1886	0.275	54.6	1.000	0.60	3.28	163.71	0.0000	71003
71004	Calder at Whalley Weir	373050 436000	317.11	1232	0.395	38.4	0.957	0.55	22.08	97.34	0.0729	71004
71008	Hodder at Hodder Place	370550 439950	258.39	1602	0.330	46.2	0.969	0.60	23.54	127.28	0.0007	71008
71802	Ribble at Halton West	385100 455200	206.68	1441	0.387	45.7	1.000	0.61	21.55	104.93	0.0027	71802
71804	Dunsop at Footholme	365300 452950	24.93	1914	0.297	53.8	0.993	0.60	4.27	187.08	0.0057	71804
72002	Wyre at St Michaels	346650 441050	276.56	1253	0.369	44.2	0.950	0.56	17.60	74.53	0.0010	72002
72006	Lune at Kirkby Lonsdale	361500 477950	510.31	1652	0.424	43.0	0.999	0.71	31.65	174.59	0.0108	72006
72818	New Mill Brook at Carvers Bridge	347900 438000	65.08	1076	0.394	39.7	0.998	0.51	9.47	29.42		72818
72820	Burnes Gill at Tebay (M6)											72820
73005	Kent at Sedgwick	350900 487550	212.38	1725	0.514	38.1	0.984	0.71	18.92	158.65	0.0117	73005
73007	Troutbeck at Troutbeck Bridge	340550 500850	23.94	2221	0.392	49.5	1.000	0.71	6.47	290.74	0.0000	73007
73008	Bela at Beetham	349600 480450	132.15	1290	0.535	32.5	0.965	0.68	13.43	89.32	0.0026	73008
73803	Winster at Lobby Bridge	342300 488550	22.20	1508	0.539	35.2	0.998	0.71	4.71	122.26	0.0002	73803
73804	Brathay at Brathay Hall	336650 503450	57.44	2747	0.437	49.3	0.923	0.71	9.73	305.68	0.0012	73804
74001	Duddon at Duddon Hall	319550 489550	85.69	2265	0.337	53.7	0.986	0.71	10.78	215.66	0.0002	74001
75006	Newlands Beck at Braithwaite	323950 524050	33.81	2372	0.459	41.8	1.000	0.64	6.86	384.63	0.0008	75006
75007	Glenderamackin at Threlkeld	331150 524800	62.99	1732	0.389	45.5	1.000	0.62	8.76	188.73	0.0003	75007
76005	Eden at Temple Sowerby	360400 528150	618.58	1143	0.475	37.0	0.996	0.66	29.65	101.55	0.0020	76005
76008	Irthing at Greenholme	348500 558000	333.75	1073	0.359	46.5	1.000	0.62	26.39	78.28	0.0015	76008
76011	Coal Burn at Coalburn	369450 577850	1.55	1097	0.196	58.9	1.000	0.62	1.03	49.93	0.0000	76011
76014	Eden at Kirkby Stephen	377250 509850	68.18	1484	0.413	45.5	1.000	0.69	9.95	153.37	0.0031	76014
76805	Force Beck at M6 (shop)	357750 513500	3.97	1514	0.512	35.2	1.000	0.71	1.88	52.70	0.0000	76805

Number	Name	IHDTM NGR	AREA km²	SAAR mm	BFIHOST	SPRHOST	FARL	PROPWET	DPLBAR km	DPSBAR m/km	URBEXT$_{1990}$	Number
77002	Esk at Canonbie	339700 575250	495.86	1423	0.405	44.3	0.994	0.61	33.00	168.74	0.0007	77002
79006	Nith at Drumlanrig	285750 599250	469.18	1485	0.386	44.5	0.995	0.68	32.16	156.90	0.0015	79006
80003	White Laggan Burn at Loch Dee	246800 578000	5.71	2469	0.385	49.1	0.996	0.69	2.03	252.37	0.0000	80003
83002	Garnock at Dalry	229300 648950	90.77	1717	0.369	43.9	0.966	0.61	10.20	96.61	0.0134	83002
84002	Calder at Muirshiel	230900 663650	12.27	2316	0.273	58.0	0.987	0.61	4.51	97.90	0.0000	84002
84008	Rotten Calder Water at Redlees	267950 660250	54.84	1217	0.314	42.2	0.998	0.58	12.85	53.81	0.0621	84008
84012	White Cart Water at Hawkhead	250050 662900	229.68	1308	0.413	38.0	0.947	0.60	20.70	64.71	0.1270	84012
84022	Duneaton at Maidencots	292750 625950	111.21	1302	0.368	47.9	1.000	0.71	15.29	121.07	0.0000	84022
85002	Endrick Water at Gaidrew	248350 686700	219.14	1484	0.454	41.6	0.984	0.65	16.89	110.97	0.0008	85002
96001	Halladale at Halladale	289050 956250	194.04	1096	0.298	55.6	0.969	0.69	13.37	56.31	0.0000	96001
202004	Muff at Eglinton	253400 421050	26.83	1051	0.402	40.0	1.000	0.61	5.52	68.86	0.0230	202004
202005	Muff at Muff Glen	252400 418950	14.60	1064	0.405	39.3	1.000	0.61	3.99	75.29	0.0000	202005
202006	Castle at Gortenny	253050 419250	5.69	1070	0.318	46.8	1.000	0.61	2.85	57.98	0.0000	202006
203046	Rathmore at Rathmore Bridge	319950 383750	29.42	1079	0.367	40.6	1.000	0.52	7.97	59.27	0.0000	203046
203049	Clady at Clady Bridge											203049
203050	Ballysally Blagh at University of Ulster	306950 417750	22.19	1246	0.451	36.9	1.000	0.61	5.75	72.03	0.0049	203050
203094	Cloghmills Water at Clogh Mills											203094
203095	Killagan Water at Killagan Bridge											203095
204003	Tow at Fairhill	311700 440600	23.79	1153	0.582	27.2	1.000	0.61	4.37	78.73	0.0236	204003
204004	Beaghs Burn at Beaghs Bridge	317750 429750	2.79	1559	0.232	59.8	1.000	0.61	2.01	104.97	0.0000	204004
205101	Blackstaff at Easons	337000 373100	12.04	921	0.580	29.9	1.000	0.52	3.79	61.27	0.1523	205101
205105	Cotton at Grandmere Park	336250 331100	3.19	1462	0.433	43.4	1.000	0.53	1.71	261.96	0.0000	205105
206007	Tullybrannigan at Bonny's	242200 342350	12.04	1176	0.369	40.2	1.000	0.58	3.14	81.89	0.0000	206007
236052	Corlough at Raw Bridge	233050 346300	16.46	1153	0.532	31.7	0.994	0.60	3.77	100.70	0.0000	236052
236053	Pubble at Ratoran											236053

A.6 Catchment descriptors given in Table A.4

A brief description of each of the variables shown in Table A.4 is given below.

ALTBAR   Mean altitude of the catchment (metres above sea level).

ASPBAR   Mean direction of all the inter-nodal slopes in the catchment (bearing in degrees, where north is zero). Represents the dominant aspect of catchment slopes.

ASPVAR   Invariability of slope directions, where values near to zero indicate that there is considerable variability in the aspect of catchment slopes. Values approaching one indicate that catchment slopes tend to face one particular direction.

LDP   Longest drainage path (km), defined by recording the greatest distance from a catchment node to the defined outlet. Principally a measure of catchment size but also reflects the catchment configuration.

RMED-1D   Median annual maximum 1-day rainfall (mm).

RMED-2D   Median annual maximum 2-day rainfall (mm).

RMED-1H   Median annual maximum 1-hour rainfall (mm).

$SAAR_{4170}$ Standard period (1941-70) average annual rainfall (mm).

SMDBAR   Mean SMD for the period 1961-90 calculated from MORECS month-end values (mm).

URBCONC   Concentration of urban and suburban land cover. High index values (approaching one) indicate concentrated urban and/or suburban land cover. Not defined when URBEXT < 0.005 or in Northern Ireland where the resolution of CORINE land cover data is too coarse.

URBLOC   Location of urban and suburban land cover. Low index values indicate that development is near the catchment outlet. Not defined when URBEXT < 0.005.

Table A.4 *Catchment descriptors provided for information only – values for 252 Flood Event Archive catchments*

Number	Name	IHDTM	NGR	AREA km²	ALTBAR m	ASPBAR degrees	ASPVAR	LDP km	RMED-1D mm	RMED-2D mm	RMED-1H mm	$SAAR_{170}$ mm	SMDBAR mm	URBCONC	URBLOC	Number
3003	Oykel at Easter Turnaig	240150	900150	331.92	296.9	62.5	0.065	31.02	45.4	65.2	9.4	1962	3.65			3003
7001	Findhorn at Shenachie	282550	833550	415.87	559.9	22.9	0.106	50.98	39.4	56.9	10.3	1429	9.36			7001
7003	Lossie at Sheriffmills	319250	862600	217.07	192.6	2.8	0.349	39.36	37.5	48.1	9.1	890	24.79			7003
7006	Lossie at Torwinny	311350	848900	20.56	347.0	23.7	0.458	12.13	42.4	54.6	9.7	963	24.79			7006
8009	Dulnain at Balnaan Bridge	297850	824750	272.27	461.0	94.0	0.193	44.28	33.1	46.8	9.1	1056	9.38			8009
19001	Almond at Craigiehall	316500	675350	386.19	176.6	20.9	0.245	46.91	35.0	46.1	8.6	905	18.71	0.730	0.768	19001
19002	Almond at Almond Weir	300250	665150	44.36	202.8	39.5	0.268	19.46	34.0	46.1	8.6	1022	15.39	0.697	0.696	19002
19005	Almond at Almondell	308600	668450	239.27	219.4	6.0	0.262	31.88	35.4	47.8	8.7	977	17.79	0.709	0.598	19005
20001	Tyne at East Linton	358950	676650	307.06	174.1	3.0	0.253	43.29	34.7	48.9	8.5	735	24.69			20001
21018	Lyne Water at Lyne Station	320800	640150	180.58	304.5	129.2	0.093	29.95	33.7	44.0	8.5	1005	20.31			21018
21028	Mezion Burn at Mezion Farm	323100	623050	56.31	509.8	105.1	0.197	13.30	48.6	65.5	11.1	1638	6.82			21028
21030	Megget Water at Henderland	406600	601650	345.96	284.2	120.5	0.159	48.54	34.3	44.7	9.1	951	21.57			21030
22009	Croquet at Rothbury	404250	550800	117.97	362.8	48.1	0.284	23.07	41.2	52.1	10.4	958	13.15			22009
23002	Derwent at Eddys Bridge	377750	586050	283.49	325.0	114.5	0.135	35.38	39.0	51.2	10.5	1321	11.98			23002
23005	North Tyne at Tarset	367150	560950	323.09	429.8	12.3	0.198	35.48	41.5	56.8	10.7	1470	10.84			23005
23006	South Tyne at Featherstone	386950	583350	345.10	285.0	128.5	0.109	47.67	32.7	44.0	9.4	1024	20.08			23006
23008	Rede at Rede Bridge	378800	587750	345.00	300.0	148.7	0.258	17.49	34.1	45.0	9.7	1064	13.51			23008
23010	Tarset Burn at Greenhaugh	364400	594600	95.85	407.9	192.6	0.148	12.29	38.3	50.9	10.6	1401	12.96			23010
23011	Kielder Burn at Kielder			58.86												23011
23998	Redesdale RD3	382550	595850	1.95	306.1	36.3	0.782	2.38	30.9	40.0	9.3	971	22.58			23998
23999	Redesdale RD2	383350	595950	4.13	290.5	44.6	0.734	3.33	31.0	40.2	9.2	955	22.58			23999
24003	Wear at Stanhope	398250	539000	173.21	471.0	72.1	0.173	23.28	42.4	55.3	10.4	1307	13.09			24003
24004	Bedburn Beck at Bedburn	411950	532150	74.32	315.9	94.7	0.342	17.05	34.8	45.1	10.0	949	13.15	0.650	0.804	24004
24005	Browney at Burn Hall	425900	538800	178.35	197.5	90.2	0.257	34.10	33.3	43.0	9.9	751	18.61			24005
24007	Browney at Lanchester	416350	546100	44.65	252.3	73.2	0.389	14.45	34.8	44.8	10.1	795	13.15			24007
25003	Trout Beck at Moor House	375750	533500	11.69	656.5	45.1	0.572	5.94	53.1	75.8	11.7	2028	10.80			25003
25004	Skerne at South Park	428350	513050	255.19	100.1	154.0	0.266	48.20	28.9	37.2	9.9	682	34.71	0.722	0.719	25004
25005	Leven at Leven Bridge	444500	512100	193.57	126.6	300.6	0.244	42.34	33.3	42.7	10.1	726	32.71	0.573	0.948	25005
25006	Greta at Rutherford Bridge	403250	512250	86.73	402.1	55.6	0.311	23.52	40.3	54.4	10.7	1263	11.77			25006
25011	Langdon Beck at Langdon	385200	530900	12.73	543.8	208.6	0.401	6.64	44.2	59.5	10.7	1454	13.15			25011
25012	Harwood Beck at Harwood	385050	530900	24.89	537.5	143.2	0.257	9.62	49.3	68.7	11.1	1736	12.76			25012
25019	Leven at Easby	458550	508550	15.06	215.9	255.9	0.049	9.21	37.8	52.0	10.5	854	28.73			25019
25809	Bog Weir at Moor House	377300	532700	0.05	529.9	109.5	0.724	0.36	55.5	79.9	11.8	1997	10.80			25809
25810	Syke Weir at Moor House	377200	533200	0.04	534.2	88.0	0.778	0.33	55.4	79.8	11.8	1995	10.80			25810
25811	Long Weir at Moor House	377050	531750	0.10	565.6	103.9	0.906	0.57	55.7	80.3	11.9	2010	10.80			25811
27001	Nidd at Hunsingore Weir	442650	452900	490.05	196.5	93.8	0.225	74.93	38.6	48.9	11.4	970	27.30	0.784	0.600	27001
27010	Hodge Beck at Bransdale Weir	462800	494350	18.87	322.1	161.2	0.234	9.86	36.0	47.4	10.4	1040	27.10			27010
27026	Rother at Whittington	439250	374250	167.04	163.9	77.0	0.227	18.17	35.2	43.6	10.4	796	31.11	0.742	0.733	27026
27027	Wharfe at Ilkley	411050	448150	447.51	354.6	162.8	0.128	63.57	43.5	58.0	11.1	1382	12.26			27027
27031	Colne at Colne Bridge	417350	419900	244.77	246.2	53.9	0.240	27.75	44.4	60.1	11.1	1134	16.75	0.701	0.573	27031
27034	Ure at Kilgram Bridge	418850	486000	511.89	364.9	84.1	0.143	60.08	45.3	59.7	11.1	1342	11.67			27034
27035	Aire at Kildwick Bridge	401400	445750	282.42	231.2	169.8	0.125	37.61	39.3	52.8	10.5	1135	12.29	0.604	0.605	27035
27051	Crimple at Burn Bridge	428350	451900	8.13	174.8	86.2	0.416	5.03	37.8	45.7	12.8	864	37.97			27051
28016	Ryton at Serlby Park	463950	389600	237.57	68.9	79.0	0.251	44.66	31.6	41.7	11.4	626	36.11	0.763	1.116	28016
28023	Wye at Ashford	418250	369750	152.17	339.7	122.4	0.124	26.29	37.4	51.1	10.0	1201	19.73	0.556	1.208	28023
28026	Anker at Polesworth	426250	303250	370.40	107.8	255.4	0.089	39.70	31.7	39.5	10.7	680	41.81	0.759	1.074	28026
28033	Dove at Hollinsclough	366850	366850	7.96	407.9	110.8	0.223	6.12	41.6	55.6	10.5	1363	19.73			28033
28041	Hamps at Waterhouses	408100	350350	36.91	327.9	110.8	0.228	15.61	35.4	44.5	10.5	1064	25.45			28041
28070	Burbage Brook at Burbage	425850	380250	8.36	385.8	212.3	0.343	5.91	38.8	52.3	10.1	990	31.11			28070
28997	Upper Smisby	434350	318800	1.13	168.3	153.8	0.423	1.66	31.2	37.6	10.9	705	41.81	0.917	1.030	28997

Number	Name	IHDTM NGR	AREA km²	ALTBAR m	ASPBAR degrees	ASPVAR	LDP km	RMED-1D mm	RMED-2D mm	RMED-1H mm	SAAR$_{4170}$	SMDBAR mm	URBCONC	URBLOC	Number
28998	Lower Smisby	435400 318200	2.49	159.5	145.0	0.459	3.02	31.2	37.7	10.9	704	41.81	0.569	1.151	28998
28999	Cliftonthorpe	435700 318950	1.12	168.8	145.1	0.526	1.92	31.4	37.7	11.0	704	39.88			28999
29001	Waithe Beck at Brigsley	525150 401700	108.28	93.7	36.5	0.191	24.38	32.1	40.1	10.3	730	44.66			29001
29002	Great Eau at Claythorpe Mill	541600 379150	80.69	67.6	70.3	0.193	17.82	34.8	41.6	11.2	718	44.61	0.280	0.697	29002
29004	Ancholme at Bishopbridge	503150 390950	58.92	27.8	62.0	0.330	15.48	29.0	36.7	11.3	635	46.63			29004
30001	Witham at Claypole Mill	484250 348150	296.04	86.1	26.4	0.139	52.79	31.7	41.1	10.9	632	45.90	0.625	0.880	30001
30004	Partney Lymn at Partney Mill	540350 367500	59.94	64.9	90.5	0.271	17.24	33.9	41.3	11.3	696	44.30	0.395	0.868	30004
30017	Witham at Colsterworth	492850 324750	50.23	123.2	80.0	0.283	14.17	32.4	42.5	12.1	649	44.07	0.399	0.798	30017
31005	Welland at Tixover	496850 299650	419.59	110.8	98.0	0.107	56.84	31.7	40.4	12.1	644	41.60	0.592	1.061	31005
31006	Gwash at Belmesthorpe	503800 309550	149.49	103.0	100.3	0.339	37.94	30.2	39.5	11.8	638	42.65	0.526	0.861	31006
31010	Chater at Fosters Bridge	496100 303100	68.86	112.8	108.6	0.168	23.41	30.6	39.6	12.2	640	41.60			31010
31021	Welland at Ashley	482050 291500	247.19	115.3	105.2	0.098	32.24	32.0	40.7	12.1	654	41.60	0.649	1.057	31021
31023	West Glen at Easton Wood	496650 325850	4.41	107.7	84.9	0.369	3.86	33.1	42.7	11.7	647	46.27			31023
32801	Flore at Experimental Catchment														32801
32999	Easton Maudit	488400 259300	15.73	92.7	16.2	0.272	7.05	30.2	38.0	12.0	621	40.19	0.439	0.943	32999
33014	Lark at Temple	575650 273100	278.43	59.2	18.1	0.149	32.99	28.0	36.8	10.6	608	46.84	0.604	1.025	33014
33015	Ouzel at Willen	488250 240650	279.06	109.0	356.9	0.077	42.66	30.7	38.4	10.2	658	39.71	0.653	0.750	33015
33029	Stringside at White Bridge	571700 300450	97.08	25.2	203.3	0.180	19.39	28.4	36.3	11.1	633	50.14	0.640	1.245	33029
33045	Wittle at Quidenham	602550 287750	27.65	42.4	293.3	0.223	9.94	27.6	34.0	11.0	627	42.07	0.539	0.870	33045
33809	Bury Brook at Bury Weir	528600 283850	61.97	31.0	45.2	0.232	22.05	28.5	36.4	11.4	558	50.75	0.495	0.723	33809
33996	Toddington	502050 228400	0.88	136.5	99.4	0.700	1.92	30.2	37.4	10.4	645	42.70	0.872	1.365	33996
33997	Letchworth	521050 233650	8.46	91.0	314.8	0.323	6.58	28.8	35.4	10.6	582	42.70	0.718	0.783	33997
33998	Bedford	510050 249050	23.34	42.1	345.2	0.570	10.27	29.9	37.2	10.7	550	49.92	0.508	1.012	33998
33999	Barton-Le-Clay														33999
34003	Bure at Ingworth	619050 329750	168.09	50.1	127.7	0.242	24.80	29.6	37.1	11.3	686	40.97	0.417	1.052	34003
34005	Tud at Costessey Park	617150 311150	72.02	46.3	64.0	0.151	25.43	28.6	36.1	11.3	643	42.07	0.670	1.238	34005
34007	Dove at Oakley Park	617400 277050	140.10	50.8	37.5	0.143	25.28	26.5	34.8	10.6	601	46.40	0.412	1.045	34007
34011	Wensum at Fakenham	591850 329300	162.10	62.0	49.3	0.122	25.99	30.4	38.6	11.1	701	41.82	0.493	0.944	34011
35008	Gipping at Stowmarket	605950 257850	127.43	62.3	69.5	0.149	17.65	26.7	34.0	10.5	606	46.40	0.619	0.470	35008
36008	Stour at Westmill	582850 246450	223.63	89.2	123.0	0.123	40.91	28.7	36.3	10.7	606	47.66	0.579	0.970	36008
37001	Roding at Redbridge	541500 188250	301.20	67.6	124.3	0.096	64.28	31.2	39.4	11.2	610	43.54	0.733	0.427	37001
37003	Ter at Crabbs Bridge	578500 210750	77.81	59.4	150.1	0.216	28.72	28.8	36.9	11.5	591	40.80	0.419	0.826	37003
37007	Wid at Writtle	568450 206050	135.73	69.0	63.2	0.179	27.86	31.8	38.7	11.7	606	46.15	0.677	1.077	37007
37008	Chelmer at Springfield	571150 206950	190.13	77.4	131.8	0.176	45.09	28.7	35.7	11.3	600	40.80	0.637	0.528	37008
37031	Crouch at Wickford	574850 193550	70.37	36.6	86.9	0.243	16.02	31.5	38.0	11.9	594	49.30	0.769	1.016	37031
37999	North Weald	549450 203750	1.53	102.8	17.8	0.590	2.06	32.3	40.5	11.6	617	40.80	0.455	0.078	37999
38003	Mimram at Panshanger Park	528350 213150	130.53	120.7	133.5	0.184	32.01	30.0	38.1	10.6	641	42.70	0.658	0.860	38003
38007	Canons Brook at Elizabeth Way	543200 210550	20.80	74.6	334.9	0.378	7.77	31.8	38.9	11.1	611	40.80	0.760	0.880	38007
39004	Wandle at Beddington Park	529450 165450	118.34	144.7	345.5	0.283	23.87	33.3	43.8	11.0	768	37.50	0.698	0.618	39004
39005	Beverley Brook at Wimbledon Common	521700 171850	39.71	41.2	346.3	0.325	17.37	33.3	39.9	10.4	634	44.39	0.870	1.016	39005
39007	Blackwater at Swallowfield	473200 164650	360.37	88.2	351.6	0.185	37.25	32.0	41.3	11.8	711	38.48	0.680	1.137	39007
39012	Hogsmill at Kingston Upon Thames	518350 168700	72.89	71.7	342.5	0.380	21.18	33.0	42.4	10.7	684	41.75	0.780	0.760	39012
39017	Ray at Grendon Underwood														39017
39018	Ock at Abingdon	448450 196900	248.23	87.4	67.8	0.196	34.36	32.1	39.5	9.7	646	39.14	0.625	0.915	39018
39022	Loddon at Sheepbridge	471850 165050	176.49	94.1	31.0	0.281	31.00	32.4	41.1	11.1	759	37.90	0.610	1.184	39022
39025	Enborne at Brimpton	456800 164950	142.13	120.1	38.8	0.279	26.89	33.2	43.5	11.2	795	38.24	0.454	0.910	39025
39026	Cherwell at Banbury	445650 241250	204.60	139.8	154.0	0.117	30.04	33.8	41.9	11.4	700	40.98	0.601	0.755	39026
39036	Law Brook at Albury	504600 146900	16.00	139.1	335.7	0.342	8.86	35.3	47.5	11.9	836	35.11			39036
39052	The Cut at Binfield	485300 171400	50.20	74.8	341.3	0.182	13.88	32.4	40.8	12.6	688	43.20	0.696	0.861	39052
39053	Mole at Horley	527050 143250	91.59	87.6	9.9	0.301	17.60	35.8	47.6	11.7	825	35.11	0.732	0.928	39053

Number	Name	IHDTM NGR	AREA km²	ALTBAR m	ASPBAR degrees	ASPVAR	LDP km	RMED-1D mm	RMED-2D mm	RMED-1H mm	SAAR4170 mm	SMDBAR mm	URBCONC	URBLOC	Number
39092	Dollis Bk at Hendon Lane Bridge	524050 189350	23.76	88.9	135.4	0.196	11.95	33.5	43.7	10.9	703	44.55	0.845	0.840	39092
39813	Mole at Ifield Weir	524500 136250	13.13	96.7	357.2	0.426	5.40	36.5	48.3	11.8	844	35.11	0.756	0.870	39813
39814	Crawters Brook at Hazlewick														39814
39830	Beck at Rectory Road														39830
39831	Chaffinch Brook at Beckenham														39831
39990	Wingrave														39990
39991	Tring														39991
39992	Stevenage	526800 222750	4.02	107.1	152.7	0.449	4.82	30.5	37.8	10.8	638	42.70	0.733	1.148	39992
39993	South Hinskey	450650 203950	1.51	114.2	77.6	0.559	2.71	31.6	39.3	10.0	650	38.03			39993
39994	Luton														39994
39995	Hook														39995
39996	Holme Green	482550 167000	10.21	80.8	303.7	0.496	6.15	31.8	40.7	12.5	673	43.20	0.764	1.250	39996
39997	Bicester														39997
39998	Beenham	458450 169450	3.29	110.5	59.9	0.387	3.40	30.0	39.4	11.2	700	39.21	0.500	0.767	39998
39999	Aylesbury														39999
40004	Rother at Udiam	577450 124650	205.36	80.6	112.8	0.112	31.20	36.6	48.8	11.6	861	35.61	0.517	0.980	40004
40006	Bourne at Hadlow	563200 149550	50.21	97.7	155.8	0.208	16.32	33.6	44.7	11.7	733	35.58	0.564	1.044	40006
40007	Medway at Chafford Weir	551600 140650	252.40	108.3	28.0	0.062	29.24	34.8	47.2	11.7	852	35.47	0.605	1.229	40007
40008	Great Stour at Wye	605050 147150	226.07	76.9	205.4	0.162	35.37	33.7	44.0	11.9	750	37.69	0.664	0.721	40008
40009	Teise at Stone Bridge	571850 140050	134.43	93.1	50.5	0.114	22.50	35.0	47.9	11.8	809	35.52			40009
40010	Eden at Penshurst	552150 143850	224.88	82.6	137.0	0.107	33.56	32.9	44.1	11.4	764	35.33	0.549	1.220	40010
41005	Ouse at Gold Bridge	542750 121500	182.26	76.9	176.6	0.160	29.18	35.9	47.5	11.7	836	35.20	0.690	0.976	41005
41006	Uck at Isfield	545900 118950	87.84	72.5	217.5	0.179	17.62	35.1	46.5	11.5	837	36.01	0.664	0.614	41006
41007	Arun at Park Mound	503700 121400	401.33	61.4	179.8	0.073	47.94	35.1	46.7	11.4	801	35.65	0.736	1.142	41007
41015	Ems at Westbourne	475450 107250	57.93	97.1	197.3	0.352	17.02	40.0	50.7	10.0	959	37.63	0.481	0.813	41015
41020	Bevern Stream at Clappers Bridge	542150 116450	35.23	51.4	52.0	0.258	14.52	37.1	49.0	11.5	881	37.34	0.448	1.122	41020
41021	Clayhill Stream at Old Ship	544850 115300	7.09	20.7	252.5	0.244	6.47	35.3	45.8	11.4	803	37.76			41021
41022	Lod at Halfway Bridge	493250 122350	52.22	82.1	147.4	0.152	18.27	38.5	49.3	10.9	886	37.23			41022
41025	Loxwood Stream at Drungewick	505850 130750	93.81	69.2	113.8	0.153	27.60	36.1	48.7	11.6	806	36.39	0.353	0.828	41025
41028	Chess Stream at Chess Bridge	521850 117400	24.96	43.1	334.0	0.332	11.39	36.5	46.9	11.4	847	37.26	0.565	0.972	41028
41801	Hollington Stream at Hollington	578800 110050	3.47	69.7	203.8	0.351	4.19	33.2	44.3	11.1	778	37.76	0.902	0.985	41801
45002	Exe at Stoodleigh	294250 117650	420.87	283.8	167.6	0.150	55.44	45.8	62.3	12.1	1421	18.09			45002
45003	Culm at Wood Mill	302100 105950	288.69	153.4	232.3	0.054	29.70	36.0	47.0	11.1	996	28.71			45003
45004	Axe at Whitford	326250 95400	288.58	137.6	124.9	0.035	36.06	40.1	51.9	11.4	1053	29.75			45004
45009	Exe at Pixton	293450 126150	147.81	309.2	185.1	0.204	35.76	47.7	65.5	12.2	1446	17.20			45009
45011	Barle at Brushford	292700 125850	128.01	346.6	152.7	0.171	40.13	52.4	69.4	12.9	1671	16.34			45011
46003	Dart at Austins Bridge	274950 66050	248.90	327.1	131.0	0.148	38.03	63.1	83.1	13.8	1706	21.83			46003
46005	East Dart at Bellever	265750 77650	22.29	458.3	144.6	0.256	13.27	67.1	92.1	14.2	2013	22.11			46005
46802	Swincombe at Swincombe Intake	263200 71850	14.18	401.8	0.8	0.212	5.40	67.2	86.8	14.5	1921	21.84			46802
46805	Bala Brook at Bala Intake	267350 62800	5.59	392.6	127.8	0.517	3.45	66.5	88.7	14.3	2156	21.86			46805
47007	Yealm at Puslinch	257550 51200	56.42	168.5	196.6	0.290	18.56	48.1	63.2	12.5	1481	21.46	0.593	0.511	47007
47008	Thrushel at Tinhay	239850 85550	112.71	162.8	227.2	0.172	20.57	38.5	49.1	12.0	1227	17.78			47008
47011	Plym at Carn Wood	252250 61400	79.56	277.6	249.1	0.296	20.00	54.1	68.0	13.3	1587	21.02	0.494	0.717	47011
47013	Withey Brook at Bastreet	224550 76450	15.93	286.7	227.1	0.030	6.89	48.6	66.5	13.0	1763	20.92			47013
48004	Warleggan at Trengoffe	215850 67250	25.21	218.6	206.1	0.209	12.40	44.2	63.4	12.2	1518	23.86			48004
48005	Kenwyn at Truro	182150 44950	19.09	82.4	114.4	0.191	8.83	36.0	49.2	11.0	1107	27.09	0.853	0.449	48005
48009	St Neot at Craigshill Wood	218400 66200	22.86	231.4	186.7	0.326	13.38	45.0	64.0	12.2	1617	23.86			48009
49003	De Lank at De Lank	213250 76550	21.70	283.1	245.3	0.165	7.70	47.7	66.3	12.5	1725	23.34			49003
51002	Horner Water at West Luccombe	289450 145950	20.49	340.6	23.9	0.287	12.03	50.9	68.4	12.5	1444	16.34			51002
52004	Isle at Ashford Mill	335950 118850	87.42	93.0	31.4	0.265	17.39	39.1	51.2	11.4	937	29.19	0.793	1.126	52004

Number	Name	IHDTM	NGR	AREA km²	ALTBAR m	ASPBAR degrees	ASPVAR	LDP km	RMED-1D mm	RMED-2D mm	RMED-1H mm	SAAR$_{4170}$ mm	SMDBAR mm	URBCONC	URBLOC	Number
52005	Tone at Bishops Hull	320450	125050	203.63	143.8	68.2	0.178	39.93	36.2	48.8	11.1	991	34.09	0.828	0.648	52005
52006	Yeo at Pen Mill	357350	116050	216.17	95.3	55.1	0.072	29.31	37.6	46.9	11.2	903	32.58	0.708	0.642	52006
52010	Brue at Lovington	359150	131800	139.52	104.7	218.3	0.167	22.44	34.1	44.2	10.7	882	32.93	0.492	0.804	52010
52016	Currypool Stream at Currypool Farm	322000	138200	15.72	181.1	63.1	0.457	8.93	36.6	48.2	11.5	969	35.33			52016
52020	Gallica Stream at Gallica Bridge	357050	109850	16.44	119.1	0.0	0.261	7.05	41.0	50.2	11.5	1027	32.55			52020
53005	Midford Brook at Midford	376350	161150	147.40	125.3	52.4	0.151	23.25	37.9	50.9	11.2	971	32.93	0.626	1.070	53005
53007	Frome(somerset) at Tellisford	380650	156250	261.85	143.2	55.2	0.176	39.51	37.5	48.9	11.2	967	33.38	0.646	0.772	53007
53008	Avon at Great Somerford	396450	183200	305.11	118.6	113.2	0.280	33.57	33.0	42.0	10.3	835	32.99	0.562	0.870	53008
53009	Wellow Brook at Wellow	374000	157950	73.47	135.3	46.2	0.221	17.79	38.2	52.1	11.3	1020	32.93	0.623	0.964	53009
54004	Sowe at Stoneleigh	433200	273250	263.29	103.7	144.3	0.194	33.19	33.0	42.0	10.8	690	41.44	0.836	0.837	54004
54006	Stour at Kidderminster	383050	276750	311.45	113.4	250.4	0.078	41.56	31.2	38.8	10.7	700	38.61	0.824	1.158	54006
54010	Stour at Alscot Park	420650	250850	316.96	122.0	1.1	0.114	42.72	34.2	41.9	10.9	678	39.27	0.567	0.985	54010
54011	Salwarpe at Harford Mill	386850	261950	186.20	82.5	209.2	0.234	28.99	30.7	37.0	10.6	675	44.67	0.712	1.034	54011
54016	Roden at Rodington	358900	314250	261.90	89.6	119.3	0.105	46.37	29.0	36.5	9.4	712	35.19	0.520	0.865	54016
54019	Avon at Stareton	433150	271500	346.32	118.8	272.6	0.125	60.30	31.6	39.6	11.5	692	41.13	0.756	0.823	54019
54020	Perry at Yeaton	343250	319200	183.18	102.3	128.7	0.116	34.16	29.0	37.5	9.2	776	24.45	0.532	1.130	54020
54022	Severn at Plynlimon Flume	285300	287200	8.68	500.2	115.1	0.433	5.65	72.9	97.8	13.2	2251	9.36			54022
54027	Frome at Ebley Mill	383000	204550	197.11	178.9	153.8	0.128	29.29	35.2	46.6	10.4	888	35.33	0.582	0.558	54027
54034	Dowles Brook at Dowles	376650	276500	42.07	128.2	75.8	0.125	14.09	33.1	44.2	11.2	758	38.57			54034
54090	Tanllwyth at Tanllwyth Flume															54090
54999	Drayton DT2															54999
55008	Wye at Cefn Brwyn	282800	283700	10.56	495.8	142.8	0.362	5.74	75.3	101.4	13.2	2394	9.36			55008
55012	Irfon at Cilmery	299450	250550	246.41	333.4	135.5	0.112	38.83	50.0	66.4	10.8	1640	9.52			55012
55021	Lugg at Butts Bridge	350350	258900	365.13	232.3	135.0	0.197	52.22	35.0	44.9	10.1	951	26.60	0.549	0.471	55021
55022	Trothy at Mitchel Troy	350150	211250	142.41	114.7	139.2	0.127	32.66	37.9	47.8	9.9	944	27.87			55022
55025	Llynfi at Three Cocks	316550	237450	131.48	238.8	354.5	0.038	20.06	39.2	49.7	11.1	1000	16.66			55025
55026	Wye at Ddol Farm	297650	267450	172.68	387.4	124.2	0.104	37.16	52.6	69.9	13.4	1611	10.99			55026
55034	Cyff at Cyff Flume	282250	284200	3.11	481.1	121.4	0.399	3.83	78.3	106.1	13.4	2414	9.36			55034
56002	Ebbw at Rhiwderyn	325900	188750	212.29	316.1	183.1	0.181	41.40	52.7	70.0	11.8	1527	18.98	0.629		56002
56003	Honddu at The Forge Brecon	305000	229850	62.53	311.5	175.0	0.216	20.75	43.1	56.6	10.4	1252	16.32		1.004	56003
56004	Usk at Llandetty	312700	220450	556.56	328.2	104.6	0.067	52.41	52.3	70.3	11.4	1491	13.18			56004
56005	Lwyd at Ponthir	332850	192400	98.33	283.9	136.5	0.264	27.88	53.6	68.1	11.7	1468	18.95	0.709	0.670	56005
56006	Usk at Trallong	294550	229650	193.99	344.3	47.1	0.051	24.16	59.5	81.9	12.2	1663	11.24			56006
56011	Sirhowy at Wattsville	320450	191150	76.26	320.2	164.8	0.182	33.71	53.5	71.8	11.9	1537	18.80	0.636	0.950	56011
57004	Cynon at Abercynon	308050	195600	103.54	270.4	169.9	0.109	28.69	66.8	90.0	13.1	1766	14.77	0.617	0.802	57004
57005	Taff at Pontypridd	308300	189650	451.99	320.1	156.1	0.140	45.74	63.6	94.7	12.7	1842	17.05	0.639	0.742	57005
57006	Rhondda at Trehafod	305250	191000	102.57	328.6	117.2	0.163	24.93	71.8	94.9	13.7	2201	17.25	0.638	0.705	57006
58001	Ogmore at Bridgend	290300	179350	157.97	211.0	185.9	0.185	25.01	54.3	72.3	12.5	1844	16.92	0.649	0.784	58001
58002	Neath at Resolven	281450	201650	190.93	318.1	198.0	0.169	31.62	63.8	88.1	12.5	1975	11.25	0.642	0.650	58002
58003	Ewenny at Ewenny Priory	291550	178100	63.85	84.5	211.2	0.237	14.73	43.2	58.2	11.6	1374	17.22	0.652	0.739	58003
58006	Mellte at Pontneddfechan	291350	208100	65.18	400.9	194.6	0.280	17.48	63.5	86.4	12.5	2111	11.25	0.603	1.276	58006
58008	Dulais at Cilfrew	277900	200950	43.36	229.1	257.5	0.196	15.55	51.8	73.6	11.5	1757	11.25	0.656	0.727	58008
58009	Ewenny at Keepers Lodge	292150	178250	63.25	85.2	211.2	0.237	14.07	43.3	58.2	11.6	1381	17.22			58009
60002	Cothi at Felin Mynachdy	250850	222500	298.54	231.4	183.9	0.113	51.31	51.0	68.1	11.6	1637	13.66			60002
60003	Taf at Clog-y-fran	223950	215850	216.73	124.8	177.5	0.089	36.60	43.3	60.4	11.5	1410	21.72			60003
60006	Gwili at Glangwili	242950	222050	130.98	188.1	194.1	0.136	26.09	51.9	70.2	12.3	1614	17.23			60006
60007	Tywi at Dolau Hirion	276200	236050	220.53	350.5	165.7	0.110	39.08	51.1	68.0	11.2	1744	9.63			60007
61001	Western Cleddau at Prendergast Mill	195250	217850	197.76	108.4	206.4	0.108	29.45	42.5	57.8	11.6	1282	24.96			61001
61003	Gwaun at Cilrhedyn Bridge	200400	235000	31.29	231.1	294.5	0.175	11.05	50.8	66.7	12.0	1468	24.96			61003
62002	Teifi at Llanfair	243450	240450	517.05	242.7	272.4	0.091	73.28	43.3	59.3	10.7	1414	14.06			62002

Number	Name	IHDTM NGR	AREA km²	ALTBAR m	ASPBAR degrees	ASPVAR	LDP km	RMED-1D mm	RMED-2D mm	RMED-1H mm	SAAR₄₁₇₀ mm	SMDBAR mm	URBCONC	URBLOC	Number
63998	Trawsgoed														63998
63999	Pwllpeiran	281050 278750	1.97	533.2	197.4	0.329	3.02	60.8	79.8	12.3	2106	9.41			63999
64001	Dyfi at Dyfi Bridge	274350 301900	464.56	281.2	222.2	0.071	39.92	58.4	75.6	11.1	1838	9.28			64001
65001	Glaslyn at Beddgelert	259200 347650	67.23	339.0	208.8	0.072	17.22	80.0	105.9	13.0	3030	10.37			65001
65801	Nant Peris at Tan-yr-allt	260750 358050	10.30	527.5	307.5	0.187	5.46	90.8	123.9	14.3	3639	7.41			65801
66002	Elwy at Pant Yr Onen	302150 370300	218.63	269.5	33.9	0.161	40.26	42.8	59.1	10.1	1084	12.89			66002
66004	Wheeler at Bodfari	310600 371550	62.94	206.9	239.9	0.081	13.83	33.3	44.1	10.1	854	33.31			66004
66006	Elwy at Pont-y-gwyddel	295350 371550	191.40	284.3	27.5	0.160	29.70	43.9	60.8	10.1	1128	12.31			66006
66011	Conwy at Cwm Llanerch	280300 358250	339.86	341.6	19.9	0.010	31.83	64.0	85.8	11.7	2165	7.61			66011
67003	Brenig at Llyn Brenig Outflow	297500 354050	22.17	418.9	172.2	0.247	7.57	42.0	58.1	10.2	1301	7.55			67003
67005	Ceiriog at Brynkinalt Weir	329650 337250	111.94	384.7	98.7	0.186	30.21	41.3	55.3	10.3	1251	18.95			67005
67008	Alyn at Pont-y-capel	333450 353950	227.16	232.1	62.4	0.179	50.03	35.0	45.5	10.1	902	25.16	0.683	0.557	67008
67010	Gelyn at Cynefail	284350 341950	12.89	423.1	234.6	0.020	7.42	61.9	84.4	12.2	2046	7.41			67010
68006	Dane at Hulme Walfield	384600 364250	151.10	262.9	260.4	0.207	33.91	36.6	45.8	10.4	1059	20.25	0.731	0.381	68006
68010	Fender at Ford	327950 388150	17.59	44.6	7.9	0.212	8.91	30.0	38.9	10.4	784	33.31	0.849	0.827	68010
68014	Sandersons Brook at Sandbach														68014
69008	Dean at Stanneylands														69008
69011	Micker Brook at Cheadle														69011
69012	Bollin at Wilmslow	384850 381550	67.89	183.6	319.1	0.238	22.67	33.5	43.6	10.3	923	19.73	0.735	1.010	69012
69013	Sinderland Brook at Partington	372700 390500	45.08	37.2	327.5	0.472	16.93	31.3	41.3	10.8	823	30.06	0.749	1.113	69013
69018	Newton Brook at Newton Le Willows	358400 393300	32.25	49.4	143.5	0.315	16.86	34.4	46.5	11.6	908	32.19	0.774	1.016	69018
69019	Worsley Brook at Eccles	375350 397850	23.74	60.4	188.7	0.555	12.30	34.3	46.3	11.2	962	23.12	0.771	0.997	69019
69020	Medlock at London Road	384750 397550	52.72	153.6	233.2	0.426	21.42	38.0	51.7	11.2	1053	16.50	0.821	0.866	69020
69027	Tame at Portwood	390450 391900	146.60	258.0	254.8	0.278	44.58	42.4	56.3	11.4	1181	17.09	0.770	0.598	69027
69031	Ditton Brook at Greens Bridge	345550 386650	48.76	37.2	174.5	0.258	11.86	30.5	42.1	11.0	877	34.56			69031
69034	Musbury Brook at Helmshore	377400 421300	3.14	318.5	71.8	0.477	3.18	43.9	62.4	12.1	1474	19.69			69034
69802	Etherow at Woodhead														69802
70006	Tawd at Newburgh	346900 410850	28.32	71.4	307.5	0.224	13.03	36.2	47.4	11.4	979	19.69	0.691	1.144	70006
71003	Croasdale at Croasdale Flume	370600 454750	10.66	345.4	148.2	0.348	5.99	55.3	75.4	12.0	1794	12.50			71003
71004	Calder at Whalley Weir	373050 436000	317.11	221.2	291.8	0.147	39.95	40.6	55.1	10.8	1211	16.43	0.769	0.842	71004
71008	Hodder at Hodder Place	370550 439950	258.39	245.2	165.9	0.131	41.10	50.9	69.0	11.4	1533	12.73			71008
71802	Ribble at Halton West	385100 455200	206.68	316.6	200.1	0.098	41.11	44.9	61.7	11.1	1483	12.07			71802
71804	Dunsop at Footholme	365300 452950	24.93	364.2	205.6	0.198	8.63	59.1	81.3	12.5	1866	12.50			71804
72002	Wyre at St Michaels	346450 441050	276.56	146.9	250.6	0.365	37.36	41.6	54.0	10.7	1253	14.37	0.633	0.688	72002
72006	Lune at Kirkby Lonsdale	361500 477950	510.31	315.6	275.9	0.081	53.04	54.5	75.0	11.9	1622	7.34			72006
72818	New Mill Brook at Carvers Bridge	347900 438000	65.08	60.4	264.9	0.335	18.67	36.8	48.5	10.3	1060	18.81	0.631	1.169	72818
72820	Burnes Gill at Tebay (M6)														72820
73005	Kent at Sedgwick	350900 487550	212.38	235.0	181.6	0.155	32.98	54.1	74.7	11.5	1756	7.24	0.650	0.431	73005
73007	Troutbeck at Troutbeck Bridge	340550 500850	23.94	348.0	205.6	0.232	11.40	68.7	93.5	13.0	2152	7.24			73007
73008	Bela at Beetham	349600 480450	132.15	131.6	248.0	0.200	27.73	43.6	56.5	10.5	1302	8.42			73008
73803	Winster at Lobby Bridge	342300 488550	22.20	100.6	143.4	0.112	11.79	49.5	65.0	11.1	1508	7.22			73803
73804	Brathay at Brathay Hall	336650 503450	57.44	287.9	92.0	0.160	16.09	84.1	121.7	14.3	2859	6.89			73804
74001	Duddon at Duddon Hall	319550 489550	85.69	315.0	157.0	0.087	21.41	62.3	83.9	12.7	2361	6.89			74001
75006	Newlands Beck at Braithwaite	323950 524050	33.81	353.7	42.5	0.252	12.02	63.3	84.7	12.4	2377	9.43			75006
75007	Glenderamackin at Threlkeld	332150 524800	62.99	353.8	347.0	0.153	18.10	56.0	75.2	11.5	1837	12.44			75007
76005	Eden at Temple Sowerby	360400 528150	618.58	283.1	322.5	0.105	60.86	41.0	56.5	10.7	1210	8.93			76005
76008	Irthing at Greenholme	348500 558000	333.75	225.0	219.2	0.144	60.56	35.1	46.5	10.4	1073	11.52			76008
76011	Coal Burn at Coalburn	369450 577850	1.55	306.0	163.9	0.491	1.79	39.3	52.4	10.6	1163	11.73			76011
76014	Eden at Kirkby Stephen	377250 509850	68.18	391.2	308.8	0.212	22.50	50.8	71.0	11.7	1383	8.10			76014
76805	Force Beck at M6 (shop)	357750 513500	3.97	326.7	319.7	0.280	3.68	50.6	70.4	12.0	1508	7.24			76805

Number	Name	IHDTM NGR	AREA km²	ALTBAR m	ASPBAR degrees	ASPVAR	LDP km	RMED-1D mm	RMED-2D mm	RMED-1H mm	SAAR4170 mm	SMDBAR mm	URBCONC	URBLOC	Number
77002	Esk at Canonbie	339700 575250	495.86	279.3	182.1	0.143	59.90	44.6	58.6	11.6	1506	11.36			77002
79006	Nith at Drumlanrig	285750 599250	469.18	327.6	32.5	0.075	59.02	46.3	63.6	10.8	1581	8.72			79006
80003	White Laggan Burn at Loch Dee	246800 578000	5.71	440.5	2.9	0.367	4.22	71.8	99.9	14.3	2141	7.91			80003
83002	Garnock at Dalry	229300 648950	90.77	201.2	150.6	0.302	19.94	48.5	63.2	10.9	1693	12.52	0.679	0.537	83002
84002	Calder at Muirshiel	230900 663650	12.27	358.4	50.6	0.383	8.60	57.6	80.4	12.5	2248	12.52			84002
84008	Rotten Calder Water at Redlees	267950 660250	54.84	192.2	21.1	0.293	22.03	37.3	52.1	9.2	1183	15.38	0.827	0.701	84008
84012	White Cart Water at Hawkhead	250050 662900	229.68	148.3	7.8	0.248	37.19	40.7	56.6	9.7	1271	13.00	0.843	0.747	84012
84022	Duneaton at Maidencots	292750 625950	111.21	341.3	68.1	0.110	31.13	41.3	57.3	9.9	1332	7.89			84022
85002	Endrick Water at Gaidrew	248350 686700	219.14	192.2	318.8	0.112	39.95	41.7	56.6	9.9	1432	9.07			85002
96001	Halladale at Halladale	289050 956250	194.04	174.5	1.5	0.137	28.36	33.2	46.3	8.2	1055	7.62			96001
202004	Muff at Eglinton	253400 421050	26.83	109.9	331.6	0.353	10.58	32.7	44.4	7.6	1046	12.90	0.815	0.271	202004
202005	Muff at Muff Glen	252400 418950	14.60	121.2	346.1	0.454	6.04	32.8	43.9	9.4	1065	12.90			202005
202006	Castle at Gortenny	253050 419250	5.69	130.4	128.4	0.108	6.87	32.7	43.1	9.2	1058	12.90			202006
203046	Rathmore at Rathmore Bridge														203046
203049	Clady at Clady Bridge	319950 383750	29.42	192.5	290.8	0.471	14.22	36.6	49.2	10.7	1066	17.29			203049
203050	Ballysally Blagh at University of Ulster														203050
203094	Coughmills Water at Cough Mills	306950 417750	22.19	209.9	264.1	0.456	10.88	39.0	52.2	9.1	1246	12.18			203094
203095	Killagan Water at Killagan Bridge														203095
204003	Tow at Fairhill	311700 440600	23.79	117.9	80.0	0.182	9.32	36.2	49.5	8.0	1150	12.18	0.858	0.211	204003
204004	Beaghs Burn at Beaghs Bridge	317750 429750	2.79	333.0	148.4	0.302	3.39	48.8	64.7	9.4	1601	12.18			204004
205101	Blackstaff at Easons														205101
205105	Cotton at Grandmere Park	337000 373100	12.04	60.3	268.4	0.211	7.61	36.1	47.5	10.3	968	17.29	0.937	0.817	205105
206007	Tully Brannigan at Bonny's	336250 331100	3.19	265.2	44.0	0.569	3.08	66.0	82.5	12.6	1522	16.67			206007
236052	Corlough at Raw Bridge	242200 342350	12.04	155.1	346.1	0.454	6.04	32.8	43.9	9.4	1085	13.54			236052
236053	Pubble at Ratoran	233050 346300	16.46	157.8	128.4	0.108	6.87	32.7	43.1	9.2	1106	12.42			236053

Index